# THE Slenderella COOK BOOK

# THE Slenderella COOK BOOK

*by Myra Waldo*

G. P. PUTNAM'S SONS
NEW YORK

Library of Congress Catalog

Card Number: 57-13298

MANUFACTURED IN THE UNITED STATES OF AMERICA

VAN REES PRESS • NEW YORK

# Foreword

The implications in weight control for good health and nutrition are exceedingly great. Well-conducted programs for the control of body weight are a means of directing food and health habits into channels that will be of lasting benefit to all persons. On the other hand, improper programs may be ineffective and even detrimental to health.

It has been demonstrated that weight control is far more than a nutritional program. It enters into the diverse fields of medicine, psychology, sociology, biochemistry and home economics.

In the Slenderella program for figure proportioning, the importance of proper eating habits has been stressed. There are many impediments and obstructive influences to adherence to a weight control dietary program. Furthermore, once ideal weight is attained, it can only be maintained if new dietary habits have been formed and ingrained; otherwise, the lost weight will be quickly regained. To those who are constantly faced with the problem of weight control, there must be continuous reminders to adhere to the program, for the first relapse is quickly followed by a second and the whole program soon collapses

Since the Slenderella program recognizes these facts, the need for an entirely new concept in cook books was apparent. To be enjoyed, food must be interesting and palatable. This is particularly true for those whose caloric intake must be restricted.

It is unfortunate that fats which make food tasty are high in calories. The carbohydrates which are easily convertible into body fats also are craved by the obese. The problem, then, is to prepare foods so that their caloric value is decreased, but at the same time their palatableness and appetite appeal are not lost but even enhanced. In addition, a variety of foods must be offered not only because it increases acceptance of the suggested food regime, but also aids in assuring that all essential foods will be eaten.

No matter what dietary program is used, the first essential must be that it will not interfere with good health, but will be conducive to well-being and vigor. This implies that the food will be adequate in proteins of high biologic value, vitamins, and minerals. It is also recognized that some fat is essential for normal nutrition.

The recipes in this cook book have been designed with these facts uppermost in mind. They are not bizarre, but cover a wide variety of foods. Appetite appeal has not been lost but increased. The caloric value of each dish has been reduced materially from the way in which these dishes usually have been prepared. It is certain that this book will add to the armamentarium of all those who seek weight control. It equally presents the type of cookery that will appeal to those who are committed to the pace of modern living: young, middle-aged or elderly.

William I. Fishbein, M.D.

# *Contents*

# Introduction

The American way of life places considerable emphasis upon youthful vigor and a slender form. A glance through any magazine will show you that the nation's ideal figure is slim and attractive.

Those who are overweight add years to their appearance and detract considerably from their chances for success, both social and financial. Fat people are self-conscious, emotionally insecure and at a disadvantage in a civilization that rewards those who conform to the American concept.

With the tremendous interest in good food, the problem has become even more acute and difficult for the weight watcher. By following this book, you will eat delicious, tempting meals and not be required to consume outlandish, monotonous, "dietetic" creations so common with diets.

Weight reduction, followed by weight control, is the only solution for the tremendous number of overweight people in our country. This book teaches you *how* to achieve that desired result.

Follow it, bring your weight to its proper level, and keep it there.

MYRA WALDO

# THE
# Slenderella
# COOK BOOK

# The Psychology of Weight Control

One of the most important factors in the well-being of a person is weight control. Intelligent overweight people want to bring their weight within proper bounds, but maintaining the correct weight is the problem of everyone in the family.

This book, therefore, is intended for the entire family—father, mother and children. Those of normal weight will continue to retain their natural slimness, and the overweight person will learn how to lose unsightly fat while eating his favorite dishes.

Overweight is the blight of American civilization. With shorter working hours, an abundance of food and increased leisure, more men and women are faced with the battle against added weight.

We have become a nation of calorie counters; everyone is an expert on diets. Nevertheless, one of every four adults in our country remains overweight. Almost all of them make more or less sporadic efforts to lose weight, and some occasionally do, but the losses are brief and inevitably followed by rapid gains. In the past years we have seen freak diets of all types—bananas and skim milk, "blitz" diets of cottage cheese and canned peaches, lamb chops and pineapple, mother's milk formulas, hard-boiled eggs and grapefruit, 3-day "miracle" diets, 8-day "health" diets, 10-day "wonder" diets, and 18-day "Hollywood" diets! All of these, if followed conscientiously, bring about a brief loss of weight, but only at the risk of health, boredom and ravenous hunger.

Extreme diets, based principally upon one or two foods, are impracticable and do not offer any easy road to the solution of diet problems.

### Eat your favorite foods

This book offers a completely new and different method of weight control based upon eating precisely what you always do, including all of those dishes you prefer and enjoy. It is not necessary to live on cottage cheese and lettuce leaves for weeks on end; nor do you have to eat lamb chops and pineapple until the very thought is abhorrent. A wide range of choice, rather than the monotonous restrictions imposed by most diets, is essential to prevent food binges. When your favorite foods are readily available, they no longer have the charm and attraction of forbidden pleasures. Therefore, you will find all of your preferred dishes in this book. You can and should eat them, because all of the recipes have been reduced in calories. Minimum amounts of fats, oils and sugars are used in their preparation, without appreciably altering the finished dish.

You'll find that a reduction of only several hundred calories a day will reduce and control weight the easiest—and only permanent—way. Scientists have learned that there are approximately 3600 calories in a pound of body weight. If you eat your regular, favorite foods, as prepared by the recipes in this book, your weight will decrease gradually. For example, by merely cutting down 300 calories a day (an extremely modest amount) below the amount of calories required to maintain your present weight, in six months you will have omitted 54,000 calories and lost 15 or more pounds. And yet, you won't have actually been on a reducing diet!

### Why you're overweight

Before you can lose weight and maintain the loss, it is necessary to understand why you're overweight and have that tendency. Everyone has a pat excuse: "It runs in my family," "It's my glands," "I lead a sedentary life," and, of course, "My metabolism is low." None of these excuses holds water. Scientists have investigated all possible reasons and demonstrated that not more than an occasional person has a legitimate physiological basis for gaining weight other than the one obvious and inescapable reason—eating too much. It is possible that there is a *slight* degree of variation from one person to another in regard to the burning of food within the body, but the fact remains that a lowered intake brings about a weight reduction in *all* cases.

Serious consideration, therefore, cannot be given to the customary excuses. Weight accumulates because of excess caloric intake; weight is reduced by lowering intake and requiring the body to burn up its store of fat. Don't worry about the harmful effects of losing weight; your body will not use up vital tissue, only fat, to make up any caloric deficiencies.

Admittedly, certain sociological factors have contributed toward our national weight problem. They are (1) the industrial revolution within the home, (2) the changing pattern of social life, and (3) psychological tensions of modern life.

**The industrial revolution within the home**

Fifty years ago, the modern woman of her day arose at dawn, cleaned her home, prepared three meals a day, baked bread and cakes, washed laundry by hand, took care of several children, and was *physically active all day.* Today, although housework has not been eliminated, much of the heavy drudgery has been minimized by the genius of American engineers. We have dishwashers, vacuum cleaners, clothes washers, ironers; we cook by gas or electricity instead of wood fire. Life, generally speaking, has become considerably less arduous for the housewife. The busiest suburban housewife, even though she is active throughout the day, is not using her *larger* muscles, and it is these that burn up energy. The *smaller* muscles, used in driving a car, shopping,

or in preparing dinner, for example, use up comparatively little energy. But we have inherited the food patterns of our grandparents, eating much as they did.

**The changing pattern of social life**

Modern society has emphasized increased leisure time. The fourteen-hour day of our grandparents has been reduced to about seven, a large portion of the free time being devoted to recreation and entertainment. The great social impact has been in the direction of commercial, scheduled entertainment. We have become a nation of spectators—viewers, not participants. We view baseball, football, television, motion pictures. At football games we eat frankfurters; at the motion pictures, it's popcorn; at home while watching television, the family raids the refrigerator. A generation or two ago, we would have been active, working longer hours at stores, factories or on farms; now we sit comfortably by during extra hours of free time, watching someone else perform and simultaneously consuming extra and unneeded calories. The more leisure the more social life, and with it, coffee and cake, pizzas, cocktail parties and hors d'oeuvres.

In order to maintain what they consider their social and financial prestige, most people serve the foods customarily associated with social and financial success. If guests are expected, tradition and mores demand that the food be rich and elaborate, and therefore high in calories. The meal must have several courses, cream soups, meat, potatoes, vegetables in butter, a salad with an oil dressing, a rich dessert, coffee with cream and sugar. Before the meal, cocktails and hors d'oeuvres. After dinner, more drinks. In an evening of this sort, the guest is offered more calories than are normally required for two complete days—six complete meals! Small wonder that modern social life causes many of us to gain weight and retain it, in spite of all efforts to reduce.

**Psychological tensions of modern life**

Many psychiatrists have asserted that overweight is primarily a psychological problem. Their reasoning may be summarized as follows. Immediately after birth, an infant is primarily concerned with food obtained orally by breast feeding or from the nipple of a bottle. Anything and everything within reach is placed in the mouth—the infant's chief area of sensation. As the child grows older, he sucks his thumb, bites his fingernails, puts pencils in his mouth and otherwise continues the oral pattern. Almost all of us outgrow childish mannerisms, but few rid ourselves of them completely.

The simplest of all human tastes is for sweet foods; it is only in the maturing process that we begin to appreciate sour, salt and bitter tastes, and learn to enjoy pickles, oysters, cheese, olives and other foods normally disliked by children. Physiologically, a sweet taste is pleasing to a child just as a bitter one is not. Many mothers, knowing this, bribe children into eating important and vital foods by promising sweet desserts for finishing meat, vegetables and milk. Food, in the infantile mind, then ceases to be what it should always be—nutrition, pure and simple. It partakes of a "reward" in the child's subconscious and he soon learns to equate sweet foods with accomplishment, reward, and—most of all—approbation by his parents. Denial or withholding of sweets means disapproval to the childish mind.

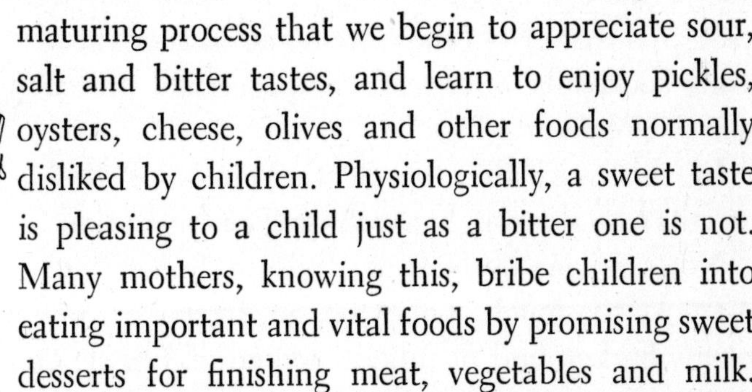

Coupled with the reward problem are mothers who overfeed their children. These women, according to researchers, are often emotionally insecure. They are worried; they experience anxieties about their husband's love, their personal appearance or dozens of other problems. They seek to

transfer these disappointments and anxieties by overgratifying their children—protecting them too much from the world or overfeeding them—thus (in their subconscious) indicating to the world the great love they bear for their children. Thus an emotional background is created in which there is a distinct association of food as representing security, protection and, of course, a reward for good behavior.

As the years go by, the child becomes an adult and presumably mature, but it is a rare person who does not carry over from childhood certain signs of immaturity—unaccountable loss of temper, prejudices, tantrums, lengthy daydreaming, finger tapping, nervousness and so on. Few of us fully achieve our life's goal, most people making a reasonable compromise with reality. Others reject reality and its daily quota of disappointments. Their subconscious, to ease the shocks of everyday life, leads them back into a fantasy of childhood when their parents protected them from the world—and so they eat to bring back, subconsciously, the peace and protection of childhood.

In this way, they repeat the errors of their parents who also sought to release *their* frustrations.

Not everyone overeats as a release. Some drink or smoke too much. They, too, are frustrated, but their childhood, physiology, background or inheritance are different. Drug addicts, of course, are extreme examples of those attempting to escape reality.

Most young women manage to keep their weight within reasonable bounds before marriage regardless of inheritance or childhood. Once married, doubts may arise about their domestic life, their appearance, their husband's love, their sex life—all leading to fears, frustrations, anxieties. What results? They slip back into that delightful Never Never Land of childhood, protected from the cruel world by their doting parents—and what better way of achieving that blissful feeling than by eating "reward" food?

Always the foods of childhood: the secretly gobbled chocolate cake, the ice-cream soda, candy—all the beloved simple pleasures of children with their primitive desires for the sweetest and least sophisticated of foods.

#### Working toward a solution

What is there to do about the problem? Recognize once and for all that no excuse is satisfactory, and that regardless of the reason you ascribe for your excess weight, care and attention to what you eat will reduce your weight—and keep you reduced.

If you have been overweight for a consistent number of years, or have a tendency to gain weight, recognize the probability that you'll have to watch your weight for the rest of your life. The subconscious control of weight and appetite that many people have must be replaced by a *conscious* mental check on your part. You can and must think out your overweight problem for yourself. Determine, for your own private information, why you have an excessive desire for food, and what prompts you to overeat. When disturbed by a problem, don't eat to calm yourself. Buy a new hat if you must, but certainly don't eat. Food is for nutrition, not to furnish you with an emotional panacea. Separate eating and food from your emotional life; if you can determine what association causes you to eat when troubled, you'll have most of the problem under control. If you have a weight problem, it'll be necessary to fight it relentlessly, *mostly by thinking it out*. You're going to break with your old food habits, your old eating pattern. It will be necessary for you to resist them in the same fashion that an alcoholic fights a Scotch and soda, in the same manner a chain smoker resists a cigarette. Food addiction, much as alcoholic or smoking excesses, may be even worse for your general health, well-being and life span than either of those two habits.

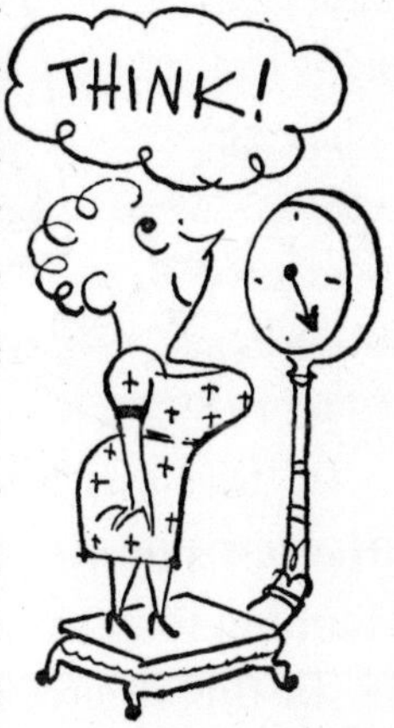

Eating is an everyday business. Most people manage with a reasonable breakfast. Even lunch isn't too difficult to keep within bounds. But later in the day, when emotional stresses make themselves felt, there comes the drive to eat and eat. Don't put something into your mouth merely because you're bored, troubled or irritated. Even if you think you're hungry, stop! Are you? Or is it just a habit pattern, much as you always put on your coat in exactly the same way every day of your life? Develop the habit of *thinking* before you eat.

**All about calories**

The body requires energy in the form of food in order to function. As a rough example, your body may be compared to a steam engine, taking in a heating material (food) and water (fluids). The food is burned in the mechanism and the burning brings the body temperature to 98.6 degrees, the normal temperature. In cold weather, the body works harder than in warm, and burns more energy to bring it to the required temperature. That is why our appetite demands heavy, substantial heating foods when the thermometer reads 30° and calls for crisp salads (low-calorie) and cooling drinks when the hot summer sun shines. But awake or asleep, our system is at work burning food to keep us alive.

In this regard, scientists have measured food energy and introduced a word that has become an important part of our everyday language, *calorie*. But actually, what is a calorie? It is an artificial measurement, admittedly, but is roughly the amount of heating power required to raise the temperature of a pint of water by 8° F.

How was it determined that an apple, for example, has 100 calories? This was learned by means of a bomb calorimeter, so-called because it is a glass-enclosed device in the rounded shape of a bomb. The food to be tested is placed in it and fired by an electric impulse. As the apple burns, it throws off heat; the heat raises the temperature of a measured quantity of water, and the number of calories in the food is determined. Thus, we have a unit for measuring the fuel values of the foods we eat. But unfortunately for the sake of simplicity, not all calories react within the human body in the same fashion. To understand this, it is necessary to learn about the three different types of food—proteins, carbohydrates and fats. (Actually, there is a fourth source of energy, alcohol, which we'll discuss later.)

*Proteins*, as most people have heard, are required by the body to build up its structure from day to day. Although carbohydrates and fats are quickly utilized for energy purposes, the proteins' primary function is to repair and restore the body's tissues. Of course, if an excess of protein is consumed, it may occasionally be used for energy.

Proteins are a complex combination consisting of many smaller units known as *amino acids* of which about twenty-five are known to science. The human body has the power to manufacture about fifteen amino acids, but ten must be furnished by the food we eat; these latter are called "essential amino acids." Good health cannot be maintained without the essential amino acids and the diet must include a fair proportion of protein food in order to supply the body with those it cannot manufacture. Foods which have *all* the essential amino acids are called "complete proteins"; those with some but not all are described as "incomplete proteins." The best-known complete-protein foods are meats, fish, poultry, eggs and milk. While all foods classified as protein contain some amino acids, it is only those of animal origin which have the complete structure. Next in order of importance as a source of protein are the legumes, including green beans, lima beans, peas and peanuts, followed by cereals, both cooked and dry. Fruits and vegetables (other than the legumes) may have some protein.

*Carbohydrates* supply the body with energy. It has been estimated that the average American consumes about two-thirds of his total diet in the form of carbohydrates, too high a proportion in the opinion of experts. Much of the energy supplied is made available to the body quickly, and athletes therefore eat lumps of sugar immediately before a contest as a source of immediate energy. Carbohydrate foods may be divided into starches and sugars. The most common starches include flours, breads, cakes and certain vegetables (the potato, for instance). Sugar foods

include syrups, jams, fruits and table sugar.

*Fats* are also used by the body to furnish energy and actually supply twice as much, in proportion to their weight as do the proteins and carbohydrates. The foods highest in fats are butter, milk, cream, fatty meats, egg yolks and all of the edible fatty oils (such as lard and olive oil). When we consume in excess of the body's requirements, it is stored in the form of fat. Nature is economical, and uses the most compact form. Surplus carbohydrates must be converted by the body into fat before storing, but excess fat is almost ready for storage without chemical conversion.

### The chemistry of metabolism

When your body obtains less than its required food supply, it draws upon the reservoir of fat, thus causing a loss of weight. When you eat more than your bodily requirements, the excess is stored, thus resulting in a weight increase. It is as simple as that.

There are approximately 3600 calories in each pound of body weight. Thus, if you eat 3600 calories more than your body requires, you will gain one pound. Equally, if you consume 3600 less calories than is necessary for your needs, you'll lose one pound. But there are additional complications, inasmuch as the body must burn up calories in order to utilize the food you've eaten. It must be converted chemically into substances the system can cope with. Fats require the least conversion since the body customarily stores excess food energy in the form of fat. Only 5 per cent of the food value consumed is expended in converting food fats into storage fats, and therefore 95 per cent of this is available to the body. Carbohydrates are almost equally available. But protein is entirely different, as the metabolic system must work strenuously in order to convert the meat or fish we eat into substances which the body needs. It requires about 35 per cent of the value of protein food in order to convert it into substances useful to the human body. Thus when you eat 100 calories of protein, 35 calories are burned up, leaving only 65 calories available, a bargain that no dieter should pass up. In the caloric computations, some regard is given to this factor, often called the "specific dynamic action" of food. But the inescapable fact remains that carbohydrates and fats are comparatively simple foods, while proteins have complex amino-acid structures requiring a considerable expenditure of energy by the human system before the food energy is available. To put it another way, let us consider two impossible diets, merely for illustrative purposes. If a person lived on nothing but 1200 calories a day of whipped cream, at the end of the week he would have lost two pounds, assuming he was still alive. Then say a second dieter lived on nothing but 1200 calories a day of lean meat; at the end of the week, he would have lost considerably more than the whipped cream dieter because of the specific dynamic action of protein foods. Neither of these can be recommended, for both are harmful.

Fats make many foods palatable, but only very small amounts are essential to human nutrition. Carbohydrates, on the other hand, form an important substance in the body by conversion into *glycogen.* This is stored in the liver which releases small quantities gradually into the blood stream in the form of *glucose,* thus maintaining at a steady rate the percentage of sugar in the blood stream. The liver acts as a reserve depot in the event the body does not obtain carbohydrates, but the storage supply is sufficient for only about one day's use. Once the liver obtains its required supply of glycogen, the excess carbohydrates are converted into fat and stored in the muscles. Therefore, it is obvious that carbohydrates should not be eliminated completely from the diet because the body works more efficiently when the diet contains carbohydrates, but the intake should be limited.

**WOMEN**

| Height (with shoes * on) | | Weight in Pounds (as ordinarily dressed) | | |
|---|---|---|---|---|
| Feet | Inches | Small Frame | Medium Frame | Large Frame |
| 4 | 11 | 104-111 | 110-118 | 117-127 |
| 5 | 0 | 105-113 | 112-120 | 119-129 |
| 5 | 1 | 107-115 | 114-122 | 121-131 |
| 5 | 2 | 110-118 | 117-125 | 124-135 |
| 5 | 3 | 113-121 | 120-128 | 127-138 |
| 5 | 4 | 116-125 | 124-132 | 131-142 |
| 5 | 5 | 119-128 | 127-135 | 133-145 |
| 5 | 6 | 123-132 | 130-140 | 138-150 |
| 5 | 7 | 126-136 | 134-144 | 142-154 |
| 5 | 8 | 129-139 | 137-147 | 145-158 |
| 5 | 9 | 133-143 | 141-151 | 149-162 |
| 5 | 10 | 136-147 | 145-155 | 152-166 |
| 5 | 11 | 139-150 | 148-158 | 155-169 |

* 2-inch heels

**MEN**

| Height (with shoes * on) | | Weight in Pounds (as ordinarily dressed) | | |
|---|---|---|---|---|
| Feet | Inches | Small Frame | Medium Frame | Large Frame |
| 5 | 2 | 116-125 | 124-133 | 131-142 |
| 5 | 3 | 119-128 | 127-136 | 133-144 |
| 5 | 4 | 122-132 | 130-140 | 137-149 |
| 5 | 5 | 126-136 | 134-144 | 141-153 |
| 5 | 6 | 129-139 | 137-147 | 145-157 |
| 5 | 7 | 133-143 | 141-151 | 149-162 |
| 5 | 8 | 136-147 | 145-156 | 153-166 |
| 5 | 9 | 140-151 | 149-160 | 157-170 |
| 5 | 10 | 144-155 | 153-164 | 161-175 |
| 5 | 11 | 148-159 | 157-168 | 165-180 |
| 6 | 0 | 152-164 | 161-173 | 169-185 |
| 6 | 1 | 157-169 | 166-178 | 174-190 |
| 6 | 2 | 163-175 | 171-184 | 179-196 |
| 6 | 3 | 168-180 | 176-189 | 184-202 |

* 1-inch heels

Source: Metropolitan Life Insurance Company

**How many calories do you need each day?**

METHOD #1: This is an individual problem because no two people are exactly alike, physically or emotionally, nor do they expend the same amount of energy. However, certain basic starting points are known. Generally speaking, most people require 15 calories for each pound of their *ideal* or *desired* weight. This does not refer to your present weight, assuming you're overweight. Find your ideal weight from chart at left. Be sure to classify yourself correctly; don't stretch a point by putting yourself in the "large frame" category when in fact it's "medium."

To illustrate, let us assume that you are 5 feet 4 inches in height and have a medium frame. Consulting the 5-foot 6-inch category (inasmuch as the chart allows for 2-inch heels), you learn that your weight should range from 130 to 140 pounds, or say 135 as an average when dressed, but not including a coat.

As mentioned previously, tests have shown that approximately 15 calories are required each day to maintain a pound of weight for the average housewife or office worker. Physically active people (those performing hours of heavy labor) require about 20 calories per pound and occasionally even more. Thus, an average woman would require 15 calories for each of her 135 pounds of *ideal* weight (you may disregard the few pounds of clothing involved). A simple multiplication shows she must obtain 2025 calories to maintain that weight.

METHOD #2: This is the number of calories expended per hour by the average person in everyday activities:

| | | | |
|---|---|---|---|
| Sleeping | 70 | Washing dishes | 150 |
| Sitting up | 100 | Vacuuming house | 150 |
| Reading | 110 | Sweeping, with broom | 170 |
| Office work | 120 | Walking, slow pace | 200 |
| Sewing, knitting | 120 | Golfing | 250 |
| Typing | 130 | Steady exercise (tennis, etc.) | 400 |
| Ironing | 150 | Running | 500 |
| Standing, filing | 150 | | |

Using the above table, let's run off a test on yourself. Assume that you sleep 8 hours daily, work at an office 7 hours, travel to and from work 1 hour, spend about 7 hours at normal social life (talking, reading, eating meals, etc.), and take a slow walk (including walking to and from transportation, shopping, etc.) for 1 hour daily.

The figures on p. 26 are rounded off for convenience. Those who are over 45 years of age should subtract 100 calories from the total because of slower metabolic rate; if over 65, subtract 200 calories. If you live at a high altitude (say, over 4,000 feet above sea level), your metabolism works faster because of the thinner atmosphere and therefore 100 calories should be added to your total count. Those who reside at sea level in a warm climate (Florida, for example) should deduct 100 calories.

| | |
|---|---|
| 8 hours sleep (at 70 calories) | = 560 |
| 7 hours office work (at 120 calories) | = 840 |
| 1 hour travel time (at 120 calories) | = 120 |
| 7 hours social life (at 110 calories) | = 770 |
| 1 hour walking (at 200 calories) | = 200 |
| Total | 2490 calories per day |

Now you can ascertain your caloric needs by comparing the totals reached in methods #1 and #2. Let us suppose that the total for method #1 is 2100 calories and for method #2 is 2300 calories; this balances out at 2200 calories per day. Now it is a simple matter to compute the caloric intake permitted to lose, say, 1 pound per week. Dividing 3600 calories (the number in a pound) by 7 (the days in a week) results in a daily figure of 514, or 500 for convenience as a guide to weight loss. If you consume 500 calories per day less than your body requires, you will lose 1 pound each week. Assuming, as in the above illustration, that your normal requirements are 2200 calories a day, you would subtract 500 and find that your daily caloric quota is 1700 to lose the required pound each week. To lose 2 pounds per week, 1000 calories must be omitted from the day's quota; deducted from the 2200 allowance, this would permit only 1200 calories daily, about as low as you should go under any circumstances. It is always advisable to have a physician give you a physical check-up before commencing a diet. Beginning on page 37, you'll find 30 days of menus for 1200-, 1500- and 1800-calorie diets.

*Alcohol:* Inasmuch as a great many adult Americans drink to a greater or lesser degree, the problem of alcoholic beverages as it affects diets cannot be overlooked. Alcohol has calories, too, just as do proteins, fats and carbohydrates. In fact, the number of calories in a mixed drink is startlingly high. Because the body lacks the equipment to convert alcohol into fat, it changes it into a substance for expenditure in the form of energy, oxidizing it at a steady rate. For this reason, those who drink excessively, and eat very little food, will not gain weight because the body cannot store the excess alcoholic calories in the form of fat. However, if you drink and then eat, your system will first burn the calories of alcohol and then those provided by the food, resulting in a weight gain if the total intake is excessive.

Alcohol is a depressant and has a narcotic effect when taken in more than very moderate quantities. It acts as a stimulant only if consumed in small amounts.

On diets, one plain alcoholic drink per day is permissible (although due caloric allowance must be made). The 1800-calorie diets in this book make allowance for a moderate amount of alcohol, if you so desire. A very small quantity produces a more vigorous heartbeat and a slight increase in blood pressure. An increased supply of blood is brought close to the skin, causing the body to throw off more heat, the familiar warm sensation customarily experienced after a drink. If you can do without liquor while bringing your weight back to normal, do so. However, if it is part of your daily pattern to have a pre-dinner drink you may continue, because the only way to stay on a diet is to follow a long-range plan. If you prefer, you may have two glasses of dry (not sweet) red or white wine with your dinner, if your calorie allowance is 1800 or over. But don't forget to tally up the calories; your system will, even if you don't.

# Dieting with the Family

The most difficult part of dieting, without any doubt, is eating completely different foods from the other members of your family. The Slenderella Cook Book eliminates forever this unpleasant aspect of weight control. Everyone in the family can eat the same delicious but calorie-reduced dishes.

Dieters *must* (and this cannot be overemphasized) adhere to the size of serving as specified in each recipe; nondieters can have larger servings plus supplementary bread, butter and whole milk. In this fashion, the dieters and nondieters will be eating the same foods, but those who are not watching their weight will be able to make up the calorie differential. And remember one important fact—*every adult*, even those at a normal weight, should know the number of calories he requires to maintain his correct weight. A very slight change in eating habits usually brings about a decided weight change; learn to watch your calories and avoid exceeding your quota. It is never too early or too late to groove in your consciousness a proper pattern of eating.

The size of servings set forth in the book are adequate for everyone (even though, in some cases, they are smaller than your customary portions). If you want to develop proper eating habits, avoid second helpings except very occasionally. Meat, in particular, is basically high in calories and that fact cannot be mitigated by pointing out that it is a protein food. Remember that the average steak, as served in a good steak restaurant, contains from 1200 to 1600 calories. This does not allow a weight watcher much leeway for other foods. You can and should eat meat, but limit the size of portions to what you can spare and still have a well-rounded, healthful diet. On the other hand, chicken and fish are quite low in calories, thus permitting the dieter to have a greater quantity.

The menus in this book are balanced so that children are well provided for, with minor additions. Childhood, as we all know, is the time when food habits are instilled, so give them the proper foundation for adult life. Don't permit them to eat carelessly, so that in later life they find it necessary to bring their weight down.

# A Few Suggestions on Food for Children

Infants under one to two years of age require a special diet; your doctor will prescribe the proper foods for your child. From two to six years of age, generally described as the "preschool age," the child's diet should emphasize foods that keep him in good health and also assist him to grow in size.

Some children will eat almost anything that is placed before them while others will linger and dawdle over each mouthful. The slow or poor eater should be encouraged to eat, but threats or promises are not recommended; food should be treated as a matter of course, and should not be overemphasized, no matter how trying it may be to the harassed mother. Children in the preschool age group are changing constantly in their food habits; this is easily noticed in their volatile likes and dislikes. They often go on food "jags"—that is, they develop a violent preference for a particular food or foods and eat it regularly and steadily day after day, until finally they become satiated and refuse it completely.

Preschool children should be encouraged to eat a wide *variety* of foods, since no one food will supply all the necessary elements for health. Here are the foods which *must* be included daily:

1 (or more) servings of leafy green and yellow vegetables; dark-green and yellow vegetables are especially valuable.

1 (or more) servings of oranges, grapefruit, tomatoes, raw cabbage, salad greens, or other good sources of vitamin C; also good are tomato juice, cantaloupe, raw pineapple or other fresh fruits.

2 (or more) servings of potatoes and other vegetables and fruit; in wintertime you may substitute prunes, dried fruits and similar foods for the more expensive vegetables and fruits.
3 to 4 cups of milk; fresh, unsweetened evaporated or powdered milk are all satisfactory; cheese or ice cream can be partly used as substitutes.
1 (or more) servings of meat, poultry, fish and eggs; these protein foods are very valuable to the growing child; serve the child at least 4 eggs weekly.
3 servings of bread, flour foods and cereals; at least 1 serving at each meal.
Fats should be included in the diet; butter and fortified margarine are the commonest sources.

If these foods are included in the daily diet, the child may eat any other desired foods (with a few exceptions), but with poor eaters it is of the utmost importance that these vital foods be included in the day's intake before the child's own preferences come into play. A child may eat candies, cookies or other sweets providing they do not impair his appetite for the more important health-giving foods listed above. But sweets are valuable to the growing child since they supply quick energy, and most children burn up fabulous numbers of calories in their play.

Bear in mind that children are mimics; they imitate what they see. If you want your child to grow up with good eating habits, be sure that you have them yourself and set a good example. Drink some milk in order to encourage your child to drink his. If you refuse to eat many foods, you can't reasonably expect your child to grow up and enjoy a wide variety of foods.

Desserts, or other foods highly regarded by children, should never be offered as a prize or reward. If you do so, the child will naturally place a false value upon them, and will also learn to regard the less interesting foods (such as fish or vegetables) as unpleasant. Treat goodies in as matter-of-fact a fashion as possible.

If a child is served with meat, potatoes and vegetables, he may finish his meat first, then eat the potatoes and finally the vegetables. Other children like to eat from all three foods more or less simultaneously. This is completely harmless, and the child should be permitted to eat in either fashion. Also, some children like to eat small amounts frequently during the day. While it is more convenient to have regular meal hours for the child, with difficult or "problem" eaters it should be remembered that the most important point is that the child should receive the proper foods and not just eat snacks. It might be advisable to seat the child at his regular place (when eating between meals) in order to create a semblance of meal-like regularity, and avoid placing undue emphasis upon the pleasure of between-meal eating.

Between the ages of six to fourteen, most children thrive best on what might be described as a light diet, chiefly based upon simple, wholesome foods. The usual caloric allowance is from 2,000 to 2,500.

# Eating Out

The complete bore, comedians say, was born in Texas, educated at Harvard, served in the Marines, and is always bragging about his grandchildren. To that list might be added the person who always talks about his diet.

When you're invited to someone's home for dinner, *don't* bore the group by discussing your diet. It may be fascinating to you, but not necessarily to others. *Don't* sit down at a festive dinner table, complete with flowers, candlelight and a wide selection of fine dishes on which the hostess has expended considerable time and effort, and announce proudly, "I'm afraid I'll just have to wait for the coffee. I'm on a diet." That kind of a pall cast on a party might make you quite unpopular with the hostess who has planned the meal for weeks and probably worked on it for several days.

It's all completely unnecessary. You *can* eat proper weight-control foods even at a banquet, by using a little thought. Contrary to general belief, most foods are not basically fattening but end up that way because of preparation and the addition of gravies and sauces. If your first course is a fruit or sea-food cocktail, no undue problem is encountered. With pastry-wrapped foods, eat only the filling. And be sure *not* to sit there like a martyr, looking down ruefully at your plate in the hope that someone will notice and commiserate with you. That's a purely childish desire to attract attention and gain sympathy, a favorite device of youngsters who scream and have tantrums when their parents leave them with a baby sitter. You're above all that, or you can't be seriously interested in reducing or weight control.

With soups, you can have all you want of clear soups and bouillons, but if it's creamed, eat just a few, say 3, tablespoons—no more! Don't put your spoon down ostentatiously, so that your hostess casts a disconcerted glance in your direction. Engage your neighbors in conversation and no one will notice.

Poultry, meats and fish are usually acceptable to dieters. If the food has been fried, lift off the exterior with a knife and fork. Trim away all excess fats on meats, but again, it isn't necessary to call attention to yourself.

Vegetables (other than the creamed or heavily sauced types) are the one place in the meal where you can go overboard and have as large a portion as you like. Even potatoes are permitted (except for fried or creamed styles), but just take a modest portion. Don't even nibble at the au gratin or hash-browned potatoes; don't even tempt your will power. Salads may be dangerous, if they have oil or mayonnaise. Just take a small amount.

As for desserts, if it's a fruit or simple dessert, no prohibition is involved. It's those rich concoctions that are so troublesome to the weight watcher. All you can do, if you're eating it, is to remove any whipped cream or sauces and eat as sparingly as you can. Again, don't flaunt your self-sacrifice; no one *really* cares except you. When coffee is served, why not have it black? If not, have very little cream; try to wean yourself away from it completely. Avoid sugar. Use Sucaryl or saccharine if you must.

You're going to be greatly surprised to learn that if you don't announce you're on a diet or put a sad, woebegone expression on your face, most people won't even notice that you're weight conscious. If your principal goal is to arouse sympathy or to attract attention, that's very disappointing. If you're serious about controlling your weight, it's an achievement because it proves you can live your normal life and still watch the calories.

In restaurants, the luncheon suggestions in the 1200-, 1500- and 1800-calorie menus will be suitable. You should experience no difficulty at all. Dinners in restaurants are more easily controlled than at someone's home because there's no sensitive hostess to contend with and the menu usually has a wide enough selection to permit a fairly free choice. Don't order carelessly; look the menu over and make a proper choice—that is, what you want to eat and yet not go outside of your caloric allowance.

### Appetizer or Soup

*Recommended:* Sea-food cocktails (without Russian dressing) ; clear soups; bouillons; clam or beef broth; fresh vegetable soup; tomato, grapefruit or sauerkraut juice; caviar; fresh fruit cup; grapefruit, melon; celery and radishes.
*Go easy with:* Clam chowder; barley, chicken-noodle, onion soup; Scotch broth; gumbos; olives; smoked trout; sturgeon; pineapple or prune juice; pickled herring; chopped chicken livers.
*Special occasions only:* Cream soups, minestrone, bean, lentil, oxtail, pepperpot, pea or potato soup; canned fruit cocktail; smoked ham; smoked salmon; Italian antipasto; pâté de foie gras.

### Main Course

*Recommended:* Any broiled fish (except shad, salmon or swordfish) ; small steak; broiled or boiled chicken; veal; broiled sweetbreads; broiled calf's liver or chicken livers; kidneys; boiled beef; squab; tongue; pheasant; quail; rabbit; venison; steamed clams; broiled or boiled lobster; frogs' legs; broiled scallops.
*Go easy with:* Broiled shad, salmon or swordfish; roast pork or ham; lamb chops; roast leg of lamb; lamb stew; chipped beef; chicken croquettes; roast beef; pot roast; beef stew; hamburgers; corned beef; kippered herring.
*Special occasions only:* Fried fish or shellfish; frankfurters; sausages; pizza; spaghetti or noodle dishes; fried chicken; chicken à la king; duck; goose, turkey and dressing; corned-beef hash; large "restaurant-style" steaks; spareribs; oyster stew.

### Vegetables

(All of the following are plain boiled, without dressings or sauces other than 1 teaspoon butter.)

*Recommended:* Asparagus; green beans, bean sprouts; beet greens; broccoli; cabbage; carrots; cauliflower; celery; cress; cucumbers; dandelion greens; eggplant; endive; lettuce; mushrooms; mustard greens; green peppers; radishes; sauerkraut; spinach; summer squash; Swiss chard; tomatoes; turnip greens.

*Go easy with:* French artichokes; beets; Brussels sprouts; kohlrabi; okra; onions; green peas; red peppers; potato, baked or boiled; winter squash; turnips.

*Special occasions only:* Beans, dried; lima beans; corn; dried peas; fried onions; sweet potatoes; white potatoes, fried, hashed-brown, au gratin; boiled or fried rice.

**Desserts**

*Recommended:* Fresh fruit cup; grapefruit; melon, fresh berries; any fresh fruit; cup custard; water ices; angel-food cake; coffee or vanilla ice cream (1 small scoop); frozen custard (1 small scoop); small piece any cheese and 2 crackers.

*Go easy with:* Baked apple; applesauce; fruit gelatin desserts; stewed fruit; milk sherbets; cornstarch puddings; coffee or vanilla ice cream (average serving); rice pudding; bread pudding; prune whip, jelly roll; small fruit tart; plain coffee cake; plain doughnut (1); canned fruits (no syrup); custard pie.

*Special occasions only:* ice cream with fruit or nuts; peach, cherry, pineapple, banana or chocolate ice cream; apple brown Betty; tapioca pudding; cheese cake; pastries of all types; fruit, layer or iced cakes; strawberry shortcake; butter cake; fruit pies; chocolate pudding.

# 1200-Calorie Menus for 30 Days

**Breakfast**

*Choice of:*
Orange juice (4 ounces)
Grapefruit juice (4 ounces)
Tomato juice (8 ounces)

1 egg, boiled or poached
1 slice bread
1 teaspoon butter or margarine

Coffee or tea with Sucaryl or saccharin and 2 tablespoons milk (this applies to lunch and dinner as well)

**Lunch**

*Choice of:*
Sandwich made with 2 pieces of bread (toasted or untoasted), no mayonnaise or butter:
Cheese (2 thin slices, any cheese)
Bacon and tomato
Roast beef
Sliced chicken
Corned beef (lean)
Fried egg
Sliced egg
Ham (1 thin slice)
Hamburger (small)
Pastrami (lean)
Bologna (2 thin slices)

Tongue (3 thin slices)

*or*

Broiled, boiled or steamed fish
(any variety but salmon, shad or swordfish)

*or*

Vegetable, fruit or sea-food salad
(no mayonnaise or cream dressing)

Coffee or tea

**Before Retiring**

1 8-ounce glass of skim milk or buttermilk

| **Dinner Menus** | *For children add:* |
|---|---|
| Fillet of Beef in Wine Sauce | Fruit juice |
| Baked Stuffed Potatoes | Butter on potato |
| Roast-pepper Salad | Bread and butter |
| Meringue Surprise | Milk |
| Coffee | |
| | |
| Stuffed Breast of Veal | Fruit Cup |
| Green Beans in Tomato Sauce | Bread and butter |
| Baked Acorn Squash | Milk |
| Mocha Cake | |
| Coffee | |
| | |
| Manhattan Clam Chowder | Potato |
| Broiled Liver | Bread and butter |
| Marinated String Beans | Milk |
| Cucumber Salad | |
| Pumpkin Pie | |
| Coffee | |

| **Dinner Menus** | *For children add:* |
|---|---|
| Cream of Tomato Soup<br>Baked Fried Chicken<br>Sauerkraut in White Wine<br>Baked Potato<br>Lime Pie<br>Coffee | Bread and butter<br>Butter on potato<br>Milk |
| Smoked Beef Tongue<br>Hot German Potato Salad<br>Coleslaw with Sour Cream<br>Nut Torte<br>Coffee | Vegetable soup<br>Bread and butter<br>Milk |
| Roast Fillet of Beef<br>Red Coleslaw<br>Braised Broccoli<br>Dessert Pancakes<br>Coffee | Tomato juice<br>Bread and butter<br>Potato<br>Milk |
| New England Clam Chowder<br>Chicken Livers en Brochette<br>Peas, French Style<br>Sautéed Cabbage<br>Banana Ice Cream<br>Coffee | Bread and butter<br>Milk |
| Cheddar Cheese Soup<br>Baked Scallops<br>Succotash<br>Baked Stuffed Tomatoes<br>Chocolate Cake<br>Coffee | Bread and butter<br>Milk |

| **Dinner Menus** | *For children add:* |
|---|---|
| Boiled Shrimp with Cocktail Sauce<br>Chicken Chow Mein<br>Boiled rice<br>Chocolate Chiffon Pie<br>Coffee | Bread and butter<br>Salad<br>Milk |
| Cold Cream of Cucumber Soup<br>Baked Veal Loaf<br>Italian Green Salad<br>Mocha Meringue Rice Pudding<br>Coffee | Baked potato and butter<br>Milk |
| Brown Cabbage Soup<br>Chicken Cacciatore<br>1 cup boiled Egg Noodles<br>Green Beans<br>Lemon Meringue Pie<br>Coffee | Bread and butter<br>Butter on vegetable<br>Milk |
| Chicken Soup<br>Norwegian Hamburgers<br>Mushroom Sauté<br>Baked Potato<br>Apple Snow Pudding<br>Coffee | Bread and butter<br>Milk |
| Shrimp Gumbo<br>Broiled Sweetbreads<br>Potatoes au Gratin<br>Braised Celery<br>Ice-cream Dessert<br>Coffee | Bread and butter<br>Milk |
| Cream of Spinach Soup<br>Fillet of Sole, Bonne Femme<br>Mixed Vegetable Casserole<br>Boiled Potato<br>Coconut Cake<br>Coffee | Bread and butter<br>Butter on potato<br>Milk |

| **Dinner Menus** | *For children add:* |
| --- | --- |
| Tomato Juice<br>Meat Loaf<br>French Fried Potatoes<br>Harvard Beets<br>Strawberry Sponge<br>Coffee | Bread and butter<br>Milk |
| Veal Ragout<br>Baked Stuffed Potato<br>Tomatoes and Okra<br>Chocolate Ice Cream<br>Coffee | Tomato Soup<br>Bread and butter<br>Milk |
| Stuffed Cabbage<br>Baked Potato<br>Nesselrode Pie<br>Coffee | Vegetable Soup<br>Bread and butter<br>Salad<br>Milk |
| Clear Vegetable Soup<br>Pork-chop-and-apple Casserole<br>Baked Acorn Squash<br>Baked Custard<br>Coffee | Bread and butter<br>Potato<br>Milk |
| Tomato Bouillon<br>Baked Fish, Italian Style<br>Swiss Potatoes<br>Baked Carrots<br>Green Salad<br>Devil's-food Cake<br>Coffee | Bread and butter<br>Milk |
| Beef Soup<br>Beef Fricassee<br>Green Peas and Potato Casserole<br>Cucumber Salad<br>Orange Whip<br>Coffee | Rice in soup<br>Bread and butter<br>Milk |

| **Dinner Menus** | *For children add:* |
|---|---|
| Black-bean Soup<br>Deep-dish Chicken Pie<br>Salad à la Grecque<br>Apple Charlotte<br>Coffee | Bread and butter<br>Spinach<br>Milk |
| Pistou Soup<br>Lamb and Rice Casserole<br>Creamed Spinach<br>Green-pepper Salad<br>Custard Pie<br>Coffee | Bread and butter<br>Milk |
| Okra Chowder<br>Salmon Divan<br>Savoyard Potatoes<br>Asparagus<br>Cheese Cake<br>Coffee | Bread and butter<br>Milk |
| Vegetable Soup<br>Curried Chicken Stew<br>¾ cup boiled noodles<br>Baked Lettuce<br>Coconut Cream Pie<br>Coffee | Bread and butter<br>Butter on noodles<br>Milk |
| Cream of Spinach Soup<br>Eggs, Butcher Style<br>½ cup Boiled rice<br>Mixed Vegetable Casserole<br>Strawberry Fluff Pie<br>Coffee | Bread and butter<br>Milk |

# 1500-Calorie Menus for 30 Days

**Breakfast**

*Choice of:*
Orange juice (4 ounces)
Grapefruit juice (4 ounces)
Tomato juice (8 ounces)

1 egg, boiled or poached
1 slice bread
1 teaspoon butter or margarine
2 slices bacon
*or*
½ cup cooked or dry cereal
1 teaspoon sugar
1 cup skim milk

Coffee or Tea
with Sucaryl or saccharin
and 2 tablespoons milk
(this applies to lunch and dinner)

**Lunch**

*Choice of:*
Sandwich made with 2 pieces of bread (toasted or untoasted), no mayonnaise or butter:

Cheese (2 thin slices, any cheese)
Bacon and tomato
Roast beef
Sliced chicken

Sliced turkey
Corned beef (lean)
Fried egg
Sliced egg
Ham (1 thin slice)
Hamburger (small)
Bologna (2 thin slices)
Tongue (3 thin slices)
Salami (2 thin slices)
Tunafish (drained)

*or*

Broiled, boiled or steamed fish (any variety but salmon, shad or swordfish)

*or*

Vegetable, fruit or sea-food salad (no mayonnaise or cream dressing)

*Choice of:*

Fruit Cup
Melon
Any fresh fruit
Applesauce
Angel Cake
Canned fruit (no syrup)
Cup Custard
Jello
Coffee or Tea

**Before Retiring**

1 8-ounce glass of skim milk or buttermilk

| **Dinner Menus** | *For children add:* |
|---|---|
| Roast Fillet of Beef | Tomato juice |
| Baked Potato | Butter on potato |
| Baked Stuffed Tomatoes | Milk |
| Coconut Cake | |
| Coffee | |
| | |
| Clear Broth | Rice in broth |
| Duck with Orange Sauce | Bread and butter |
| Peas, French Style | Milk |
| Swiss Potatoes | |
| French Cream | |
| Coffee | |

| **Dinner Menus** | *For children add:* |
|---|---|
| Shrimp Gumbo<br>Baked Tongue<br>Savoyard Potatoes<br>Tomato Vegetable Salad<br>Deep-dish Apple Pie<br>Coffee | Bread and butter<br>Milk |
| Chicken Broth<br>Pot Roast<br>Boiled Potato<br>Creamed Carrots<br>Mocha Biscuit<br>Coffee | Butter on Potato<br>Bread and butter<br>Milk |
| Scotch Broth<br>Chicken Divan<br>Buttered Beets<br>Lima Beans in Yogurt<br>Italian Green Salad<br>Gingerbread<br>Coffee | Bread and butter<br>Whipped cream on ice cream or gingerbread<br>Milk |
| Roast Loin of Pork<br>Sweet-and-sour Red Cabbage<br>Candied Sweet Potato<br>Italian Green Salad<br>Devil's-food Cake<br>Coffee | Juice<br>Bread and butter<br>Milk |
| Beef Stew<br>1 cup boiled Egg Noodles<br>Home-style Salad<br>Nut Cake<br>Coffee | Fruit Cup<br>Bread and butter<br>Butter on noodles<br>Milk |

| **Dinner Menus** | *For children add:* |
| --- | --- |
| Barbecued Spareribs<br>Lobster Cantonese<br>½ cup boiled rice<br>Ice-cream Dessert<br>Coffee | Bread and butter<br>Green peas<br>Milk |
| Clear Vegetable Soup<br>Stuffed Capon<br>Candied Sweet Potatoes<br>Deviled Tomatoes<br>Cheese Cake<br>Coffee | Crackers with soup<br>Bread and butter<br>Milk |
| Anchovy Salad<br>Veal Paprika<br>½ cup rice<br>Sautéed Artichokes<br>Chocolate Chiffon Pie<br>Coffee | Bread and butter<br>Butter on rice<br>Milk |
| Marinated Roast Beef<br>Green Pea and Potato Casserole<br>Broiled Stuffed Mushrooms<br>Strawberry Fluff Pie<br>Coffee | Bread and butter<br>Whipped cream on pie<br>Milk |
| Black-bean Soup<br>ChickenTetrazzinni<br>Stuffed Artichokes<br>Chiffonade Salad<br>One-egg Cake<br>Coffee | Bread and butter<br>Milk |

| **Dinner Menus** | *For children add:* |
|---|---|
| Chicken Soup<br>Veal Parmigiana<br>Italian-style Green-pepper Sauté<br>Swiss Potatoes<br>Endive Salad<br>Baked Bananas<br>Coffee | Bread and butter<br>Milk |
| Philadelphia Pepper Pot<br>Baked Trout Meunière<br>Potatoes au Gratin<br>Carrots and Apples<br>Spinach Salad<br>Chocolate Custard<br>Coffee | Bread and butter<br>Milk |
| Cream of Spinach Soup<br>Beef Roulades<br>Baked Potato<br>Mixed Salad with Cottage Cheese<br>Mocha Biscuit<br>Coffee | Bread and butter<br>Milk |
| Vegetable Soup<br>Veal Ragout<br>Potato Soufflé<br>Green Beans<br>French Cream<br>Coffee | Bread and butter<br>Butter on beans<br>Milk |
| Roast Fresh Ham<br>Hot German Potato Salad<br>Sauerkraut Slaw<br>Peach Pie<br>Coffee | Tomato juice<br>Bread and butter<br>Milk |

| **Dinner Menus** | *For children add:* |
|---|---|
| 3 Pickled Clams<br>Roast Turkey<br>Glazed Onions<br>Baked Mashed Sweet Potatoes<br>White Cake<br>Coffee | Butter on potato<br>Bread and butter<br>Ice cream with cake<br>Milk |
| Pan-broiled Steak<br>Potatoes in sour cream<br>Home-style Salad<br>Baked Pears<br>Coffee | Fruit juice<br>Bread and butter<br>Cream with pears<br>Milk |
| Fish Chowder<br>Chicken Livers Sauté<br>Baked Stuffed Potatoes<br>Brussels Sprouts and Chestnuts<br>Banana Ice Cream<br>Coffee | Biscuit and butter<br>Milk |
| Roast Leg of Lamb<br>French Fried Onions<br>Baked Potato<br>Tomato-vegetable Salad<br>Pound Cake<br>Coffee | Butter on potato<br>Ice cream with pound cake<br>Milk |
| Onion Soup<br>Veal-chop Casserole<br>Broccoli Amandine<br>Potatoes in sour cream<br>Apple Charlotte<br>Coffee | Biscuit and butter<br>Whipped cream on Apple Charlotte<br>Milk |
| Shrimp in Wine Sauce<br>Brunswick Stew<br>Biscuit<br>Salad à la Grecque<br>Custard Pie<br>Coffee | Butter with biscuit<br>Milk |

| **Dinner Menus** | *For children add:* |
|---|---|
| ½ grapefruit<br>Baked Ham<br>Braised Celery<br>Baked Carrots<br>Sauerkraut Slaw<br>Cocoa Ice Cream<br>Coffee | Baked sweet potato<br>Milk |
| Pistou Soup<br>Curried-beef Pie<br>Sautéed Beans<br>Carrot Salad<br>Dessert Pancakes<br>Coffee | Baked potato with butter<br>Roll and butter<br>Milk |
| Caesar Salad<br>Broiled Steak<br>Green Beans<br>Baked Potato<br>Lemon Pudding<br>Coffee | Butter on potato<br>Whipped cream with pudding<br>Milk |
| Okra Chowder<br>Shish Kebob<br>½ cup boiled rice<br>Roast-pepper Salad<br>Baked apple<br>Coffee | Bread and butter<br>Butter on rice<br>Cream on apple<br>Milk |
| Cold Cream of Cucumber Soup<br>Swordfish Sauté Provençal<br>French Fried Potatoes<br>Sautéed Artichokes<br>Strawberries Parisienne<br>Coffee | Bread and butter<br>Milk |

| **Dinner Menus** | *For children add:* |
| --- | --- |
| Split-pea Soup<br>Sautéed Liver<br>Sweet-potato-and-apple Casserole<br>Brussels Sprouts<br>Wilted Lettuce<br>Berry Pie<br>Coffee | Roll and butter<br>Milk |
| Cream of Tomato Soup<br>Beef Stroganoff<br>Mixed-vegetable Casserole<br>½ cup fine noodles<br>Pineapple Fluff<br>Coffee | Butter on noodles<br>Whipped cream on Pineapple Fluff<br>Milk |

# 1800-Calorie Menus for 30 Days

**Breakfast**

*Choice of:*
Orange juice (4 ounces)
Grapefruit juice (4 ounces)
Tomato juice (8 ounces)

2 eggs, any style
1 slice bread
1 teaspoon butter or margarine
2 slices bacon
*or*
½ cup cooked or dry cereal
1 teaspoon sugar
1 cup skim milk

Coffee or tea
1 teaspoon sugar, or Sucaryl or saccharin
with 2 tablespoons milk

(this applies to lunch and dinner as well)

**Lunch**

*Choice of:*
Sandwich made 2 pieces of buttered bread (toasted or untoasted), no mayonnaise:

Cheese (2 thin slices, any cheese)
Bacon and tomato
Roast beef
Sliced chicken

Chicken salad
Sliced turkey
Corned beef (lean)
Fried egg
Egg salad
Sliced egg
Ham (1 thin slice)
Hamburger (small)
Bologna (2 thin slices)
Tongue (3 thin slices)
Salami (2 thin slices)
Tunafish (drained)

*or*

Broiled, boiled or steamed fish (any variety but salmon, shad or swordfish)

*or*

Salad (any type) but avoid those with excessive mayonnaise or dressings

*Choice of:*

Fruit Cup
Melon
Any fresh fruit
Applesauce
Angel Cake
Cup Cake (no icing)
Canned fruit (no syrup)
Cup Custard
Jello
Muffin
Rice Pudding
Coffee or Tea

**Before Retiring**

1 8-ounce glass of skim milk or buttermilk

**Dinner**

*Choice of:*

100 calories of any selection from the Appetizer section

*or*

1 ounce rye, bourbon or Scotch whiskey, straight, or with water or soda

*or*

2 wineglasses (3½ ounces each) of any dry (not sweet) white or red wine with your dinner

*or*

1 8-ounce glass of beer

| **Dinner Menus** | *For children add:* |
| --- | --- |
| Shrimp Curry<br>Roast Loin of Pork<br>Sweet-and-Sour Cabbage<br>Baked Potato<br>Coffee Sponge<br>Coffee | Bread and butter<br>Milk |
| Watercress Soup<br>Veal Parmigiana<br>Baked Stuffed Tomatoes<br>Savoyard Potatoes<br>Refrigerator Cheese Cake<br>Coffee | Bread and butter<br>Milk |
| Clear Broth<br>Duck with Sauerkraut Stuffing<br>Applesauce<br>Potato Soufflé<br>Chocolate Ice Cream<br>Coffee | Noodles in broth<br>Bread and butter<br>Milk |
| Purée Mongol<br>Norwegian Hamburgers<br>French Fried Potatoes<br>Broccoli Amandine<br>Cinnamon Cake<br>Coffee | Bread and butter<br>Milk |
| Sole Amandine<br>Broiled Liver<br>Savoyard Potatoes<br>Sautéed Beans<br>Green Salad<br>Chocolate Roll<br>Coffee | Bread and butter<br>Milk |

| **Dinner Menus** | *For children add:* |
|---|---|
| Vegetable Soup | Bread and butter |
| Spareribs and Sauerkraut | Milk |
| Mashed Potato | |
| Strawberries Parisienne | |
| Coffee | |
| | |
| Baked Crab Meat | Bread and butter |
| Fillet of Sole Veronique | Milk |
| Swiss Potatoes | |
| Peas, French Style | |
| 1 slice bread | |
| Banana Ice Cream | |
| Coffee | |
| | |
| Onion Soup | Bread and butter |
| Stuffed Chicken in Casserole | Milk |
| Baked Stuffed Potatoes | |
| Baked Lettuce | |
| Roast-pepper Salad | |
| Charlotte Russe | |
| Coffee | |
| | |
| Cream of Mushroom Soup | Bread and butter |
| Roast Beef | Milk |
| Sweet Potato and Apple Casserole | |
| Belgian-style Endive | |
| Chocolate Custard | |
| Coffee | |

| **Dinner Menus** | *For children add:* |
| --- | --- |
| Shrimp Gumbo<br>Beef-and-potato Pie<br>Salad à la Grecque<br>1 slice bread<br>Pumpkin Pie<br>Coffee | Bread and butter<br>Milk |
| Black-bean Soup<br>Sautéed Chicken with olives<br>Brussels Sprouts<br>Savoyard Potatoes<br>Green Salad and 1 slice bread<br>French Cream<br>Coffee | Bread and butter<br>Milk |
| Vegetable Soup<br>Pot Roast<br>Hungarian Sauerkraut<br>Boiled Potato<br>Cream Puff<br>Coffee | Bread and butter<br>Butter with potato<br>Milk |
| Coquille St. Jacques<br>Stuffed Peppers<br>Baked Potato<br>Cucumber Salad<br>Berry Pie<br>Coffee | Bread and butter<br>Milk |
| Fish Chowder<br>Poached Salmon with Egg Sauce<br>Broccoli Amandine<br>Corn Sauté<br>1 slice bread<br>Orange Chiffon Cake<br>Coffee | Bread and butter<br>Milk |

| **Dinner Menus** | *For children add:* |
| --- | --- |
| Corn Chowder<br>Veal, Hunter's Style<br>Green Beans<br>Spinach Salad<br>1 slice bread<br>Banana Delight<br>Coffee | Bread and butter<br>Milk |
| Celery Remoulade<br>Broiled Steak<br>Baked Potato<br>Harvard Beets<br>Meringue Surprise<br>Coffee | Bread and butter<br>Milk |
| 4 Glazed Shrimp<br>Braised Loin of Veal<br>Broccoli Amandine<br>Boiled Potato<br>Dessert Pancakes<br>Coffee | Bread and butter<br>Milk |
| Okra Chowder<br>Chicken Marengo<br>Au Gratin Potatoes<br>Baked Carrots<br>Green-pepper Salad<br>Peach Pie<br>Coffee | Bread and butter<br>Milk |
| Sautéed Shrimp<br>Sukiyaki<br>½ cup boiled rice<br>Ice-cream Dessert<br>Coffee | Bread and butter<br>Milk |

| **Dinner Menus** | *For children add:* |
|---|---|
| Stuffed Artichokes<br>Ham in Coffee Sauce<br>Braised Celery<br>Swiss Potatoes<br>Gingerbread<br>Coffee | Bread and butter<br>Milk |
| Spring Lamb Stew<br>Endive Salad<br>1 slice bread<br>Deep-dish Apple Pie<br>Coffee | Tomato Soup<br>Bread and butter<br>Milk |
| Purée Mongol<br>Chicken Liver Paprika<br>Baked Potato<br>Eggplant Parmigiana<br>Apple Betty<br>Coffee | Bread and butter<br>Milk |
| Onion Soup<br>Shish Kebob<br>½ cup boiled rice<br>Baked Stuffed Tomatoes<br>Spring Salad<br>Pineapple Fluff<br>Coffee | Grated cheese on soup<br>Bread and butter<br>Milk |
| Clams Casino<br>London Broil<br>Potatoes in Sour Cream<br>Braised Celery<br>Blancmange<br>Coffee | Bread and butter<br>Milk |

| **Dinner Menus** | *For children add:* |
|---|---|
| Cream of Spinach Soup<br>Veal-chop Casserole<br>½ cup fine Noodles with 2 tablespoons Spaghetti Sauce<br>Italian Green Salad<br>Cherry Pie<br>Coffee | Bread and butter<br>Milk |
| Cream of Mushroom Soup<br>Roast Fresh Ham<br>Candied Sweet Potatoes<br>Glazed Onions<br>Cherry Compote<br>Coffee | Bread and butter<br>Plain Cake<br>Milk |
| Clear Broth<br>Boeuf Bourgignon<br>½ cup boiled rice<br>Braised Broccoli<br>Orange Chiffon Cake<br>Coffee | Bread and butter<br>Butter on rice<br>Milk |
| Lentil Soup<br>Chicken, Spanish Style<br>Biscuit<br>Green-bean Salad<br>Berry Pie<br>Coffee | Butter with biscuit<br>Milk |
| Manhattan Clam Chowder<br>Fish Mousse<br>Green-pea-and-potato Casserole<br>1 slice bread<br>Apple Charlotte<br>Coffee | Crackers with soup<br>Foamy Sauce on Apple Charlotte<br>Milk |

**Dinner Menus**

Scotch Broth
Tongue en Papillote
Hot German Potato Salad
Red Coleslaw
1 slice bread
Pound Cake
Coffee

*For children add:*

Butter with bread
Applesauce with cake
Milk

The symbol ⁂ indicates dishes that can be frozen.

Hors d'oeuvres and appetizers, more than any other type of food, have kept pace with the modern trend toward less fattening meals. Dips, raw vegetable bowls and sea-food appetizers are replacing the overelaborate and fussy canapés of yesteryear. This, of course, means less bread, fewer canapé bases, a paucity of mayonnaise and in general, a better approach to the calorie question.

For family meals, be sure to serve an attractive bowl of iced carrots, celery strips, cauliflower flowerets and other crisp, raw vegetables. This will help to take the edge off ravenous appetites. If you're having guests, try to have the hors d'oeuvres complement the meal itself and provide a contrast both in texture and in flavor. Two or three beautifully presented appetizers are sufficient, unless you're having a very large cocktail party.

Unusual platters and serving dishes add to the eye appeal of appetizers. Small chafing dishes are excellent for serving hot preparations. Bowls of ice are practical and inviting for sea food and other cold appetizers, so let your imagination have full rein.

## STUFFED EGGS

Use 6 hard-cooked eggs, split in half lengthwise; remove the yolks and mash. Combine with one of the following mixtures and stuff the whites.

### Fish

¼ cup cooked or canned salmon, tuna or shrimp
½ teaspoon prepared mustard
3 tablespoons special mayonnaise (see recipe)
Mashed hard-cooked egg yolks
12 capers

Chop the fish very fine and blend with the mustard, mayonnaise and yolks. Taste for seasoning and stuff the whites. Place a caper on top.

—50 calories in each half egg.

### Ham

2 tablespoons deviled ham
1 tablespoon finely chopped gherkins
3 tablespoons special mayonnaise (see recipe)
Mashed hard-cooked egg yolks
Paprika

Mix all the ingredients (except the paprika) and stuff the eggs. Sprinkle with paprika.

—45 calories in each half egg.

### Anchovy

2 tablespoons anchovy paste
3 tablespoons special mayonnaise (see recipe)
1 tablespoon finely chopped pickled onions
½ teaspoon freshly ground black pepper
Mashed hard-cooked egg yolks
1 tablespoon chopped parsley

Mix all the ingredients except the parsley and stuff the eggs. Sprinkle with the parsley.

—45 calories in each half egg.

### Smoked Turkey

3 tablespoons chopped smoked turkey
3 tablespoons special French dressing (see recipe)
Mashed hard-cooked egg yolks
1 pimento, thinly sliced

Mix together the turkey, French dressing and yolks. Stuff the eggs and garnish with a strip of pimento.

—50 calories in each half egg.

## DILL-PICKLED EGGS

2 cups cider vinegar
1 teaspoon sugar
5 Sucaryl tablets
1 teaspoon salt
5 peppercorns
2 cloves
1 teaspoon celery seed
8 hard-cooked eggs, peeled
1 onion, sliced
1 clove garlic, minced
½ teaspoon pickling spice
1 teaspoon caraway seeds
3 sprigs dill

Combine in a saucepan the vinegar, sugar, Sucaryl, salt, peppercorns, cloves and celery seed. Bring to a boil and cook over low heat 5 minutes. Strain into a 1-quart jar. Add the eggs, onion, garlic, pickling spice, caraway seeds and dill. Cover tightly and let pickle in the refrigerator 2 days before serving. Cut each egg in half and spear with a cocktail pick.

Makes 16—40 calories in each.

## STUFFED CUCUMBER SLICES

1 cucumber
¼ cup cottage cheese
1 tablespoon chili sauce
1 teaspoon Worcestershire sauce
1 tablespoon chopped parsley

Buy a straight firm cucumber, about 6 inches long. Pare it and scoop out the center with a corer or knife.

Beat together the cheese, chili sauce, Worcestershire sauce and parsley. Stuff the cucumber and chill. Slice ¼-inch thick.

Makes about 24 slices—5 calories in 1 slice.

## ALABAMA DIP

1 cucumber, pared
½ green pepper
1 clove garlic, minced
½ teaspoon salt
4 tablespoons special mayonnaise
4 tablespoons yogurt
4 tablespoons chili sauce
1 tablespoon prepared horseradish

Chop the cucumber, green pepper, garlic and salt together. Stir in the mayonnaise, yogurt, chili sauce and horseradish. Chill and serve with shrimp or crisp vegetables.

Makes about 1¼ cups—10 calories in 1 tablespoon.

## RED CAVIAR DIP

1 cup cottage cheese
1 jar (2 ounces) red caviar

Force the cheese through a sieve or run in the electric blender for a few seconds. Mix in the caviar. Turn into a serving bowl and surround with crisp fingers of green pepper.

Makes 1½ cups—20 calories in 1 tablespoon.

## CHEESE DIP

1 cup cottage cheese
2 tablespoons anchovy paste
3 tablespoons finely chopped pickled onions
3 tablespoons chopped pimentos
Raw vegetables

Mix together the cheese, anchovy paste, onions and pimento. Place in a bowl and chill.

Arrange one or all of the following around the bowl: cauliflower flowerets, baby turnips, celery stalks.

Makes 1 cup—15 calories in 1 tablespoon.

## PICKLED CLAMS

36 clams
2 cups white vinegar
12 small white onions
¾ teaspoon dried ground red peppers
1½ teaspoons salt
6 peppercorns

Buy freshly opened clams. Pour boiling water over them and let soak 3 minutes. Drain well.

Combine the vinegar, onions, red pepper, salt and peppercorns in a jar; add the clams. Cover tightly and let pickle in the refrigerator for 3 days. Spear with cocktail picks and serve. The clams keep about 2 weeks in the pickling solution.

—15 calories in 1 clam

## CLAMS PICANTE

1 green pepper
1 onion
2 tomatoes, diced
12 fresh clams or 1 can (7½ ounces) minced clams, drained
2 teaspoons Worcestershire sauce

Remove the seeds and fiber of the pepper. Chop with the onion until very fine. Add the tomatoes and clams; chop until well blended. Stir in the Worcestershire sauce.

Chill and serve in a bowl, with corn chips.

Makes 2 cups—10 calories in 1 tablespoon.

## MARINATED OYSTERS

12 oysters
½ cup special French dressing (see recipe)
3 drops Tabasco sauce

Have the oysters shucked. Mix together the French dressing and Tabasco sauce. Marinate the oysters in the mixture (in the refrigerator) for 2 hours. Drain and serve on cocktail picks.

—25 calories in each oyster.

## WATER CHESTNUTS IN BACON

12 slices bacon
24 water chestnuts
¼ cup chopped chutney

Cut the bacon in half and wrap around the water chestnuts carefully. Place on a rack in a baking pan. Bake in a 375° oven 20 minutes, or until bacon is crisp. Spear with a cocktail pick and serve with the chutney as a dip.

Makes 24—25 calories in each.

## MELON AND PROSCIUTTO

12 paper-thin slices Prosciutto or Parma ham
24 1-inch cubes of melon

Be sure the ham is very thin—almost transparent. Cut each slice in half and wrap around the melon cubes. Spear with a cocktail pick and serve cold.

Makes 24—25 calories in each serving.

## STUFFED ENDIVE

3 endive
2 ounces Roquefort cheese
2 tablespoons cottage cheese
2 tablespoons milk
Paprika

Wash and dry the endive. Separate the leaves carefully (save the hearts for salad).

Cream the Roquefort cheese, cottage cheese and milk together. Stuff each leaf and chill until ready to serve. Sprinkle with the paprika.

Makes about 24—10 calories in each.

## EGGPLANT CAVIAR ❋

1 small eggplant
2 tablespoons olive or salad oil
2 onions, chopped
2 green peppers, chopped
2 tablespoons tomato paste
1½ teaspoons salt
½ teaspoon freshly ground black pepper
1 teaspoon sugar
1 tablespoon lemon juice

Peel and dice the eggplant. Heat the oil in a skillet; sauté the onions, eggplant and green peppers 20 minutes, stirring frequently. Stir in the tomato paste, salt, pepper and sugar. Cook over low heat 10 minutes, mixing frequently. Add the lemon juice. Chill and serve with thin fingers of pumpernickel.

Makes about 3 cups—10 calories in 1 tablespoon.

## CHICKEN-LIVER CAPS

24 mushroom caps
6 chicken livers
2 tablespoons butter or margarine
1¼ teaspoon salt
½ teaspoon pepper

Wash and dry the mushrooms. Wash and dry chicken livers; remove any discolored spots and cut each liver into 4.

Melt the butter in a skillet and sauté the mushrooms lightly. Remove and keep warm. Sauté the livers in the same skillet. Pierce a piece of liver with a cocktail pick, and then the mushroom, rounded side down. Sprinkle with salt and pepper.

Makes 24—25 calories in each.

## DEVILED CHICKEN BALLS

- ¾ cup cooked or canned chopped chicken
- 2 tablespoons finely chopped parsley
- 2 tablespoons grated onion
- 2 teaspoons curry powder
- 3 tablespoons special mayonnaise (see recipe)
- 1 teaspoon prepared mustard
- 2 tablespoons dry bread crumbs
- ½ teaspoon paprika

Blend together the chicken, 1 tablespoon parsley, the onion, curry powder, mayonnaise and mustard. Shape into ½-inch balls.

Mix the bread crumbs, paprika and remaining parsley together. Roll the balls in the mixture and chill. Spear with a cocktail pick and serve.

Makes about 12—20 calories in each.

## COCKTAIL SAUSAGES ❋

- ⅛ pound lean beef, ground
- ⅛ pound lean veal, ground
- ¼ cup grated carrot
- 1 teaspoon salt
- ¼ teaspoon freshly ground black pepper
- ⅛ teaspoon oregano
- 1 tablespoon paprika
- 1 teaspoon salad oil
- ½ cup chopped scallions (green onions) optional

Mix together the beef, veal, carrot, salt, pepper and oregano. Shape into sausages ¼-inch wide by ¾-inch long. Roll in the paprika.

Oil a pan and place the sausages on it. Broil in a hot broiler about 3 inches from the heat until browned on all sides. Serve the scallions in a bowl as a dip, if desired.

Makes about 24—10 calories in each.

## CHEESE MERINGUES

- 2 egg whites
- 2 teaspoons anchovy paste
- ¼ cup grated Parmesan cheese
- ⅛ teaspoon nutmeg
- 1 teaspoon salad oil

Turn oven on and set at 300°.

Beat the egg whites until stiff peaks are formed. Fold in the anchovy paste, Parmesan cheese and nutmeg.

Drop by the teaspoon onto a lightly oiled baking sheet. Bake 20 minutes, or until delicately browned and set. Remove from the baking sheet and serve hot or cold.

Makes about 24—15 calories in each serving.

## HOT COTTAGE CHEESE BALLS

- 1 cup cottage cheese
- 1 tablespoon caraway seeds
- 1 egg yolk
- 2 tablespoons flour
- ⅛ teaspoon freshly ground black pepper
- 1 tablespoon melted butter
- 16 pretzel sticks

Turn oven on and set at 350°.

Mix all the ingredients together. Use 1 tablespoon of the mixture to make small balls. Place on a baking sheet.

Bake about 10 minutes or until browned. Pierce with a pretzel stick and serve.

Makes 16—25 calories in each.

## CHEESE PUFFS

- 2 tablespoons milk
- 2 teaspoons butter or margarine
- ¼ teaspoon salt
- ½ cup sifted flour
- 1 egg
- 1 egg yolk
- 4 tablespoons grated Parmesan cheese
- Dash cayenne pepper

Turn oven on and set at 400°.

Combine the milk, butter and salt in a saucepan; bring to a boil and add the flour all at once, stirring constantly. Remove from the heat and add the egg; beat well and add the egg yolk. Beat again and stir in the cheese and cayenne pepper.

Wet a baking sheet with cold water and drop the mixture onto it by the teaspoon. Bake 15 minutes, or until browned and puffed.

Makes about 18—25 calories in each.

## PICKLED HERRING

- 6 fillets of salt herring
- 1 cup white vinegar
- ¼ cup water
- ¼ teaspoon liquid Sucaryl
- 3 onions, sliced thin
- 1 teaspoon pickling spice
- 2 bay leaves

Soak the herring in water to cover overnight; change the water several times. Drain and cut each fillet into 2-inch pieces.

Combine the vinegar, water and Sucaryl in a saucepan; bring to a boil and let boil 2 minutes.

In a glass jar or bowl, arrange layers of the herring, onions, pickling spice and bay leaves. Pour the vinegar mixture over all. Cover and let pickle in the refrigerator at least 48 hours before serving. Spear with cocktail picks or serve on plates.

Makes about 24 pieces—25 calories in each.

## PEPPER CAPONATINA ❊

- 6 green peppers
- 2 tablespoons olive oil
- 3 onions, thinly sliced
- 3 tomatoes, peeled and diced
- 1 teaspoon salt
- ¼ teaspoon freshly ground black pepper
- ⅓ cup wine vinegar

Wash and dry the peppers. Slice lengthwise, discarding the seeds and fibers.

Heat the oil in a saucepan. Add the peppers, onions, tomatoes, salt and pepper. Cover and cook over low heat 1 hour, stirring frequently. Add the vinegar and cook 10 minutes. Turn into a jar or bowl. Cover and refrigerate for 2 days before using. The Caponatina will keep about 10 days. Serve with very thinly sliced bread squares.

Makes about 3 cups—10 calories in 1 tablespoon.

## CHOPPED HERRING APPETIZER

4 salt herring fillets
½ small onion
½ apple, peeled and cored
2 hard-cooked egg yolks
3 tablespoons cider vinegar
1 slice dry white bread
2 teaspoons salad oil
½ teaspoon sugar

Soak the herring in water to cover overnight; change the water 3 times. Drain. Carefully remove any bones; chop the herring, onion, apple and egg yolks together. Pour the vinegar over the bread and add with the oil and sugar. Continue chopping until well blended. Chill and serve.

Makes about 2 cups—20 calories in 1 tablespoon.

## PICKLED MUSHROOMS

18 mushrooms
1 cup special garlic dressing (see recipe)

Buy small uniform mushrooms. Wash, dry and peel them. Place in a jar and pour the dressing over them. Refrigerate for 2 days before using. Turn the jar several times to distribute the dressing. Drain and serve on cocktail picks.

Makes 18—10 calories in each mushroom.

## STUFFED MUSHROOMS

18 mushrooms
1 teaspoon salt
⅛ teaspoon pepper
½ teaspoon paprika
2 tablespoons grated onion
2 tablespoons Parmesan cheese
1 teaspoon oil

Buy medium-sized mushrooms. Wash and dry them; remove the stems and chop fine. Combine with the salt, pepper, paprika, onion and cheese. Mix well and stuff the mushrooms.

Oil a baking pan and arrange the mushrooms on it. Bake in a 375° oven 10 minutes. Spear with cocktail picks and serve hot.

Makes 18—10 calories in each.

## CHIPPED-BEEF ROLLS

¼ cup cottage cheese
2 tablespoons grated onion
⅛ teaspoon Worcestershire sauce
⅛ teaspoon freshly ground black pepper
12 slices chipped beef

Mix together the cottage cheese, onion, Worcestershire sauce and pepper. Place a teaspoon of the mixture on each slice of beef and roll up tight. Fasten with cocktail picks. Chill and serve.

Makes 12—35 calories in each.

## TARTAR BALLS

- ½ pound sirloin steak
- ¼ cup chopped onions
- ⅛ teaspoon minced garlic
- ¾ teaspoon salt
- ½ teaspoon freshly ground black pepper
- 1 egg white
- ¼ cup chopped parsley

It is advisable to grind the beef at home, or if possible scrape it with a sharp knife into very small pieces. Add the onions, garlic, salt and pepper.

Shape teaspoons of the mixture into balls; roll in the egg white and then the parsley. Chill until ready to serve. Spear with cocktail picks.

Makes about 30—25 calories in each.

## DEVILED CRAB-MEAT BALLS ✲

- ½ pound crab meat, fresh or canned
- 2 tablespoons finely chopped onion
- 2 tablespoons finely chopped parsley
- 1 teaspoon salt
- ¼ teaspoon white pepper
- ¼ teaspoon dry mustard
- 1 egg yolk
- 1 tablespoon sherry
- 4 tablespoons dry bread crumbs
- 1 teaspoon salad oil

Flake the crab meat very fine; blend with the onion, parsley, salt, pepper, mustard, egg yolk and sherry. Shape teaspoons of the mixture into balls and roll lightly in the bread crumbs.

Grease a baking pan with the oil and arrange the balls on it. Bake in a 400° oven 10 minutes or until browned.

Makes about 32—10 calories in each.

## HAM BALLS

- ¼ pound lean boiled ham
- 2 hard-cooked eggs
- ½ teaspoon salt
- ¼ teaspoon pepper
- 3 tablespoons special mayonnaise (see recipe)
- 4 tablespoons crushed rice flakes

Grind or chop the ham and eggs very fine. Add the salt, pepper and mayonnaise. Shape into ½-inch balls and roll in the rice flakes. Chill and spear with cocktail picks.

Makes about 24—30 calories in each.

## TONGUE KABOBS

- 6 slices boiled tongue, ½-inch thick
- 18 small pickled onions
- 18 cucumber cubes

Cut each slice of tongue in 6 pieces. Thread cocktail picks alternately with the tongue, onions and cucumbers, starting and ending with the tongue.

Makes 12 kabobs—30 calories in each.

## GRAPEFRUIT VINAIGRETTE

- 1 grapefruit
- ½ cup special vinaigrette sauce (see recipe)

Peel grapefruit and segment it carefully, removing all the white fibers. Marinate in the vinaigrette sauce 1 hour. Drain and serve on cocktail picks.

Makes about 12—15 calories in each.

## TONGUE ROLLS

- 1/3 cup cottage cheese
- 1/2 teaspoon dry mustard
- 2 teaspoons grated onion
- 2 teaspoons prepared horseradish
- 12 thin slices of tongue
- 4 tablespoons chopped parsley

Mix the cheese, mustard, onion and horseradish together. Trim edges of tongue and spread the slices with the cheese mixture. Roll up tightly. Cut in half. Fasten with toothpicks and dip the ends in chopped parsley. Chill until ready to serve.

Makes 24—15 calories in each.

## TONGUE PATÉ

- 1/4 pound boiled tongue
- 2 tablespoons chopped onion
- 2 teaspoons prepared horseradish
- 1/2 teaspoon paprika
- 3 tablespoons special mayonnaise (see recipe)

Grind the tongue and onion in a food mill or chop very fine. Blend in the horseradish, paprika and mayonnaise. Heap in a bowl and chill until ready to serve.

Makes about 1 1/4 cups—15 calories in 1 tablespoon.

## SHRIMP PASTE

- 1/2 pound shrimp, cooked and cleaned
- 1 1/2 tablespoons butter or margarine
- 1/2 teaspoon salt
- 1/8 teaspoon pepper
- 1/8 teaspoon nutmeg

Grind the shrimp in a food chopper, chop very fine or purée in the electric blender. Combine with the butter, salt, pepper and nutmeg in a saucepan. Bring to a boil, stirring constantly. Pack in a mold or cup and chill. Serve with celery or carrot sticks.

Makes 1 cup—20 calories in 1 tablespoon.

## CALVES' BRAINS VINAIGRETTE

- 3 calves' brains
- 4 cups water
- 2 tablespoons vinegar
- 1 teaspoon salt
- 1 onion
- 1 carrot, sliced
- 2 sprigs parsley
- 1 bay leaf
- 1/4 teaspoon thyme

Wash the brains; remove the membranes, soak in cold water 30 minutes. Drain and combine with the 4 cups water, the vinegar, salt, onion, carrot, parsley, bay leaf and thyme. Bring to a boil; cover and cook over low heat 20 minutes.

To serve hot, drain and slice. To serve cold, let the brains cool in the liquid (in the refrigerator). Then drain and slice. In either case, serve with vinaigrette sauce (see recipe).

Serves 6—105 calories in each serving.

## SWEDISH SHRIMP BOWL

- ½ cup tarragon vinegar
- 1 bay leaf
- 6 crushed peppercorns
- ½ teaspoon thyme
- 1 pound shrimp, cooked and cleaned
- ½ cup special Russian dressing (see recipe)

Mix together the vinegar, bay leaf, peppercorns and thyme. Marinate the shrimp in the mixture (in the refrigerator) 2 hours. Drain.

Arrange on a serving plate with the Russian dressing in the middle, or hang the shrimp on a bowl of dressing.

Makes about 18—15 calories in each.

## GLAZED SHRIMP

- 2 teaspoons gelatin
- 2 tablespoons cold water
- ⅓ cup special French dressing (see recipe)
- 2 tablespoons ketchup
- 1 pound shrimp, cooked and cleaned

Soften the gelatin in the water 5 minutes. Place over hot water and stir until gelatin dissolves. Cool 5 minutes; add the dressing and ketchup. Mix well.

Spear the shrimp with cocktail picks and dip into the gelatin mixture. Chill and then dip again. Chill until set.

Makes about 18—15 calories in each.

## CHOPPED BRAINS

- 2 calves' brains
- 1 tablespoon vinegar
- 2 teaspoons salt
- 1 onion, chopped
- 1 tablespoon olive oil
- ¼ teaspoon freshly ground black pepper
- 3 tablespoons lemon juice

Wash the brains and soak in cold water 10 minutes. Drain; cover with fresh water and add the vinegar and salt. Bring to a boil; cover and cook over low heat 20 minutes. Drain and remove the membrane. Chop the brains and onion together. Blend in the olive oil, pepper and lemon juice. Chill and serve on crisp lettuce.

Serves 6—60 calories in each serving.

## CHOPPED CHICKEN LIVERS ❋

- 1 pound chicken livers
- 1 onion, chopped
- 2 tablespoons rendered chicken fat or melted butter
- 1 hard-cooked egg
- 1½ teaspoons salt
- ½ teaspoon freshly ground black pepper
- ¼ cup chicken broth, fresh or canned

Sauté the livers and onion in the fat for 5 minutes. Cover and cook over very low heat 5 minutes.

Chop the mixture with the egg, or grind in a food chopper or blender. Stir in the salt, pepper and chicken broth. Mix well and taste for seasoning.

Serves 6—165 calories in each serving.

# SOUPS

The symbol ✻ indicates dishes that can be frozen.

Hot in winter, or chilled in summer, soup is a delightful way to begin a dinner. You can serve it in the living room instead of cocktails, in mugs or cups. Soups are satisfying and filling, offering the bulk so necessary to a diet.

Some soups are almost meals in themselves, and they're delicious for lunch or supper with a salad to follow. Most soups keep well in your home freezer, so make fairly large quantities and keep them on hand ready to be reheated. Puréeing soup in an electric blender produces a creamy rich-tasting product. Low-caloric greens of all types can be blended into a smooth, pleasing soup with practically no food value, but just the thing to round out a meal. You'll find the investment in an electric blender very worth while.

Consommés and broths are practically calorie-free, so you can treat yourself to a cup when you feel hungry at odd hours between meals; you'll be surprised at the feeling of satiety a cup of soup can furnish. One word of caution, however—always remove the fat before serving the soup. Follow the instructions for "fat skimming" which follow and then enjoy yourself doubly, knowing that the delicious soup you're eating has very few calories.

#### Fat Skimming

Soups and stews *must* be served with as little fat as possible. There are several ways to remove it. The most efficient method requires thorough chilling, and thus the dish should be prepared enough in advance of serving to allow at least four hours for chilling. The hot saucepan or bowl of food can be placed over ice or in cold water to quickly cool it before placing it in the refrigerator until the fat congeals on the top. You can then lift it off.

When you can't spare the extra time, there are alternate methods which will accomplish almost the same results.

1. Place a few ice cubes in the soup or stew. The fat will adhere to them. Discard the ice, then reheat and serve.
2. Lettuce or cabbage leaves immersed in the soup or stew will also pick up the grease. Discard and replace with fresh ones, until the grease is all removed.
3. Place a paper towel or napkin over the soup or stew. The grease will be absorbed by it.

### CHICKEN SOUP ❄

1 4-5 pound fowl
9 cups water
1 onion
3 stalks celery
6 sprigs parsley
2 leeks
1 carrot, quartered
1 turnip, peeled and sliced
1 parsnip
2 teaspoons salt
8 peppercorns, gently bruised

Ask the butcher for some extra chicken feet and necks. Combine the chicken, feet, necks and water in a saucepan; bring to a boil and carefully skim the top. Add the onion, celery, parsley, leeks, carrot, turnip, parsnip, salt and peppercorns. Cover and cook over low heat 3 hours.

Remove the chicken and use it in other dishes. Strain the soup and remove all the fat (See Fat Skimming). Serve as soup, or pour into jars for later use.

Serves 6—60 calories in each serving.

## SOUP COLORING

1 cup sugar
⅔ cup water

Boil the sugar and half the water until a very dark brown. Add the remaining water carefully, as it may spatter, and cook over very low heat until syrupy. Strain and pour into a bottle. Use about 1 teaspoon to give pale soups or stock a darker color. Don't worry about the calories, they are infinitesimal.

## BELGIAN CHICKEN-SOUP DINNER

2 2-pound broilers
Veal bones
7 cups water
2 stalks celery
1 celery root, peeled and sliced
4 sprigs parsley
2 teaspoons salt
½ teaspoon pepper
1 lemon, peeled and sliced thin
1 cup dry white wine
1 tablespoon butter
½ cup dry bread crumbs

Have the broilers left whole. Ask the butcher for a veal knuckle, some veal bones and chicken feet for the stock.

Combine the livers, gizzards, hearts (of the broilers), the bones, water, celery, celery root, parsley, salt, pepper and lemon in a saucepan. Bring to a boil and skim the top. Cover and cook over medium heat for 2 hours. Strain and skim the fat (See Fat Skimming).

In a casserole, place the broilers, stock, wine and butter. Cover and cook over low heat 45 minutes, or until the broilers are tender. Remove the chicken and cut into serving pieces. Stir in the bread crumbs. Serve the chicken in deep plates or bowls with the soup over it.

Serves 6—155 calories in each serving.

## SCOTCH BROTH ❊

½ cup medium barley
8 cups water
1 pound lean lamb
Lamb bones
1 onion, chopped
1 stalk celery
1 package frozen mixed vegetables
2 teaspoons salt
¼ teaspoon freshly ground black pepper
2 tablespoons chopped parsley

Wash the barley thoroughly. Soak in cold water for 1 hour. Drain and combine in a saucepan with the 8 cups water, the lamb, bones, onion and celery. Cover and cook over low heat for 1½ hours. Add the vegetables, salt and pepper. Cook 30 minutes. Taste for seasoning.

Remove the meat and bones. Cut the meat into ¼-inch cubes. Serve the soup with 3 cubes in each plate, and some parsley on top.

Serves 6—155 calories in each serving.

## BEEF SOUP OR STOCK ❋

- 2 pounds beef (brisket, flank)
- Beef bones
- 2½ quarts water
- 2 cloves
- 1 onion
- 2 teaspoons salt
- ½ teaspoon pepper
- 1 bay leaf
- 3 stalks celery
- 2 carrots, sliced
- 4 sprigs parsley
- 1 parsnip, sliced

Remove as much fat as possible from the beef. Place the beef, bones and water in a saucepan; bring to a boil. Insert the cloves in the onion and add to the soup with the salt, pepper and bay leaf. Cover the saucepan and cook over low heat for 3 hours.

Add the celery (with the leaves) carrots, parsley and parsnip. Cover and cook 45 minutes.

Strain the soup. It is very important to remove all the fat, so if there is time, chill it. To speed up chilling, place the saucepan or bowl in cold water for a few minutes, then in the refrigerator until there is a solid mass of fat on top. It should be possible to remove it in one piece.

The meat will be overcooked, so if you want to serve it as "boiled beef" remove it at the end of 2½ hours cooking time, or when tender. Continue cooking the soup as specified.

For immediate serving, see Fat Skimming.

Serves 6—30 calories in each serving.

## PHILADELPHIA PEPPER POT ❋

- 1 tablespoon corn oil
- 2 onions, chopped
- ½ cup chopped celery
- 1½ cups finely chopped green peppers
- 1 tomato, cubed
- ½ pound honeycomb tripe, sliced
- 7 cups chicken broth, fresh or canned
- ¼ teaspoon thyme
- 1 bay leaf
- ½ teaspoon freshly ground black pepper
- 2 teaspoons paprika
- 2 teaspoons salt
- 1 potato, peeled and diced
- 1 tablespoon cornstarch
- 3 tablespoons cold water
- ½ cup milk

This is a really hearty soup, good for lunch or supper.

Heat the oil in a saucepan; add the onions, celery and green pepper. Sauté for 10 minutes, stirring frequently. Add the tomato, tripe, broth, thyme, bay leaf, pepper, paprika and salt. Cover and cook over low heat 1 hour. Add the potato and cook 20 minutes.

Mix the cornstarch and water to a smooth paste. Stir into the soup and cook 5 minutes. Add the milk just before serving, and taste for seasoning.

Serves 6—140 calories in each serving.

## CLEAR VEGETABLE SOUP OR STOCK ❊

- 2 tablespoons butter or margarine
- 2 onions, sliced
- 3 carrots, sliced
- 1 white turnip, sliced
- 1 bunch celery, sliced
- 1 head lettuce, shredded
- 7 cups water
- 2 tomatoes, quartered, or ¾ cup canned
- 1 bay leaf
- 4 sprigs parsley
- 2 teaspoon salt
- ½ teaspoon pepper
- 1 tablespoon Kitchen Bouquet or Pique
- 2 cloves

Melt the butter in a saucepan. Stir in the onions, carrots, turnip, celery and lettuce. Cover and cook over low heat 20 minutes, stirring a few times. Add the water, tomatoes, bay leaf, parsley, salt, pepper, Kitchen Bouquet and cloves. Bring to a boil, cover and cook over low heat 1½ hours. Strain through a fine sieve.

Serve as a clear vegetable broth or store in covered jars and use as a base for other soups or dishes.

Serves 6—40 calories in each serving.

## ONION SOUP ❊

- 2 tablespoons butter or margarine
- 4 cups thinly sliced onion
- 2 tablespoons flour
- ½ teaspoon freshly ground black pepper
- 6 cups beef stock, fresh or canned
- 6 tablespoons grated Sap Sago or Parmesan cheese

Melt the butter in a saucepan; sauté the onions over very low heat until quite brown. Stir frequently to prevent burning. Sprinkle with the flour and pepper, stirring until brown. Gradually add the stock, stirring constantly to the boiling point. Cover and cook over low heat 45 minutes. Taste for seasoning. (No salt is provided in the recipe, as it depends on the stock used.)

Serve with the grated cheese.

Serves 6—75 calories in each serving.

## PISTOU SOUP ❊

- ½ pound green beans
- 1 potato, peeled and diced
- 1 cup canned tomatoes, drained
- 6 cups water
- 1 teaspoon salt
- ⅓ cup fine egg noodles
- 1 clove garlic, minced
- ¼ teaspoon dried thyme
- ½ teaspoon dried basil
- 2 tablespoons tomato paste
- 1 tablespoon olive oil

Cut the beans in ½-inch lengths and combine with the potato, tomatoes, water and salt in a saucepan. Bring to a boil and cook over low heat 15 minutes. Stir in the noodles and cook 8 minutes. Taste for salt.

Pound together the garlic, thyme, basil and tomato paste, gradually adding the oil. Place a teaspoon of the mixture in each soup plate, or all the mixture in a tureen. Pour the soup over it.

Serves 6—85 calories in each serving.

## VEGETABLE SOUP ※

- 1 tablespoon butter or margarine
- 2 onions, sliced
- 2 carrots, sliced
- 1 cup shredded cabbage
- ½ cup sliced celery
- ½ pound green peas, shelled
- ¼ pound green beans, cut in ¼-inch pieces
- 7 cups water
- 2 teaspoons salt
- ¼ teaspoon freshly ground black pepper
- ½ teaspoon sugar
- 2 tomatoes, chopped
- 1 potato, peeled and diced
- ½ cup cooked fine egg noodles
- 1 tablespoon chopped parsley

Melt the butter in a saucepan; sauté the onions for 10 minutes, stirring frequently. Add the carrots, cabbage, celery, green peas, green beans, water, salt, pepper, sugar, tomatoes and potato. Cover and cook over medium heat 35 minutes. Stir in the noodles and parsley; cook 5 minutes longer.

Serves 6—85 calories in each serving.

## TOMATO BOUILLON ※

- 2 teaspoons butter
- 1 onion, chopped
- 6 cups tomato juice
- 1 bay leaf
- ½ cup chopped celery and leaves
- ½ teaspoon oregano
- ¼ teaspoon celery salt
- ⅛ teaspoon freshly ground black pepper
- 6 teaspoons sour cream

Melt the butter in a saucepan; sauté the onion for 5 minutes, stirring frequently. Add the tomato juice, bay leaf, celery, oregano, celery salt and pepper. Cook over low heat 15 minutes. Strain. Taste for seasoning.

Serve hot or well chilled, with a spoon of sour cream in the center.

Serves 6—40 calories in each serving.

## COLD BEET SOUP

- 6 beets, pared and quartered
- 1 onion, chopped
- 7 cups water
- 2 teaspoons salt
- 3 tablespoons lemon juice
- 1 tablespoon sugar
- 2 eggs
- 6 teaspoons sour cream

Combine the beets, onion, water and salt in a saucepan. Bring to a boil and cook over medium heat 45 minutes. Add the lemon juice and sugar; cook 5 minutes. Taste for seasoning; the soup should be both sweet and sour.

Beat the eggs in a bowl; gradually add the soup, beating constantly to prevent curdling. Chill.

Serve with a spoon of sour cream on top.

Serves 6—105 calories in each serving.

## GAZPACHO

A delicious cold vegetable soup from Spain. When serving this, do not have a salad in the same meal.

2 onions, chopped
2 cloves garlic, minced
3 green peppers, chopped
5 tomatoes, chopped
2 teaspoons salt
½ teaspoon freshly ground black pepper
2 teaspoons Spanish paprika
2 tablespoons olive oil
⅓ cup wine vinegar
1½ cups water
1 cucumber, peeled and sliced thin

Combine the onions, garlic, green peppers, tomatoes, salt, pepper and paprika; purée in an electric blender or force through a sieve. Gradually stir in the olive oil, vinegar and water.

Chill in a bowl (not metal) for 2 hours. Add the cucumbers just before serving. Croutons flavored with garlic may be served separately, if desired.

Serves 6—70 calories in each serving.

## BROWN CABBAGE SOUP

3 pounds cabbage
2 tablespoons butter or margarine
2 teaspoons sugar
½ teaspoon liquid Sucaryl
7 cups beef stock, fresh or canned
1 teaspoon salt
½ teaspoon freshly ground black pepper

Shred the cabbage finely. Melt the butter in a saucepan; add the cabbage, sugar and Sucaryl. Cook over very low heat until the cabbage is well browned (about 45 minutes), stirring frequently to prevent burning.

Stir in the stock, salt and pepper. Cover and cook over low heat 2 hours. Taste for seasoning.

Serves 6—80 calories in each serving.

## CORN CHOWDER ❄

1 slice bacon, diced
¼ cup chopped onion
½ cup diced green pepper
1 potato, pared and diced
3 cups water
¾ teaspoon salt
¼ teaspoon pepper
½ teaspoon paprika
1 bay leaf
1 tablespoon cornstarch
1½ cups skim milk
1½ cups corn kernels
2 tablespoons chopped pimento

Cook the bacon until almost crisp. Drain. Combine the bacon pieces, onion and green pepper in a saucepan. Sauté over low heat 5 minutes, stirring frequently. Add the potato, water, salt, pepper, paprika and bay leaf. Cover and cook over low heat 20 minutes.

Mix the cornstarch and milk until smooth and add to the soup, stirring constantly until it boils. Add the corn and pimentos. Cook 3 minutes.

Serves 6—90 calories in each serving.

## OKRA CHOWDER

- 1 pound okra or 1 package frozen
- 1 tablespoon butter or margarine
- 1 onion, chopped
- ½ cup chopped green pepper
- 1 cup sliced celery
- 1 cup canned tomatoes
- 5 cups water
- 1½ teaspoon salt
- ¼ teaspoon pepper
- 1 teaspoon sugar
- ½ cup cooked rice
- 2 slices crisp bacon, crumbled

Cut the ends from the okra and slice into 1-inch pieces. Melt the butter in a saucepan; sauté the okra, onion, green pepper and celery in it for 10 minutes, stirring frequently. Add the tomatoes, water, salt, pepper and sugar. Cover and cook over low heat 45 minutes. Taste for seasoning.

Divide the rice among 6 bowls, fill with the soup and sprinkle the bacon on top.

Serves 6—70 calories in each serving.

## LENTIL SOUP ❋

- 1 cup lentils
- 6 cups water
- 2 teaspoons butter
- 1 onion, chopped
- 1 clove garlic, minced
- 1½ teaspoons salt
- ¼ teaspoon pepper
- 2 teaspoons curry powder
- 2 cups chicken broth

Wash the lentils thoroughly and combine with the water in a saucepan. Cover and cook over low heat 2 hours, or until tender. Force through a sieve or purée in an electric blender.

Melt the butter in a skillet; sauté the onion and garlic 10 minutes, stirring frequently. Add to the lentils with the salt, pepper, curry powder and broth. Cook over low heat 30 minutes. If too thick, add a little water.

Serves 6—125 calories in each serving.

## SPLIT-PEA SOUP ❋

- 1 cup split peas
- 1 onion, chopped
- 1 carrot, grated
- 6 cups water
- 1½ teaspoons salt
- ¼ teaspoon pepper
- 1 bay leaf
- 2 cups chicken broth, fresh or canned

Wash the peas thoroughly and soak overnight in water to cover, if precooked variety is not used. Drain.

Combine the peas, onion, carrot and water in a saucepan. Cover and cook over low heat 1 hour. Add the salt, pepper and bay leaf. Cook 1 hour longer or until peas are tender. Force through a sieve or purée in an electric blender. Stir in the broth and cook 30 minutes. Taste for seasoning.

Serves 6—125 calories in each serving.

## PURÉE MONGOL

To split-pea soup add 2 cups canned tomatoes at the same time as the sautéed vegetables.

Serves 8—135 calories in each serving.

## BLACK-BEAN SOUP

- 1 cup black beans
- 8 cups water
- 2 teaspoons butter or margarine
- 1 onion, chopped
- 1 stalk celery, sliced
- 1 carrot, grated
- 1 teaspoon celery salt
- ¼ teaspoon black pepper
- ¼ teaspoon mustard seed
- 2 teaspoons salt
- 2 tablespoons sherry
- ¼ cup milk
- 1 hard-cooked egg, finely chopped
- 1 tablespoon finely chopped parsley

Wash the beans thoroughly, cover with water and bring to a boil. Remove from the heat and let soak 2 hours. Drain. Combine with the 8 cups water and cook over low heat while preparing the vegetables.

Melt the butter in a skillet; add the onion, celery and carrot. Sauté for 10 minutes, stirring frequently. Add to the beans with the celery salt, pepper, mustard seed. Cover and cook over low heat 3 hours. Force through a sieve or purée in an electric blender. Stir in the salt, sherry and milk. Reheat. If too thick, add a little boiling water. Taste for seasoning.

Serve with the egg and parsley sprinkled on top.

Serves 6—135 calories in each serving.

## CREAM OF SPINACH SOUP

- 2 pounds spinach or 2 packages frozen
- 4 cups chicken stock, fresh or canned
- 2 teaspoons salt
- ⅛ teaspoon pepper
- 1 bay leaf
- 1 onion, sliced
- 2 tablespoons flour
- 1 cup milk
- 1 egg yolk

If fresh spinach is used, wash carefully. Defrost frozen spinach. Combine with the stock, salt, pepper, bay leaf and onion in a saucepan. Bring to a boil and cook over low heat for 20 minutes. Discard the bay leaf and force the mixture through a sieve or purée in an electric blender. Return to saucepan.

Mix the flour with a little milk to a smooth paste, then add remaining milk. Stir into the soup, mixing steadily until the boiling point. Cook over low heat 10 minutes.

Beat the egg yolk in a bowl. Gradually add the hot soup, stirring constantly to prevent curdling. If you plan to reheat the soup, be sure it doesn't boil after the egg yolk is added.

Serves 6—60 calories in each serving.

## CREAM OF LETTUCE SOUP AMANDINE

Substitute 2 pounds lettuce for the spinach and proceed as directed in the Cream of Spinach recipe. Serve with a teaspoon of shredded toasted almonds.

Serves 6—70 calories in each serving.

## CREAM OF TOMATO SOUP ❋

- 1 can (#2½) tomatoes
- 3 tablespoons chopped onion
- ¼ teaspoon basil
- 1½ teaspoons salt
- 1 tablespoon lemon juice
- 1 tablespoon sugar
- 1 tablespoon flour
- 1½ cups skim milk
- 1 tablespoon butter

Combine the tomatoes, onion, basil, salt, lemon juice and sugar in a saucepan. Cook over low heat for 25 minutes. Force through sieve or purée in an electric blender. Return to saucepan.

Mix the flour to a smooth paste with a little milk; add to the soup with the balance of the milk and the butter, stirring until the boiling point. Cook over low heat 5 minutes.

Serves 6—85 calories in each serving.

## CREAM OF MUSHROOM SOUP

- 1 tablespoon butter
- 1 onion, chopped
- 1 pound mushrooms, chopped
- 4 cups chicken consommé, fresh or canned
- ¼ teaspoon white pepper
- 1 egg yolk
- 1 cup skim milk
- 1 tablespoon chopped parsley

Melt the butter in a saucepan; sauté the onion and mushrooms 5 minutes, stirring frequently. Add the consommé and pepper. Cover and cook over low heat 30 minutes. Force through a sieve or purée in an electric blender.

Beat the egg yolk and milk in a bowl; gradually add the mushroom mixture, beating constantly to prevent curdling. Reheat, stirring constantly, but do not let boil. Taste for seasoning, sprinkle with the parsley and serve.

Serves 6—65 calories in each serving.

## CHEDDAR CHEESE SOUP

- 2 teaspoons butter
- ¼ cup grated onion
- 2 tablespoons flour
- 3 cups chicken consommé, fresh or canned
- 2 cups skim milk
- ¾ cup grated cheddar cheese
- ¾ teaspoon paprika

Melt the butter in a saucepan; sauté the onion 5 minutes, stirring frequently. Sprinkle with the flour, then blend in the consommé. Cook over low heat 10 minutes. Add the milk, cheese and paprika, stirring until cheese melts. Taste for seasoning and serve hot.

Serves 6—95 calories in each serving.

## WATERCRESS SOUP

1 tablespoon potato starch or cornstarch
4 cups chicken consommé, fresh or canned
1 bunch watercress, chopped
1 egg yolk
1 cup skim milk

Mix the potato starch with a little consommé, then add the rest. Cook over low heat, stirring constantly until the boiling point. Cook 5 minutes. Add the watercress and cook 2 minutes.

Beat the yolk and milk in a bowl; gradually add the hot soup, stirring constantly to prevent curdling. Reheat but do not let boil. Taste for seasoning.

Serves 6—40 calories in each serving.

## CRÈME VICHYSSOISE ❄

4 leeks or 4 onions, sliced
3 potatoes, peeled and sliced
4 cups chicken stock, fresh or canned
2 stalks celery
3 sprigs parsley
2 cups milk
¼ teaspoon white pepper
1½ teaspoons Worcestershire sauce
minced chives (optional)

Wash the leeks very thoroughly and slice thin. Combine with the potatoes, chicken stock, celery and parsley. Cook over low heat 40 minutes. Discard the celery and parsley. Force the potato mixture through a sieve or purée in an electric blender. Stir in the milk, pepper and Worcestershire. Taste for seasoning and serve hot or chilled, with the chives on top if desired.

Serves 6—140 calories in each serving.

## COLD CREAM OF CUCUMBER SOUP

2 cucumbers, pared and sliced
1 onion, chopped
4 cups chicken broth, fresh or canned
¼ teaspoon white pepper
1 bay leaf
1 tablespoon cornstarch
3 tablespoons cold water
1 cup milk
1 tablespoon finely chopped dill or parsley

Combine the cucumber, onion, broth, pepper and bay leaf in a saucepan; bring to a boil and cook over low heat 20 minutes. Discard the bay leaf. Purée in an electric blender or force through a sieve. Return to the saucepan. Mix the cornstarch and water until smooth and stir it into the cucumber mixture. Cook over low heat, stirring constantly, until the boiling point. Continue to cook for 5 minutes.

Add the milk, taste for seasoning, and chill. Serve with the dill sprinkled on top. If possible use dill rather than parsley—it gives the soup a unique flavor.

Serves 6—55 calories in each serving.

## POTATO SOUP ❊

3 potatoes, pared and diced
1 onion, diced
3 cups water
1½ teaspoons salt
¼ teaspoon pepper
½ teaspoon paprika
1 cup chicken consommé, fresh or canned
1 cup skim milk

Combine the potatoes, onion, water, salt, pepper and paprika in a saucepan. Cover and cook over low heat 35 minutes. Force through a sieve or purée in an electric blender. Return to the saucepan; add the consommé and milk. Cook 10 minutes.

Serves 6—65 calories in each serving.

## MANHATTAN CLAM CHOWDER ❊

2 dozen hard-shell clams or 2 cans minced clams
2 slices bacon, diced
3 onions, chopped
1 can (#2½) tomatoes
2 carrots, pared and grated
3 cups water
1 teaspoon salt
¼ teaspoon freshly ground black pepper
1½ teaspoons diced thyme
3 potatoes, pared and cubed
1 tablespoon minced parsley

Have the fish man shuck the clams for you, but be sure he reserves the liquid. Grind the clams in a food mill, or mince them with a sharp knife. Measure the clam juice of the fresh or canned clams and add enough water to make 3 cups. (Keep the clams in the refrigerator while preparing the soup.)

Cook the bacon in a saucepan until browned; drain the fat. Sauté the onions with the bacon for 10 minutes over low heat; stir frequently. Add the tomatoes, carrots, water, clam juice, salt, pepper and thyme. Cook over low heat 30 minutes. Add the potatoes and cook 30 minutes. Stir in the clams and cook 10 minutes. Taste for seasoning.

Sprinkle with the parsley and serve.

Serves 6—105 calories in each serving.

## FISH CHOWDER ❊

1 tablespoon butter or margarine
2 onions, chopped
1 pound cod fish, cubed
Fish head
2½ teaspoons salt
½ teaspoon pepper
1 teaspoon paprika
1 bay leaf
5 cups water
2 potatoes, pared and diced
1 cup milk

Ask for a fish head when buying the fish, it adds flavor to the chowder.

Melt the butter in a saucepan. Sauté the onions for 10 minutes, stirring frequently. Add the fish, fish head, salt, pepper, paprika, bay leaf and water. Cook over low heat 30 minutes. Discard the fish head and bay leaf. Add the potatoes. Cook 10 minutes. Stir in the milk, heat and serve.

Serves 6—145 calories in each serving.

## NEW ENGLAND CLAM CHOWDER ❋

- 3 dozen soft-shell clams or 3 cans minced clams
- 3 cups water
- 1 tablespoon butter or margarine
- 2 onions, chopped
- 1 tablespoon flour
- 2 teaspoons salt
- ¼ teaspoon white pepper
- ¼ teaspoon celery salt
- 2 potatoes, peeled and diced
- 2 cups milk, scalded

Have the fish man open the clams for you, but reserve the liquid. Strain it before using it, as soft-shell clams have a tendency to be sandy. Snip off the necks of the clams and chop the soft part coarsely. Combine with the water and reserved liquid; bring to a boil and strain, reserving the liquid and clams.

Melt the butter in a saucepan; sauté the onions for 10 minutes, stirring frequently. Sprinkle the flour on the onions, then stir in the clam liquid, salt, pepper, celery salt and potatoes. Cover and cook over low heat 10 minutes. Add the milk and clams; cook 3 minutes. Taste for seasoning and serve.

Serves 6—145 calories in each serving.

## ALASKAN CLAM CHOWDER

Add ½ cup canned cream-style corn when adding the clams.

Serves 6—155 calories in each serving.

## SHRIMP GUMBO

- 2 slices bacon, diced
- 3 onions, chopped
- 1 pound okra or 1 package frozen, sliced
- 5 cups water
- 1 cup tomatoes, canned
- ½ cup diced celery
- 1 green pepper, diced
- 2 teaspoon salt
- ½ teaspoon pepper
- 2 teaspoons garlic powder
- ½ teaspoon thyme
- 1 pound uncooked shrimp, shelled and cleaned
- 1 cup cooked rice
- 3 tablespoons chopped parsley

The shrimp gumbo is actually more than just a soup. Served with salad, it becomes a complete luncheon or supper.

Cook the bacon in a saucepan until almost crisp; drain the fat. Add the onions and okra; sauté for 5 minutes, stirring frequently. Stir in the water, tomatoes, celery, green pepper, salt, pepper, garlic powder and thyme. Cover and cook over low heat 30 minutes. Add the shrimp; cook 10 minutes. Taste for seasoning.

Serve with the rice and sprinkle with parsley.

Serves 6—125 calories in each serving.

# FISH

Fish, properly and imaginatively prepared, is regarded by gourmets as one of the greatest delicacies in the field of cookery. Freezing has made a wide variety of fresh and saltwater fish available in all parts of the country, and it is an excellent food for calorie counters. Fish furnishes protein, so necessary for good health, and is an important source of vitamins and minerals. Most fish are quite low in fat, so you can have unusual dishes without too many calories. The flesh of fish is delicate, thus overcooking should be avoided. Follow the cooking instructions as set forth in the recipes.

When buying fresh fish, be sure to select truly fresh fish. The eyes should be bright and bulgy, the gills a bright red, the flesh firm to the touch, and the scales closely adhering to the body. Use the fish within twenty-four hours of purchase.

Frozen fish should be solidly frozen when bought and kept that way until ready to defrost and cook. It is advisable to keep frozen fish in the freezer for emergencies as it thaws quickly for unexpected use.

As a rule, fish is bland and requires some preparation to enhance its enjoyment. The recipes in this section are designed to do precisely that without adding too many calories. Presentation is particularly important with fish; garnish the serving dish with colorful bits of parsley, crisp watercress, capers, lemon slices or pieces of lime.

Shellfish, so popular in the United States, offer a delightful variety to the diet. Again we must thank freezing for making it available all year round. The shellfish calorie count is low, but it is high in proteins and minerals. Always keep shellfish on ice until ready to cook and serve.

## BAKED FISH IN TOMATO SAUCE

- 3 teaspoons salt
- ½ teaspoon pepper
- 6 slices (2 pounds) fish (haddock, lake trout, whitefish)
- 3 teaspoons salad or olive oil
- ½ cup chopped onion
- ½ cup chopped celery
- ½ cup chopped green pepper
- 2 cups canned tomatoes
- ¼ teaspoon garlic powder
- 1 teaspoon chili powder
- 1 tablespoon Worcestershire sauce
- 1 bay leaf

Sprinkle 2 teaspoons salt and ¼ teaspoon pepper on the fish. Grease a baking dish with 1 teaspoon of the oil; place the fish in it and refrigerate while preparing the sauce.

Heat the remaining oil in a saucepan; sauté the onion, celery and green pepper for 10 minutes, stirring frequently. Add the remaining salt and pepper, the tomatoes, garlic powder, chili powder, Worcestershire sauce and bay leaf. Cook over low heat for 20 minutes, stirring frequently. Discard bay leaf and purée the mixture in an electric blender, or force it through a sieve.

Pour the sauce over the fish. Bake in a 350° oven for 50 minutes, or until fish is flaky. Baste frequently.

Serves 6—165 calories in each serving.

## BAKED FISH CURRY

- 1½ tablespoons butter or margarine
- 6 fillets of sole, flounder or haddock (4 ounces each)
- 2 onions, sliced
- 1 cup sliced celery
- 1 teaspoon salt
- ¼ teaspoon pepper
- 2 teaspoons curry powder
- ¾ cup milk

Turn oven on and set at 350°

Grease a baking dish with 1 teaspoon butter; place the fillets in it.

Melt the remaining butter in a skillet; sauté the onions and celery for 5 minutes. Stir in the salt, pepper, curry powder and milk. Pour over the fish.

Bake 35 minutes, or until fish flakes easily.

Serves 6—155 calories in each serving.

## BAKED STUFFED FISH

- 1 tablespoon butter or margarine
- ½ cup chopped onion
- ¼ cup chopped celery
- ½ cup chopped mushrooms
- 1 slice bread, trimmed and crumbled
- 2 teaspoons chopped capers
- 3 teaspoons salt
- ¾ teaspoon pepper
- ¼ teaspoon dried tarragon
- 1 egg, beaten
- ¼ cup milk
- 1 teaspoon paprika
- 1 2-pound fish (bass, pike, whitefish or snapper, split for stuffing)
- ½ cup dry white wine

Turn oven on and set at 350°.

Melt 2 teaspoons of the butter in a skillet; sauté the onion, celery and mushrooms for 10 minutes, stirring frequently. Remove from heat and stir in the bread, capers, 1 teaspoon salt, ¼ teaspoon pepper, the tarragon, egg and milk. Mix well and taste for seasoning.

Sprinkle the paprika and remaining salt and pepper on the fish. Stuff the fish and fasten the opening by sewing or with skewers.

Grease a baking dish with the remaining butter and place the fish in it. Bake 20 minutes; pour the wine over it and bake 50 minutes longer or until fish is flaky and browned. Baste frequently.

Serves 6—195 calories in each serving.

## CLAMS CASINO

- 36 cherrystone clams
- 4 tablespoons chopped green pepper
- 4 tablespoons chopped pimento
- 6 slices half-cooked bacon, chopped

Have the clams opened, or open them yourself. Sprinkle some of the green pepper, pimento and bacon on each clam. Place in a baking dish (or 6 individual dishes) over rock salt, if you have it.

Broil 3 inches under the heat for 5 minutes. Serve immediately with lemon wedges.

Serves 6—140 calories in each serving.

## BAKED FRIED FISH

- ¼ cup milk
- 2 teaspoons salt
- ½ teaspoon Worcestershire sauce
- 2 tablespoons minced onion
- ½ cup finely crushed cornflakes
- ¼ teaspoon dry mustard
- ½ teaspoon paprika
- 6 fillets of flounder or sole (4 ounces each)
- 1½ tablespoons melted butter or margarine

Turn oven on and set at 500°.

Mix the milk, salt, Worcestershire sauce and onion in a bowl.

Mix the cornflakes, mustard and paprika on a piece of waxed paper.

Dip the fish in the milk mixture and then in the crumb mixture. Grease a shallow baking dish with ½ tablespoon of the melted butter; arrange the fish in it. Pour the remaining butter over. Bake 20 minutes or until browned.

Serves 6—145 calories in each serving.

## BAKED MARINATED FISH

- 1 teaspoon butter or margarine
- 2 teaspoons salt
- ½ teaspoon pepper
- ¼ teaspoon garlic powder
- ½ teaspoon monosodium glutamate
- 6 slices (2 pounds) fish (striped bass, lake trout, perch)
- 2 onions, thinly sliced
- ¾ cup white wine, dry
- 1 teaspoon Worcestershire sauce
- 1 can (8 ounces) tomato sauce
- 1 small green pepper, sliced

Start this dish the night before it is to be served or early in the day, allowing at least 5 hours for marinating.

Grease a glass baking dish with the butter. Sprinkle the salt, pepper, garlic powder and monosodium glutamate on the fish. Arrange in the baking dish with the onions over it.

Mix the wine and Worcestershire sauce together and pour over the fish. Let marinate until needed. Mix the tomato sauce and green peppers together; pour over the fish.

Bake 35 minutes, basting frequently.

Serves 6—145 calories in each serving.

## BAKED FISH, PIQUANT

- 1 tablespoon olive oil
- 4 onions, sliced
- 6 slices (2 pounds) fish (perch, whitefish, snapper or similar fish)
- 2 teaspoons salt
- ½ teaspoon black pepper
- ⅓ cup water
- 1 tablespoon vinegar
- ½ teaspoon liquid Sucaryl
- 1 bay leaf
- 2 lemons, sliced thin
- 2 tomatoes, peeled and chopped
- 2 tablespoons chopped parsley

Heat the oil in a skillet; sauté the onions for 10 minutes. Arrange the fish over it and sprinkle with salt, pepper, water, vinegar and Sucaryl. Place the bay leaf, lemon slices and tomato over the fish. Cover and cook over low heat 35 minutes, or until fish flakes easily.

Taste for seasoning, sprinkle with the parsley and serve hot or well chilled.

Serves 6—185 calories in each serving.

## BAKED FISH, ITALIAN STYLE

- 2 tablespoons olive oil
- 3 onions, chopped
- 2 cloves garlic, minced
- ¼ pound mushrooms, chopped
- ¼ cup capers, drained
- 2 tablespoons ground almonds
- 1 tablespoon flour
- 6 slices (1½ pounds) fish (bass, lake trout, perch)
- ¾ cup beef broth
- ¼ teaspoon oregano
- 2 teaspoons salt
- ½ teaspoon pepper
- 3 tablespoons chopped parsley

Heat the olive oil in a large skillet (with ovenproof handle); sauté the onions and garlic 10 minutes. Stir in the mushrooms, capers, almonds and flour; cook over low heat 3 minutes.

Place the fish on the vegetables; add the broth, oregano, salt, pepper and parsley. Bake in a 400° oven 35 minutes, or until fish flakes easily. Baste occasionally.

Serves 6—165 calories in each serving.

## FISH EN PAPILLOTE

6 pieces parchment paper or aluminum foil, 12 inches square
2 tablespoons olive or salad oil
6 slices (2 pounds) fish (snapper, whitefish, perch)
2 teaspoons salt
½ teaspoon pepper
1 teaspoon paprika
2 tablespoons lemon juice

Grease each piece of paper with 1 teaspoon of the oil. Place a slice of fish on each and sprinkle with the salt, pepper, paprika and lemon juice.

Fold over the edges, sealing them well (bring 2 sides up, fold over twice, then do the two other edges like a package). Place on a baking sheet.

Bake in a 350° over for 30 minutes. Split paper and serve directly in it, or slide onto heated plates.

All the juices and flavor are retained in this method of preparation. A whole fish can be prepared in this way too.

Serves 6—150 calories in each serving.

## BAKED FINNAN HADDIE

1½ pounds finnan haddie fillets
1 onion, sliced
1 cup skim milk
1 cup water
1 tablespoon butter or margarine
1 tablespoon flour
½ teaspoon salt
½ teaspoon white pepper

Wash the fish thoroughly; cover with cold water and let soak 2 hours. Drain.

Place the fish in a baking dish. Add the onion, milk and water. Bake in a 375° over 30 minutes, or until fish flakes easily.

Drain, reserving the liquid. Melt the butter in a saucepan; stir in the flour, salt and pepper. Gradually add the reserved liquid, stirring constantly to the boiling point. Cook over low heat 5 minutes.

The finnan haddie may be served in fillets, with the sauce poured over them, or flaked and mixed with the sauce.

Serves 6—135 calories in each serving.

## SOLE AMANDINE

1½ teaspoons salt
¼ teaspoon white pepper
2 tablespoons flour
6 fillets of sole (4 ounces of each)
2 tablespoons butter
¼ cup dry vermouth
12 blanched almonds, sliced
6 slices lemon

Mix the salt, pepper and flour together. Dip the fillets in the mixture.

Melt the butter in a skillet; brown the fillets on both sides. Add the vermouth and almonds and cook over low heat 5 minutes.

Serve with a slice of lemon on each fillet.

Serves 6—180 calories in each serving.

## CURRIED SALMON

- 1½ pounds salmon
- 2 teaspoons salt
- ½ teaspoon pepper
- 1 tablespoon salad or olive oil
- 3 onions, sliced thin
- 1½ tablespoons curry powder
- ⅛ teaspoon dried ground red pepper
- 4 tablespoons seedless raisins
- 1 teaspoon liquid Sucaryl
- 2 cups white vinegar

Have the salmon sliced thin and divide it into 6 pieces. Sprinkle the salt and pepper on the fish.

Heat the oil in a skillet; brown the salmon on both sides. Carefully remove; add one of the sliced onions to the oil in the skillet and sauté until browned.

In a saucepan combine the curry powder, red peppers, raisins, Sucaryl and vinegar; bring to a boil and cook over low heat 10 minutes.

Arrange the fish, sautéed onions and raw onions in layers in a glass bowl or jar. Pour the vinegar mixture over it. Cover and refrigerate for 48 hours before serving.

You can serve 12 appetizer-sized portions with this recipe. Divide calories in half, if you do. The salmon keeps for as long as 2 weeks prepared in this manner.

Serves 6—260 calories in each serving.

## SALMON IN ASPIC

- 2 cloves
- 1 onion
- 1 bay leaf
- 3 peppercorns
- 1 stalk celery
- 3 sprigs parsley
- 1½ teaspoons salt
- 5 cups water
- 1½ pounds salmon, in one piece
- 2 tablespoons gelatin

Stick the cloves in the onion and combine with the bay leaf, peppercorns, celery, parsley, salt and water. Bring to a boil and cook over medium heat 15 minutes. Carefully place the salmon in it and cook over low heat 1 hour. Let cool in the stock for 15 minutes, then carefully remove. Discard the skin. Strain the stock.

Soften the gelatin in a little cold water; stir into the hot stock until dissolved. Pour a little over the fish, and let it set. Chill remaining gelatin mixture until it begins to set, then beat it with a rotary beater.

Place the beaten gelatin on a serving dish and arrange the fish over it. Chill. Decorate with watercress.

Serves 6—200 calories in each serving.

## SALMON DIVAN

- 2 packages frozen broccoli
- 1 tablespoon butter or margarine
- 1 tablespoon flour
- 1 teaspoon salt
- ¼ teaspoon pepper
- 1 cup skim milk
- 4 tablespoons grated American cheese
- 1 can (#2) tomatoes, drained
- 2 cans (7¾ ounces) salmon, drained
- 2 tablespoons crushed cornflakes

Turn oven on and set at 375°.

Cook the broccoli half as long as the package directs. Drain and place in a 2-quart casserole.

Melt the butter in a saucepan; blend in the flour, salt and pepper. Gradually add the milk, stirring constantly to the boiling point. Cook over low heat 5 minutes. Stir in the cheese and tomatoes.

Break the salmon into chunks and place over the broccoli; pour the sauce over all. Sprinkle with the cornflakes.

Bake 30 minutes. Serve directly from the casserole.

Serves 6—205 calories in each serving.

## CHOPPED-FISH BALLS

- 2 pounds fillet of fish (whitefish and pike)
- Head, skin and bones of fish
- 5 onions
- 3 teaspoons salt
- 1 teaspoon white pepper
- 4½ cups water
- ½ teaspoon sugar
- 1 egg, beaten
- 1 tablespoon cracker meal
- 2 carrots, sliced

Use both types of fish—the combination is good. If you want to make enough for leftovers, double the amount of fish, egg and cracker meal.

Place the head, skin and bones of the fish on the bottom of a saucepan. Slice 4 onions and arrange over them. Add 1½ teaspoons salt, ½ teaspoon pepper and 4 cups of the water. Bring to a boil and cook over low heat while preparing the fish balls.

Grind the fish and remaining onion in a food chopper. Transfer to a wooden bowl; add the sugar, egg, cracker meal and the remaining salt, pepper and water. Chop until light and fluffy (this is important, as the texture depends on the chopping). Shape into 12 balls. Drop into the fish stock. Add the carrots; cover, but allow steam to escape. Cook over low heat 1¼ hours. Taste for seasoning.

Carefully remove the fish balls and carrots. Strain the stock over the fish. Chill and serve. The stock will jell.

Serves 6—180 calories in each serving.

## POACHED SALMON WITH EGG SAUCE

- 2 teaspoons salt
- ½ teaspoon pepper
- 6 slices (2 pounds) salmon
- 3 onions, sliced
- 2 carrots, scraped and sliced
- 2 stalks celery, sliced
- 2 cups water
- 2 egg yolks
- 2 tablespoons ground almonds
- 2 tablespoons chopped dill or parsley

Sprinkle the salt and pepper on the fish. Place the onions, carrots and celery in a saucepan with the fish on top. Add the water. Bring to a boil; cover and cook over low heat 35 minutes.

Transfer the fish to a platter. Purée the vegetables and stock in a blender, or force through a sieve.

Beat the egg yolks and almonds together; gradually add the vegetable mixture, stirring steadily to prevent curdling. Reheat but do not let boil. Taste for seasoning. Pour over the fish, sprinkle with the dill and serve.

Serves 6—165 calories in each serving.

## PAPRIKA FISH

- 1 tablespoon butter or margarine
- 4 onions, chopped
- 2 teaspoons paprika
- 6 (2 pounds) slices fish (sea bass, lake trout, whitefish)
- 2 teaspoons salt
- ½ teaspoon freshly ground black pepper
- 1 cup water
- ½ cup yogurt or buttermilk

Melt the butter in a deep skillet; sauté the onions for 10 minutes, stirring frequently. Blend in the paprika. Arrange the fish over the onions; season with the salt and pepper. Add the water and bring to a boil. Cover and cook over low heat 45 minutes. Taste for seasoning.

Carefully remove the fish to a serving dish. Stir the yogurt into the sauce; heat but do not boil. Pour over the fish and serve.

Serves 6—165 calories in each serving.

## SWORDFISH SAUTÉ PROVENÇAL

- 1½ pounds swordfish, cut ¼-inch thick
- 2 teaspoons butter or margarine
- 1 onion, finely chopped
- 2 teaspoons salt
- ½ teaspoon freshly ground black pepper
- ½ teaspoon basil
- 2 tomatoes, chopped
- ½ teaspoon garlic powder
- 6 ripe black olives, sliced

Cut the fish into 6 pieces. Melt the butter in a skillet; sauté the swordfish and onion for 5 minutes, turning the fish once. Add the salt, pepper, basil, tomatoes and garlic powder. Cover and cook over low heat 15 minutes, or until fish flakes easily. Add the olives, heat and serve.

Serves 6—280 calories in each serving.

## BROILED SHAD

2 pounds boned shad
1½ teaspoons salt
½ teaspoon pepper
1 teaspoon paprika
1 tablespoon butter
2 tablespoons grated American cheese

Season the shad with the salt, pepper and paprika. Place in a lightly greased shallow baking pan, skin side up.

Broil (with the gauge set at 400°) for 5 minutes. Carefully turn fish, skin-side down, sprinkle with the cheese and broil 15 minutes, or until fish flakes easily.

Serves 6—225 calories in each serving.

## SHAD ROE SAUTÉ

Roe of 3 shad
1 onion
1 teaspoon salt
2 tablespoons butter
2 tablespoons chopped parsley
6 slices crisp bacon

Combine the roe, onion, salt, and water to cover, in a deep skillet. Bring to a boil and cook over low heat 15 minutes. Drain carefully.

Melt the butter in a skillet; lightly brown the roe on both sides. Season with salt and pepper. Transfer to a heated serving dish. Place a piece of bacon on each half roe and serve with wedges of lemon.

Serves 6—225 calories in each serving.

## BAKED TROUT MEUNIÈRE

6 brook trout
½ cup skim milk
2 teaspoons salt
½ teaspoon pepper
3 tablespoons flour
2 tablespoons butter or margarine
2 tablespoons chopped parsley

Wash and dry the trout, remove the heads if you like, but they are usually served with the heads.

Dip the fish first in the milk, then sprinkle with the flour, mixed with the salt and pepper. Melt the butter in a baking dish and arrange the trout in it.

Bake in a 425° oven 20 minutes or until browned. Sprinkle the parsley on top and serve with lemon wedges.

Serves 6—155 calories in each serving.

## TROUT AMANDINE

Add 10 blanched sliced almonds to the fish after 15 minutes of baking time.

Serves 6—165 calories in each serving.

## FILLET OF SOLE BONNE FEMME

1½ teaspoons salt
¼ teaspoon white pepper
6 fillets of sole (4 ounces each)
1 tablespoon butter or margarine
1 onion, finely chopped
½ pound mushrooms, thinly sliced
½ cup dry white wine
1 teaspoon flour
3 tablespoons light cream
2 tablespoons chopped parsley

Sprinkle the salt and pepper on the fillets.

Melt the butter in a skillet. (Use one that can be brought to the table if possible.) Sauté the onion and half the mushrooms for 3 minutes. Arrange the fillets over this and cover with the remaining mushrooms. Pour the wine over all; cover the skillet and cook over medium heat for 15 minutes or until fish flakes easily.

Mix the flour and cream until smooth; add to the skillet, mixing steadily until the boiling point. Cook 2 minutes, basting once or twice.

Sprinkle with the parsley and serve.

Serves 6—155 calories in each serving.

## SCALLOPED FISH

1 tablespoon butter or margarine
1 onion, minced
3 tablespoons minced green pepper
1 tablespoon flour
½ teaspoon salt
¼ teaspoon pepper
1 cup skim milk
1 teaspoon Worcestershire sauce
2 cups cooked, flaked haddock or canned salmon
4 tablespoons grated American cheese
4 tablespoons crushed cornflakes

Melt the butter in a saucepan; sauté the onion and green pepper for 10 minutes, stirring frequently. Blend in the flour, salt and pepper. Gradually add the milk, stirring constantly to the boiling point. Add the Worcestershire sauce and cook 5 minutes.

Turn oven on and set at 400°.

In a 1½ quart casserole arrange alternate layers of the fish and sauce. Mix cheese and cornflakes and sprinkle on top.

Bake 25 minutes, or until browned.

Serves 6—165 calories in each serving.

## STEAMED CLAMS

36 clams (soft-shell steamers)
½ cup water
6 tablespoons melted butter

Wash and scrub the clams very thoroughly; combine in a deep kettle with the water. Cover, bring to a boil, and cook over low heat until the clams open.

Strain the broth through cheesecloth to remove the sand, taste for seasoning and serve in cups, along with the clams. Serve 1 tablespoon butter for each in a shallow dish.

Serves 6—200 calories in each serving.

## FILLET OF SOLE VERONIQUE

1½ teaspoons salt
¼ teaspoon white pepper
6 fillets of sole (4 ounces each)
½ cup dry white wine
1 tablespoon lemon juice
1 tablespoon butter
1 tablespoon flour
¾ cup skim milk
½ cup seedless white grapes

Sprinkle the salt and pepper on the sole. Place in a lightly greased baking dish (not metal). Add the wine and lemon juice. Cover the dish with a piece of aluminum foil. Bake in a 350° oven 15 minutes.

Melt the butter in a saucepan; blend in the flour and ¼ teaspoon salt. Gradually add the milk, stirring constantly to the boiling point. Cook 3 minutes.

Pour over the fish and sprinkle the grapes around it.

Place under the broiler until browned, about 5 minutes.

Serves 6—145 calories in each serving.

## FISH SALAD

1 pound haddock or cod
1½ cups water
1 onion
1 teaspoon salt
4 tablespoons special mayonnaise (see recipe)
1 teaspoon grated onion
1 teaspoon Worcestershire sauce
1 teaspoon chopped parsley
1 apple, peeled and diced
2 cucumbers, peeled and diced
½ cup diced celery
1 hard-cooked egg, finely chopped

Combine the fish, water, onion and salt, bring to a boil and cook over medium heat 20 minutes. Drain, flake and cool.

Mix together the mayonnaise, onion, Worcestershire sauce and parsley. Add to the fish with the apple, cucumber and celery. Toss together. Taste for seasoning.

Serve on shredded lettuce with the egg sprinkled on top.

Serves 6—125 calories in each serving.

## CRAB RAVIGOTE

1 pound crab meat, cooked or canned
¼ cup tarragon vinegar
1 teaspoon salt
½ teaspoon freshly ground black pepper
3 tablespoons chopped pimento
2 tablespoons chopped chives or scallions (green onion)
¾ cup special mayonnaise (see recipe)
2 tablespoons chopped capers

Flake the crab meat and pour the vinegar over it. Chill for 15 minutes, then drain the vinegar by pressing the crab meat gently. Add the salt, pepper, pimento, chives and ½ cup mayonnaise. Mix lightly.

Pile into 6 shells, ramekins or lettuce cups. Cover with the remaining mayonnaise and sprinkle with the capers.

Serves 6—120 calories in each serving.

## FISH MOUSSE

1½ pounds haddock or cod
1 slice onion
1 tablespoon butter
2 teaspoons flour
⅓ cup milk
1½ teaspoons salt
½ teaspoon pepper
½ teaspoon dry mustard
2 tablespoons dry sherry
2 egg yolks, beaten
3 egg whites, stiffly beaten

Turn oven on and set at 350°.

Remove the skin and bones of the fish; grind the fish and onion in a food chopper twice, using the finest blade.

Melt the butter in a saucepan; stir in the flour and gradually add the milk, mixing constantly to the boiling point. Add the fish, salt, pepper, mustard, sherry and egg yolks; mix lightly. Fold in the egg whites gently.

Turn into 6 individual baking dishes or a 1½-quart baking dish. Place in a shallow pan of hot water.

Bake 25 minutes for individual ones or 35 for large one. Carefully unmold onto heated plates and serve at once with 1 tablespoon hollandaise for each (see recipe).

Serves 6—240 calories in each serving.

## CRAB LOUIS

½ cup special mayonnaise (see recipe)
¼ cup special French dressing (see recipe)
3 tablespoons chili sauce
2 tablespoons chopped green olives
1 teaspoon Worcestershire sauce
½ teaspoon freshly ground black pepper
1 pound crab meat, cooked or canned
Shredded lettuce
3 hard-cooked eggs, chopped

Mix together the mayonnaise, French dressing, chili sauce, olives, Worcestershire sauce and pepper.

Divide the crab meat into 6 mounds and place on the lettuce. Sprinkle some egg around each mound. Cover with the dressing. Decorate with a slice of pimento if you like.

Serves 6—150 calories in each serving.

## CRAYFISH MARINIÈRE

2 tablespoons butter
36 uncooked crayfish or shrimp, cleaned
1 onion, finely chopped
¼ teaspoon dried thyme
1½ teaspoons salt
½ teaspoon freshly ground black pepper
1½ cups dry white wine
3 tablespoons chopped parsley

Melt the butter in a skillet; sauté the crayfish until they turn red (if shrimp are used, pink). Add the onion, thyme, salt, pepper and wine. Cover and cook over low heat 10 minutes (shrimp 5 minutes). Taste for seasoning, sprinkle with the parsley and serve.

Serves 6—150 calories in each serving.

## MAJORCAN FISH CASSEROLE

- 3 tomatoes, chopped, or 1 cup canned, drained
- 2 cloves garlic, minced
- 3 onions, sliced
- 2 green peppers, cut julienne fashion
- 2 teaspoons paprika
- ¼ teaspoon saffron
- 2 tablespoons olive oil
- 6 slices (2 pounds) fish (see bass, snapper, pike)
- 2½ teaspoons salt
- 2 bay leaves
- ¼ teaspoon dried ground red pepper
- 1½ cups dry white wine
- 1½ cups water
- ½ cup uncooked rice

In a saucepan, cook the tomatoes and garlic for 10 minutes over low heat. Mash until smooth, then add the onions, green peppers, paprika and saffron. Cook over low heat 15 minutes, stirring frequently.

Heat the oil in a casserole or Dutch oven; brown the fish in it on both sides. Add the salt, bay leaves, red peppers, wine, water and tomato mixture. Bring to a boil, and add the rice. Cover and cook over low heat 25 minutes. Taste for seasoning and serve hot.

Serves 6—220 calories in each serving.

## GLAZED CRAB MEAT

- 1 pound crab meat
- 6 slices crisp bacon
- ½ cup special mayonnaise (see recipe)
- ¼ cup chili sauce
- 1 teaspoon wine vinegar
- 1 teaspoon dry mustard
- ½ teaspoon paprika
- ½ teaspoon celery salt

Divide the crab meat among 6 ramekins, shells or baking dishes. Place a piece of bacon on each. Bake in a 400° oven 5 minutes.

Mix together the mayonnaise, chili sauce, vinegar, mustard, paprika and celery salt. Spread over the crab meat.

Place under the broiler for 5 minutes or until browned.

Note: Cooked haddock or cod may be prepared in the same fashion.

Serves 6—130 calories in each serving.

## FROGS' LEGS PROVENCALE

- 18 pairs frogs' legs
- 2½ teaspoons salt
- ¾ teaspoon freshly ground black pepper
- 2 tablespoons flour
- 2 tablespoons butter
- 2 cloves garlic
- 3 tablespoons chopped parsley

Wash and clean the legs; soak in cold water 2 hours. Drain and dry. Mix the salt, pepper and flour together and sprinkle on the frogs' legs.

Heat the butter in a skillet; sauté the legs until browned on both sides. Add the garlic when turning the legs. Sprinkle with the parsley and serve with lemon wedges.

Serves 6—120 calories in each serving.

## CUBAN FISH STEW

1 lobster (1 pound)
1 tablespoon olive oil
2 onions, chopped
2 cloves garlic, minced
1 pound haddock or cod, cubed
3 tablespoons uncooked rice
2 potatoes, peeled and cubed
2 cups coarsely shredded cabbage
1 cup canned tomatoes
2 tablespoons tomato paste
5 cups water
2 teaspoons salt
½ teaspoon pepper
½ teaspoon oregano

Have the fish man split the uncooked lobster for you, then it will be a simple process to remove the meat and cut it into pieces. Don't forget the claw meat, too. Reserve the shells, as it will help to flavor the stew.

Heat the olive oil in a deep saucepan; sauté the onions and garlic for 5 minutes. Add the fish, lobster and rice; cook over high heat for 5 minutes, stirring almost constantly. Add the potatoes, cabbage, tomatoes, tomato paste; water, salt, pepper, oregano and some of the lobster shells. Cook over medium heat 20 minutes. Taste for seasoning, discard the lobster shells and serve in deep bowls.

This is a complete dish—soup, fish and vegetables all in one.

Serves 6—185 calories in each serving.

## COQUILLES SAINT-JACQUES

1 pound scallops
1 cup dry white wine
¼ teaspoon thyme
1 stalk celery
2 sprigs parsley
1 bay leaf
1 teaspoon salt
½ pound mushrooms, chopped
1 onion, chopped
1 tablespoon chopped parsley
1 tablespoon butter
2 tablespoons water
1 teaspoon lemon juice
½ teaspoon pepper
1 tablespoon flour
1 egg yolk
3 tablespoons milk
Paprika

Wash and drain the scallops; combine the wine, thyme, celery, parsley and bay leaf in a saucepan. Bring to a boil and add the scallops and salt. Cook over low heat 10 minutes. Strain the stock and cut the scallops in small pieces.

Combine the mushrooms, onion, parsley, butter, water, lemon juice and pepper in a saucepan; cover and cook over low heat 10 minutes. Stir in the flour, and gradually add the reserved stock. Cook 2 minutes, stirring constantly.

Beat the egg yolk and milk in a bowl; gradually add the mushroom mixture, stirring constantly to prevent curdling. Add the scallops and taste for seasoning.

Pile into 6 individual ramekins or shells. Sprinkle with the paprika.

Place under a hot broiler until delicately browned. Serve immediately.

Serves 6—140 calories in each serving.

## MARINATED FISH

4 onions, sliced
6 slices (2 pounds) fish (whitefish, pike, haddock)
2 teaspoons salt
½ teaspoon freshly ground black pepper
2 cups water
1½ cups white vinegar
1 tablespoon sugar
⅛ teaspoon liquid Sucaryl
2 teaspoons pickling spice
2 bay leaves

Combine 2 of the onions, the fish, salt, pepper and water in a saucepan. Bring to a boil; cover and cook over low heat 35 minutes.

In a glass bowl or jar, arrange the fish and remaining onions in layers. Add the vinegar, sugar, Sucaryl, pickling spice and bay leaves to the fish stock. Bring to a boil and pour over the fish.

Let marinate in the refrigerator for at least 36 hours before using. The marinade will be jellied.

Cook twice as much fish, if you like—it can be kept for as long as 2 weeks.

Serves 6—145 calories in each serving.

## BAKED CREAMED TUNA ON TOAST

1 tablespoon butter or margarine
¼ cup minced onion
½ pound mushrooms, sliced, or 2 3-ounce cans, drained
1 tablespoon flour
1 teaspoon salt
¼ teaspoon pepper
1½ cups skim milk
2 tomatoes, cut in eighths
2 cans (7¾ ounces) tuna, drained and flaked
3 slices toast, cut into triangles
2 tablespoons chopped parsley

Turn oven on and set at 400°.

Melt the butter in a saucepan; sauté the onion and mushrooms for 5 minutes. Sprinkle with the flour, salt and pepper; mix well. Gradually add the milk, stirring constantly to the boiling point. Add the tomatoes and tuna.

Arrange the toast in a shallow baking dish; pour the tuna mixture over it. Sprinkle with the parsley.

Bake 15 minutes. Serve directly from the baking dish.

Serves 6—205 calories in each serving.

## BROILED LOBSTER

6 lobsters (1¼ pounds each)
2 teaspoons salt
½ teaspoon pepper
3 tablespoons butter or margarine

Have the lobsters split, or do it yourself. Remove the sac behind the head and the dark vein. Season with salt and pepper and spread each lobster with ½ tablespoon butter. Place on a baking pan, shells down.

Broil in a hot broiler 15 minutes. Serve with lemon wedges. If additional melted butter is served, add calories.

Serves 6—150 calories in each serving.

## MUSSELS IN WHITE WINE

48 mussels
1 cup dry white wine
6 shallots, chopped, or 3 tablespoons chopped onion
1 tablespoon butter
2 teaspoons flour
1 tablespoon chopped parsley

Wash and scrub the mussels. Combine in a saucepan with the wine and shallots. Cover and cook over high heat 5 minutes, or until the shells open. Remove mussels and keep warm.

Knead the butter and flour together; drop into the wine broth. Cook until butter melts and sauce thickens slightly. Taste for seasoning and add the parsley. Serve the mussels with some of the broth in deep plates.

Serves 6—125 calories in each serving.

## OYSTERS ROCKEFELLER

½ pound uncooked spinach
4 tablespoons chopped parsley
3 tablespoons chopped onion
½ teaspoon salt
⅛ teaspoon pepper
4 drops Tabasco sauce
2 tablespoons dry bread crumbs
2 tablespoons melted butter
36 oysters on the half shell

Chop together the spinach, parsley, onion, salt, pepper and Tabasco. Stir in the bread crumbs and butter.

Fill a baking pan with rock salt and place the oysters on it.

Bake in a 450° oven until the edges curl. Quickly spread each oyster with some of the spinach mixture and bake 5 minutes longer. Serve immediately.

Serves 6—140 calories in each serving.

## BOUILLABAISSE

2 tablespoons olive oil
3 onions, chopped fine
2 cloves, garlic
5 tomatoes, chopped fine, or 2 cups canned
1 bay leaf
1 teaspoon salt
½ teaspoon pepper
1 teaspoon saffron
1 pound assorted sliced fish (perch, pike, haddock)
5 cups boiling water
2 lobsters (1 pound each) cut up in the shell
6 shrimp, shelled and cleaned
6 clams or mussels in the shell
1 cup dry white wine

Heat the oil in a large casserole or Dutch oven; sauté the onions and garlic for 5 minutes. Add the tomatoes; cook 10 minutes. Add the bay leaf, salt, pepper, saffron, fish and boiling water. Cook over low heat 10 minutes. Carefully place the lobster in the casserole; cook 10 minutes. Add the shrimp, clams and wine. Cook 7 minutes. Taste for seasoning.

Place pieces of fish, lobster, shrimp and clams in individual casseroles or deep soup plates. Pour the soup-sauce over it.

This dish is usually served with toasted French bread.

Serves 6—190 calories in each serving.

## PICKLED HERRING, FINNISH STYLE

3 salt herring
3 onions, sliced
½ cup hot water
1½ cups white vinegar
1 tablespoon sugar
1 teaspoon liquid Sucaryl
2 tablespoons pickling spice
2 bay leaves

The 3 herring will serve 6 generously but if you want to pickle a larger quantity for future use, 6 may be pickled in the same amount of marinade.

Wash the herring thoroughly. Cover with water and let soak 24 hours; change the water at least 3 times. Drain and cut off the heads of the herring. Cut each herring (through the bone) into 4 pieces. Arrange layers of the herring and onions in a covered jar.

Combine the water, vinegar, sugar, Sucaryl, pickling spice and bay leaves, mixing well. Pour over the herring. Cover and refrigerate for 48 hours before serving.

Serves 6—100 calories in each serving.

## DEVILED CRAB MEAT

2 teaspoons butter
2 teaspoons flour
½ cup skim milk
3 tablespoons chopped onion
3 tablespoons chopped green pepper
1 teaspoon salt
1 tablespoon prepared mustard
1 teaspoon Worcestershire sauce
2 drops Tabasco sauce
3 tablespoons bread crumbs
¾ pound crab meat, cooked or canned

Melt the butter in a saucepan; blend in the flour. Gradually add the milk, stirring constantly to the boiling point. Cook over low heat 3 minutes.

Combine the onion, green pepper, salt, mustard, Worcestershire, Tabasco sauce, bread crumbs, crab meat and sauce, mixing lightly. Taste for seasoning.

Pile into shells, ramekins or individual baking dishes.

Bake in a 400° oven 10 minutes or until delicately browned.

Serves 6—85 calories in each serving.

## SAUTÉED SHRIMP

1½ pounds shrimp, peeled and deveined
2 tablespoons butter or margarine
4 tablespoons chopped parsley
1½ teaspoons salt
½ teaspoon pepper
½ teaspoon paprika

Wash and dry the shrimp. Melt the butter in a skillet; add the shrimp. Sauté for 3 minutes on each side. Add the parsley, salt, pepper and paprika when turning them.

Serves 6—135 calories in each serving.

## STUFFED CLAMS

24 large clams
¼ cup water
1 tablespoon butter or margarine
½ cup chopped mushrooms
3 tablespoons chopped onion
1 tablespoon chopped parsley
¼ cup dry vermouth
1 tablespoon bread crumbs

Wash and scrub the clams thoroughly; place in a deep kettle with the water. Cover; bring to a boil and cook over low heat until clams open.

Remove the clams from the shells, reserving half the shells. Chop the clams finely. Melt the butter in a skillet, sauté the mushrooms and onions for 3 minutes. Mix together the clams, sautéed vegetables, parsley, wine and bread crumbs. Taste for seasoning and fill the shells.

Bake in a 400° oven 5 minutes.

Serves 6—95 calories in each serving.

## CRAB MEAT IN ASPIC

2 tablespoons gelatin
2 cups chicken broth
1 hard-cooked egg, sliced
10 stuffed green olives
¼ cup diced green pepper
½ cup special mayonnaise (see recipe)
1 tablespoon wine vinegar
1 teaspoon grated onion
1 tablespoon chopped parsley
2 tablespoons chopped celery
¾ pound cooked crabmeat, fresh or canned
1 cucumber, peeled and diced

Soak the gelatin in ½ cup broth; bring the remaining 1½ cups to a boil; then add the softened gelatin, stirring until dissolved.

Rinse a 1-quart mold with cold water; arrange the egg, olives and green pepper on the bottom. Carefully pour ¾ cup of the gelatin mixture over it and chill until firm.

Mix together the mayonnaise, vinegar, onion, parsley, celery, crabmeat, cucumber and remaining gelatin mixture. Pack into the mold; chill until firm.

Carefully unmold onto shredded lettuce. Slice and serve.

Serves 6—170 calories in each serving.

## SHRIMP IN WINE SAUCE

2 tablespoons flour
1 teaspoon salt
½ teaspoon pepper
1½ pounds uncooked shrimp, shelled and cleaned
2 tablespoons olive oil
¾ cup dry white wine
2 teaspoons tomato paste
2 tablespoons boiling water
1 scallion (green onion), chopped
1 tablespoon chopped parsley

Combine the flour, salt and pepper on a piece of waxed paper; toss the shrimp in the mixture.

Heat the olive oil in a skillet; lightly brown the shrimp on both sides. Stir together the wine, tomato paste, water and scallion; add to the shrimp. Cook over low heat 5 minutes, stirring occasionally. Sprinkle with the parsley, taste for seasoning and serve.

Serves 6—135 calories in each serving.

## BAKED CRAB MEAT

- 2 tablespoons olive oil
- 2 onions, chopped fine
- 2 tomatoes, chopped
- 2 green peppers, chopped fine
- 1 clove garlic, minced
- 3 tablespoons chopped parsley
- 1 pound cooked or canned crab meat
- 1½ teaspoons salt
- ½ teaspoon pepper
- 2 eggs, beaten
- 2 tablespoons bread crumbs
- 6 stuffed green olives, sliced

Heat the oil in a skillet; sauté the onions for 10 minutes, stirring frequently. Add the tomatoes, green pepper, garlic and parsley. Cook over low heat 15 minutes. Stir in the crab meat, salt and pepper. Cook 5 minutes. Gradually add the eggs, stirring constantly until set. Taste for seasoning.

Turn the mixture into a baking dish or 6 individual ramekins. Sprinkle the bread crumbs on top and arrange the olives over all.

Bake in a 375° oven 10 minutes, or until browned.

Serves 6—135 calories in each serving.

## CRAB MEAT CREOLE

- 1 tablespoon butter or margarine
- 2 onions, finely chopped
- 1 tablespoon flour
- ¾ cup chicken broth, fresh or canned
- 1 cup canned tomatoes, drained
- 1 green pepper, diced
- 2 tablespoons chopped parsley
- ¼ teaspoon dried thyme
- ¾ pound crab meat, cooked or canned
- 8 green olives, chopped
- 2 teaspoons Worcestershire sauce
- ¼ teaspoon freshly ground black pepper
- 1 teaspoon salad oil
- 2 tablespoons bread crumbs

Melt the butter in a saucepan; sauté the onions for 5 minutes. Blend in the flour; gradually add the broth, stirring constantly to the boiling point. Add the tomatoes, green pepper, parsley and thyme. Cook over low heat 15 minutes.

Stir in the crab meat, olives, Worcestershire sauce and pepper. Taste for seasoning.

Grease a 1-1½ quart casserole with oil, and dust with the crumbs. Turn the crab-meat mixture into it.

Bake in a 375° oven 15 minutes. Serve directly from the casserole.

Serves 6—115 calories in each serving.

## SHRIMP KEBOBS

- 1 tablespoon butter
- 1 pound shrimp, cooked, shelled and deveined
- 12 small mushroom caps
- 4 slices bacon, half-cooked and cut in 2-inch pieces

Melt 1 tablespoon butter in a skillet; sauté the mushrooms 5 minutes, turning them once.

Use 6 metal skewers and thread them alternately with the shrimp, mushrooms and bacon. Place on a rack, and broil about 6 minutes in a hot broiler 3 inches under the heat. Turn a few times until the bacon is crisp.

Serve with special tartar sauce (see recipe).

Serves 6—110 calories in each serving.

## NEW ORLEANS FISH

- 2 cups water
- 1 onion, sliced
- 1 bay leaf
- 1 stalk celery
- 1½ teaspoons salt
- ¼ teaspoon pepper
- 6 fillets of sole or haddock
- 1 package frozen spinach
- 1 tablespoon butter
- ¼ pound fresh mushrooms, sliced or 1 3-ounce can
- 1 tablespoon flour
- 1 egg yolk
- 2 tablespoons dry vermouth
- 6 cooked shrimp, chopped coarsely

Combine the water, onion, celery, salt and pepper in a deep skillet. Bring to a boil and cook over medium heat 10 minutes. Gently place the fish in it. Cover and cook 20 minutes. Drain and reserve 1 cup of the stock.

Meanwhile cook the spinach as the package directs. Drain. Melt the butter in a skillet; sauté the mushrooms for 5 minutes. Stir in the flour, then gradually add the stock, stirring constantly to the boiling point.

Beat the egg yolk and vermouth in a bowl. Gradually add the sauce, stirring steadily to prevent curdling. Stir in the shrimp. Spread some of the spinach on each fillet and pour the sauce over all.

Serves 6—155 calories in each serving.

## LOBSTER AMÉRICAINE

- 3 live lobsters (2 pounds each)
- 1 tablespoon olive oil
- 1½ teaspoons salt
- 1 tablespoon butter
- 1 onion, chopped fine
- 1 carrot
- 2 tablespoons cognac
- ½ cup canned tomato sauce
- 1 tomato, peeled and chopped
- ½ cup dry white wine
- ¼ teaspoon garlic powder
- ½ teaspoon dried thyme

Remove the claws of the lobsters and crack. Chop the lobster tails (in the shells) into 4 pieces crosswise. (Ask the fish man to do this for you.)

Heat the oil in a skillet; add the lobsters and sprinkle with the salt. Cook over medium heat 5 minutes, or until lobsters turn red.

Melt the butter in a deep casserole or saucepan; sauté the onion and carrot 5 minutes. Add the lobsters. Heat the cognac in a ladle, set it aflame and pour over the lobsters. When flame dies, add the tomato sauce, tomatoes, wine, garlic powder and thyme. Cover tightly and cook over low heat 20 minutes. Taste for seasoning.

Remove meat from shells, or serve right in the shells. Serve in deep plates.

Serves 6—190 calories in each serving.

## BAKED SCALLOPS

- 1½ pounds scallops
- 2 teaspoons salt
- ½ teaspoon freshly ground black pepper
- ½ pound mushrooms, chopped
- 2 tablespoons chopped parsley
- 6 tablespoons dry white wine
- 6 teaspoons butter

Wash and drain the scallops. If bay scallops are used, leave them whole; if sea scallops, cut into 4 pieces. Arrange them in 6 ramekins, shells or baking dishes. Season with the salt and pepper, and cover with the mushrooms. Sprinkle with the parsley and 1 tablespoon of wine for each shell. Dot each with 1 teaspoon butter.

Bake in a 450° oven 12 minutes. Serve with lemon wedges.

Serves 6—140 calories in each serving.

## SHRIMP CURRY

- 2 cups water
- 1 teaspoon salt
- 1 bay leaf
- 1 stalk celery
- 1½ pounds shrimp, shelled and deveined (reserve a few shells)
- 1 tablespoon butter or margarine
- ¼ cup chopped onion
- 2 tablespoons curry powder
- ½ teaspoon powdered ginger
- ½ cup beef broth, fresh or canned
- 1 cucumber, diced
- 1 tablespoon lemon juice

Combine the water, salt, bay leaf and celery; bring to a boil. Add the shrimp and shells and cook 5 minutes. Drain and discard shells, reserving ½ cup of the shrimp stock.

Melt the butter in a saucepan; sauté the onion 5 minutes; stir in the curry powder, ginger and beef broth. Cook over low heat 15 minutes. Add the shrimp, reserved stock, cucumber and lemon juice. Cook 2 minutes.

Serve with rice, but add calories.

Serves 6—90 calories in each serving.

## SHRIMP AND GREEN PEAS, CHINESE STYLE

- 2 tablespoons peanut or salad oil
- 1½ pounds shrimp, shelled and cleaned
- 3 scallions (green onions), sliced thin, or ¼ cup chopped onion
- 1-inch piece fresh ginger or 1½ teaspoons powdered ginger
- 2 cloves garlic, minced
- 1 cup canned tiny green peas, drained
- 2 teaspoons cornstarch
- 1 teaspoon salt
- 1 teaspoon sugar
- 2 teaspoons soy sauce
- ½ cup cold water

Heat the oil in a skillet; lightly brown the shrimp on both sides. Add the scallions, ginger, garlic and peas. Cook over low heat 2 minutes.

Mix the cornstarch, salt, sugar, soy sauce and water until smooth; pour over the shrimp mixture. Stir constantly to the boiling point; cook 2 minutes. Taste for seasoning and serve immediately.

Serves 6—165 calories in each serving.

## BOILED LOBSTER

1 tablespoon butter
1 onion, chopped
1 carrot, sliced
2 stalks celery
2 quarts water
1 bay leaf
2 sprigs parsley
6 peppercorns
1 tablespoon vinegar
6 live lobsters (1½ pounds each)

Melt the butter in a saucepan; sauté the onion, carrot and celery 10 minutes. Add the water, bay leaf, parsley, peppercorns and vinegar. Cover, bring to a boil and cook over low heat 30 minutes. Strain and bring to a boil again.

Plunge the lobsters, heads down, into the boiling liquid. Cook over medium heat 20 minutes. Drain.

Split the lobsters lengthwise and remove the sac behind the head, and the vein along the back. Crack the claws. Serve hot or cold with 2 tablespoons special mayonnaise for each serving.

Serves 6—140 calories in each serving.

## STUFFED LOBSTER

6 uncooked lobsters, split (1 pound each)
2 tablespoons butter
2 onions, chopped
½ pound mushrooms, chopped
1 tablespoon flour
½ cup chicken broth
1 teaspoon salt
¼ teaspoon pepper
¼ teaspoon dried thyme
Dash of cayenne pepper
2 tablespoons dry bread crumbs
4 tablespoons grated Parmesan cheese

Remove the meat of the lobster (reserve the shells) and cut into small pieces.

Melt 1 tablespoon of the butter in a saucepan; sauté the onions and mushrooms for 10 minutes, stirring frequently. Blend in the flour; gradually add the broth, stirring constantly to the boiling point. Add the lobster meat, salt, pepper, thyme and cayenne. Cook over low heat 15 minutes, stirring occasionally. Taste for seasoning.

Fill the shells with the mixture. Mix the bread crumbs and cheese together and sprinkle on top; dot with the remaining butter.

Bake in a 400° oven 10 minutes or until browned on top.

Serves 6—180 calories in each serving.

## LOBSTER CANTONESE

- 3 lobsters (1½ pounds each)
- 1 tablespoon peanut or salad oil
- ¼ pound ground lean pork
- ¼ cup chopped water chestnuts or celery
- ½ cup bamboo shoots (optional, but delicious)
- 1 carrot, grated
- 2 scallions (green onions) chopped
- 1½ teaspoon salt
- ½ teaspoon pepper
- 1 cup chicken broth, fresh or canned
- 2 eggs
- 1 tablespoon cornstarch
- 1 tablespoon soy sauce
- 3 tablespoons cold water

Buy boiled lobsters and have them cut into several pieces or boil live lobsters in salted water for 10 minutes, then clean and cut.

Heat the oil in a deep skillet over medium heat; sauté the pork, water chestnuts, bamboo shoots, carrot, scallions, salt and pepper 15 minutes, stirring freuqently. Add the lobsters and broth. Cook over low heat 10 minutes.

Beat the eggs, and add to the mixture, stirring constantly. Mix the cornstarch, soy sauce and water until smooth. Stir into the skillet, mixing steadily to the boiling point. Cook over low heat 5 minutes. Serve immediately.

If served with rice, add calories.

Serves 6—200 calories in each serving.

## BOILED SHRIMP

- 1½ pounds shrimp
- 2 cups water
- 1 teaspoon salt
- 1 bay leaf
- ½ teaspoon shrimp spice (celery seed, thyme, cloves)
- 1 stalk celery
- 6 peppercorns

You can cook the shrimp in the shells or remove them before cooking. It is easier to do it before cooking; slip the shells off, then cut down the back to remove the black vein. Reserve a few shells for the water. If shelled after cooking, peel the shrimp, then remove black vein.

Combine the water, salt, bay leaf, shrimp spice, celery and peppercorns in a saucepan; bring to a boil and add the shrimp. Cook over medium heat 5 minutes for shelled shrimp and 8 for unshelled. Drain and cool.

Serve with cocktail sauce, or use as directed in other recipes.

Serves 6—80 calories in each serving.

## SHRIMP REMOULADE

1¼ pounds shrimp
1 onion, sliced
3 cloves garlic, minced
1 teaspoon salt
½ teaspoon pepper
1 bay leaf
2 cups water
2 tablespoons olive oil
3 tablespoons lemon juice
3 tablespoons chili sauce
1 tablespoon prepared horseradish
1 teaspoon prepared mustard
½ teaspoon paprika
2 scallions (green onions) chopped fine

Shell (reserve few shells) and remove the veins of the shrimp. Wash and drain. Combine the onion, 2 cloves garlic, salt, pepper, bay leaf, water and shells in a saucepan; cook over medium heat 10 minutes. Place the shrimp in the mixture and cook over low heat 5 minutes. Let cool in the liquid for 15 minutes, then drain and cool.

Beat together the remaining clove of garlic, the olive oil, lemon juice, chili sauce, horseradish, mustard and paprika. Stir in the scallions and shrimp. Let marinate at least 2 hours —or overnight, if possible.

Serve on shredded lettuce.

Serves 6—125 calories in each serving.

The symbol ⁂ indicates dishes that can be frozen.

A generation ago, poultry was reserved chiefly for holidays and celebrations. Today, it is one of our most typical and economical everyday foods. Chicken in particular is low in calories and high in protein, vitamins and minerals—an ideal diet food. Inasmuch as it is not fattening, servings may be larger than usual. Serve it frequently; there are so many ways to prepare poultry that you couldn't possibly tire of it.

Poultry is sold dressed (ready to be drawn) or in the more popular "ready to cook" style. Frozen poultry and chicken in parts are available, too, making it convenient to have on hand in the home freezer for large or small families. Always keep frozen poultry solidly frozen until time to thaw for cooking.

Buy the type of chicken specified in the recipes. Younger chickens have less fat and therefore, fewer calories. If older birds are used, drain away the fat. Young ducks are delicious and may be prepared in numerous ways. You *must*, however, remove as much fat as possible before cooking, and keep draining away the fat during the cooking process. In this way, the high fat calories are melted away, leaving only the lean meat. Once a Thanksgiving-only specialty, turkeys are now available the year round in small sizes (as well as large), making it practicable for any occasion.

To carve poultry, place the bird on a heated platter with the breast side up. Put a fork through the breastbone and hold firmly with the left hand. Pull the leg away from the body and sever the thigh joint. Pull the wing away from the body and sever the joint. Slice the breast against the grain. Duck may sometimes be carved in this fashion, or it may be cut into quarters, or sixths.

## ARROZ CON POLLO

- 1 3½-pound fryer, disjointed
- 3 tablespoons flour
- 2 teaspoons salt
- 2 tablespoons olive oil
- 2 onions, chopped
- 2 cloves garlic, minced
- 3 tomatoes, chopped
- 2 cups chicken broth, fresh or canned
- 1 bay leaf
- ½ teaspoon saffron
- ½ teaspoon pepper
- 1 cup uncooked rice
- 1 green pepper, diced
- 1 pimento, sliced
- 3 tablespoons sherry

Wash and dry the chicken. Mix the flour and salt together and roll the chicken in the mixture.

Heat the oil in a deep skillet or casserole. Sauté the onions and garlic for 10 minutes. Remove and brown the chicken in the oil remaining in the skillet. Return the onions, and add the tomatoes, broth, bay leaf, saffron and pepper. Cover and cook over low heat 30 minutes. Add the rice, green pepper, pimento and sherry. Cover and cook 30 minutes longer, or until chicken and rice are tender. Watch carefully to avoid burning and add a little more broth if necessary.

Serves 6—275 calories in each serving.

## BARBECUED CHICKEN

- ⅓ cup cider vinegar
- ½ cup water
- 1 teaspoon Worcestershire sauce
- 2 teaspoons sugar
- 3 tablespoons chili sauce
- 1 teaspoon salt
- ½ teaspoon pepper
- 2 teaspoons onion powder
- ¼ teaspoon garlic powder
- ¼ teaspoon dry mustard
- 1 tablespoon salad oil
- 3 1¼-pound broilers, split

Combine the vinegar, water, Worcestershire sauce, sugar, chili sauce, salt, pepper, onion powder, garlic powder and mustard in a saucepan. Bring to a boil.

Oil a baking pan and place the broilers on it skin side down. Broil under a hot broiler 10 minutes. Turn and pour the sauce over them. Continue to broil for 25 minutes, basting frequently.

Serves 6—165 calories in each serving.

## STUFFED CAPON ❋

4 teaspoons salt
1¼ teaspoons pepper
1 teaspoon ginger
1 5-pound capon
4 slices white bread, shredded
1 cup chicken broth, fresh or canned
1 onion, chopped
1 cup chopped celery
2 tablespoons chopped parsley
3 tablespoons seedless raisins
¼ teaspoon diced thyme
¼ cup milk

Mix 3 teaspoons salt, ¾ teaspoon pepper and the ginger together. Rub into the capon, inside and out.

Grind or chop the liver and gizzard. Soak the bread in the broth for 5 minutes. Remove and press out excess liquid. Combine the ground giblets, the bread, onion, celery, parsley, raisins, thyme, milk, and remaining salt and pepper. Mix well and stuff the capon. Close the opening with skewers, thread or aluminum foil. Truss the bird.

Place in a shallow roasting pan, breast side up. Roast in a 400° oven for 10 minutes; reduce heat to 350° and roast 1¼ hours longer or until tender.

Carve the bird and serve 3 slices or 1 joint with 3 tablespoons stuffing.

Serves 6—350 calories in each serving.

Note: Don't baste the capon, but turn over, if necessary, to brown the underside.

## BOUILLI
## BOILED CHICKEN DINNER

3 pounds cabbage (2 small heads, quartered)
1 yellow turnip
1 onion
2 cloves
1 5-pound fowl
1 tablespoon salt
½ teaspoon white pepper
¼ teaspoon thyme
1 bay leaf
Boiling water
1 pound green beans
6 small white onions
6 carrots, scraped
3 potatoes, peeled and halved

Put the cabbage, turnip, and onion stuck with the cloves on the bottom of a deep saucepan or kettle. Place the cleaned chicken and giblets over them; add the salt, pepper, thyme, bay leaf and enough water to just cover the chicken. Cover the saucepan tightly; bring to a boil and cook over low heat 1¾ hours.

Tie the green beans into 6 bunches with white string and add to the chicken with the onions, carrots and potatoes. Cover and cook 45 minutes. Serve the chicken on a platter surrounded with the vegetables. The soup may be served separately or saved for future use.

Serves 6—250 calories in each serving.

## STUFFED BABY CHICKEN ✻

- 1 pair sweetbreads
- 1 cup water
- 1 tablespoon vinegar
- 3 teaspoons salt
- 1 teaspoon pepper
- ½ teaspoon garlic powder
- 3 1¼-pound whole broilers
- ¼ pound mushrooms, chopped
- 1 onion, chopped
- 2 stalks celery, chopped
- 1 cup cooked medium-fine noodles
- 1 egg, beaten
- ¼ cup chicken broth, fresh or canned
- ¼ cup sherry
- 1 tablespoon butter or margarine

Wash the sweetbreads in cold water; combine in a saucepan with the 1 cup water and the vinegar. Bring to a boil and cook over low heat 10 minutes. Drain and cover with cold water for 10 minutes. Drain again; remove the membrane and cube the sweetbreads.

Mix together 2 teaspoons salt, ¾ teaspoon pepper and the garlic powder. Rub into the broilers. Grind or chop the livers and gizzards. Combine the mushrooms, onion and celery in a skillet; cook over low heat 5 minutes, stirring frequently. Add the noodles, sweetbreads, ground livers, egg, broth, sherry and the remaining salt and pepper, mixing thoroughly. Stuff the chickens and close the opening with skewers or thread.

Melt the butter in a baking pan. Arrange the chickens in it. Roast in a 425° oven 10 minutes; reduce heat to 375° and roast 35 minutes longer or until well browned and tender. Cut in half and serve with the stuffing.

Serves 6—210 calories in each serving.

## BRUNSWICK STEW ✻

- 1 5-pound stewing chicken, disjointed
- ½ pound beef, cut in ½-inch cubes
- 2 quarts water
- 2 onions, chopped
- 2 teaspoons salt
- ½ pound okra, fresh or frozen
- 2 potatoes, peeled and cubed
- 1 cup lima beans, fresh or frozen
- ½ cup canned corn kernels, drained
- 2 tomatoes, chopped
- 2 stalks celery, sliced
- 2 tablespoons catsup
- 1 tablespoon sugar
- 1 tablespoon vinegar
- Dash cayenne pepper

Combine the chicken, beef, water, onions and salt in a deep saucepan. Bring to a boil; cover and cook over medium heat 1½ hours, or until chicken is almost tender. Cut the chicken from the bones and return to the soup. Skim the fat (see Fat Skimming).

Add the okra, potatoes, lima beans, corn, tomatoes, celery and catsup. Cook over medium heat 30 minutes (the stew should be fairly thick at this point). Stir in the sugar, vinegar and cayenne pepper; cook 5 minutes. Serve in deep bowls.

An unusual soup, meat and vegetable dish all in one.

Serves 6—320 calories in each serving.

## STUFFED CHICKEN IN CASSEROLE ❋

2 slices bread, trimmed
3 tablespoons cider
1 tablespoon cognac
¼ pound calf's liver
3 teaspoons salt
¾ teaspoon pepper
3 tablespoons grated onion
2 tablespoons chopped parsley
¼ teaspoon dried marjoram
2 1¼-pound chickens
2 tablespoons butter or margarine
1 clove garlic, minced
½ pound mushrooms, cut in half
4 carrots, sliced
1 bay leaf
¾ cup dry white wine
2 potatoes, peeled and diced

Crumble the bread finely and sprinkle with the cider and cognac. Grind the calf's liver and the livers of the chickens. Mix together the bread, liver, 1 teaspoon salt, ¼ teaspoon pepper, the onion, parsley and marjoram. Chill for 1 hour.

Season the chickens with the remaining salt and pepper. Stuff loosely with the liver mixture and fasten the opening with skewers or thread. Melt the butter in a large casserole or Dutch oven and brown the chickens in it on all sides. Add the garlic, mushrooms, carrots, bay leaf and wine. Cover and bake in a 375° oven for 1 hour. Turn the chickens after ½-hour baking time and add the potatoes; baste frequently. Taste for seasoning.

Cut the chickens in thirds and serve. An easily prepared and delicious meal-in-one dish.

Serves 6—270 calories in each serving.

## BURGOO

1 4-pound fowl, disjointed
3 quarts water
3 cups canned tomatoes
1 tablespoon chili sauce
½ pound peas, shelled
½ pound green beans, cut in half
½ pound okra
1 potato, peeled and diced
2 carrots, sliced
2 green peppers, diced
2 onions, chopped
1½ pounds cabbage, shredded
1 teaspoon salt
2 tablespoons Worcestershire sauce
½ teaspoon thyme
½ teaspoon pepper
1 bay leaf
½ pound tripe, shredded (optional, but good)

Combine all the ingredients in a deep kettle. Bring to a boil; cover and cook over low heat 3½ hours. Taste for seasoning, skim the fat (see Fat Skimming), and serve in deep bowls.

This is a delicious, filling meal-in-one dish. You can double the quantities and freeze half, if you like. Just omit the potato.

Serves 6—230 calories in each serving.

## BAKED BREAST OF CHICKEN GARNI

- 6 chicken breasts
- 2 tablespoons flour
- 2 teaspoons salt
- ½ teaspoon pepper
- 2 tablespoons butter or margarine
- ¼ teaspoon garlic powder
- ½ pound mushrooms, chopped
- ¼ cup diced ham
- ½ cup shelled green peas
- 1 cup dry white wine
- 1 stalk celery
- 2 sprigs parsley
- 1 bay leaf
- 1 head lettuce

Wash and dry the chicken. Mix the flour, salt and pepper together and rub into the chicken.

Melt the butter in a deep skillet or casserole; add the garlic powder and the chicken breasts. Brown lightly. Cover the chicken with the mushrooms, ham and peas. Add the wine, celery, parsley and bay leaf. Cut the lettuce in 6 wedges, and place over all.

Bake in a 350° oven for 1 hour or until the chicken is tender.

A delicious meal-in-one dish. If you prefer another part of the chicken, you may use it.

Serves 6—175 calories in each serving.

## CHICKEN CACCIATORE ❄

- 3 tablespoons flour
- 1½ teaspoons salt
- ½ teaspoon pepper
- 1 4-pound roasting chicken, disjointed
- 1 tablespoon olive oil
- 1 onion, chopped
- 2 cups canned tomatoes
- 1 green pepper, coarsely chopped
- ¼ teaspoon dried oregano
- ¼ cup dry white wine

Mix the flour, salt and pepper together; lightly roll the chicken in the mixture. Heat the oil in a deep skillet; sauté the onion and chicken until well browned. Add the tomatoes, green pepper, oregano and wine. Cover and cook over low heat 50 minutes, or until the chicken is tender. Taste for seasoning and skim the fat.

Serves 6—150 calories in each serving.

## CHICKEN, CEYLON STYLE

- 1 cup buttermilk or yogurt
- 1 teaspoon garlic powder
- 2 2½-pound fryers, disjointed
- 2 tablespoons butter or margarine
- 2 onions, chopped fine
- 1½ teaspoons salt
- ½ teaspoon powdered ginger
- 1 tablespoon curry powder
- 1 teaspoon cornstarch

Mix the buttermilk and garlic powder in a bowl. Add the chicken and let marinate 2 hours; baste and turn frequently.

Melt the butter in a deep skillet or casserole; sauté the onions 10 minutes stirring frequently. Sprinkle with the salt, ginger, curry and cornstarch, stirring until well blended. Drain the chicken (reserve the buttermilk) and cook until chicken is lightly browned. Stir in the buttermilk. Cover and cook over low heat 1½ hours, or until chicken is tender.

Serves 6—200 calories in each serving.

## CHICKEN DIVAN

2 packages frozen broccoli
2 tablespoons cornstarch
2 cups chicken broth, fresh or canned
½ cup milk
⅓ cup grated Parmesan cheese
18 thin slices cooked chicken

Cook the broccoli 2 minutes less than the package suggests. Drain and place in a shallow baking dish.

Mix the cornstarch with a little broth in a saucepan, then gradually add the balance of the broth. Cook over low heat, stirring constantly to the boiling point. Cook 5 minutes longer. Stir in the milk and cheese. Taste for seasoning and pour half the sauce over the broccoli. Arrange the chicken over it and cover with the remaining sauce. Bake in a 475° oven 10 minutes or until delicately browned.

Serves 6—230 calories in each serving.

## CHICKEN WITH CHESTNUTS

2 tablespoons butter or margarine
1 5-pound fowl, disjointed
2 onions, chopped
2½ teaspoons salt
1 teaspoon paprika
2 tablespoons tomato paste
1½ cups water
½ pound uncooked chestnuts, peeled

Melt the butter in a heavy saucepan; sauté the chicken until brown on all sides. Stir in the onions; cover and cook until onions brown. Stir occasionally. Add the salt, paprika, tomato paste and water. Cover and cook over low heat 1 hour. Add the chestnuts, cover and cook 1 hour longer or until chicken and chestnuts are tender. Watch carefully and add a little water if necessary.

Serves 6—200 calories in each serving.

## SAUTÉED CHICKEN WITH OLIVES ❊

⅓ cup cider vinegar
2 green peppers, chopped
4 tomatoes, chopped
2 onions, chopped
½ teaspoon garlic powder
2 teaspoons salt
½ teaspoon pepper
1 teaspoon oregano
2 2-pound broilers, disjointed
1 tablespoon olive oil
2 tablespoons tomato paste
¾ cup sliced stuffed olives

Combine the vinegar, green peppers, tomatoes, onions, garlic powder, salt, pepper and oregano in a bowl. Add the chickens and mix well to coat them. Let marinate 2 hours. Remove the chickens, but reserve the marinade.

Heat the oil in a deep skillet; brown the chicken lightly on all sides. Add the marinade, tomato paste and olives. Cover and cook over low heat 45 minutes or until chicken is tender. Taste for seasoning.

Serves 6—230 calories in each serving.

## CHICKEN JAMBALAYA

2 cups canned tomatoes
1½ cups firm cooked rice
3 cups diced cooked chicken (or turkey)
1½ teaspoon salt
½ teaspoon pepper
2 onions, chopped
1 green pepper, chopped
2 stalks celery, chopped
⅛ teaspoon nutmeg

Combine all the ingredients in a casserole. Mix well and taste for seasoning.

Bake in a 375° oven 1 hour; stir once or twice. Serve directly from the casserole.

Serves 6—155 calories in each serving.

## CURRIED CHICKEN STEW ✳

1 tablespoon butter or margarine
1 onion, grated
2 cloves garlic, minced
1 teaspoon salt
2 tablespoons curry powder
2 2-pound chickens, disjointed
2 cups chicken broth, fresh or canned
6 small white onions
1 tablespoon shredded coconut

Melt the butter in a deep skillet or casserole; sauté the onion and garlic 5 minutes, stirring frequently. Sprinkle with the salt and curry powder, mixing until blended. Add the chicken and cook over low heat until browned.

Stir in the stock and onions; cover and cook over low heat 45 minutes or until chicken is tender. Taste for seasoning; sprinkle with the coconut and serve.

Serves 6—170 calories in each serving.

## CHICKEN MARENGO ✳

3 tablespoons flour
2 teaspoons salt
½ teaspoon pepper
2 2-pound chickens, disjointed
1 tablespoon olive oil
1 tablespoon cognac
2 cloves garlic, minced
1 stalk celery
2 sprigs parsley
1 bay leaf
½ teaspoon dried thyme
2 tomatoes, peeled and diced
1 cup dry white wine
½ pound mushrooms, cut in quarters
2 tablespoons chopped parsley

Mix the flour, salt and pepper together; lightly roll the chicken in the mixture.

Heat the olive oil in a skillet; brown the chicken in it. Transfer to a casserole; heat the cognac, pour it over the chicken and set it aflame. When the flames die, add the garlic, celery, parsley, bay leaf, thyme, tomatoes and wine. Cover and cook over low heat 30 minutes. Add the mushrooms and cook 15 minutes longer or until the chicken is tender. Taste for seasoning; remove the celery, parsley and bay leaf. Sprinkle with the parsley and serve directly from the casserole.

Serves 6—180 calories in each serving.

## GINGER BROILERS

3 teaspoons salt
¾ teaspoon pepper
1½ teaspoons powdered ginger
½ teaspoon garlic powder
3 1½-pound broilers, split
2 tablespoons butter or margarine
2 tablespoons water

Mix the salt, pepper, ginger and garlic powder together; rub into the broilers.

Melt the butter in a baking pan; arrange the broilers in it, skin side down.

Bake in a 400° oven 25 minutes. Reduce the heat to 350°; add the water, turn the broilers and bake 20 minutes longer.

Serves 6—165 calories in each serving.

## CHICKEN OREGANO ❊

2½ teaspoons salt
1 tablespoon olive oil
3 tablespoons lemon juice
1 5-pound roasting chicken
2 cups canned tomatoes
¾ teaspoon pepper
1½ teaspoons oregano

Combine 2 teaspoons salt, the olive oil and lemon juice; rub into the chicken. Place in a roasting pan and roast in a 375° oven 1 hour.

Mix together the tomatoes, pepper, oregano and remaining salt. Pour over the chicken. Reduce the heat to 350° and roast 1 hour longer or until chicken is tender. Baste frequently.

Serves 6—250 calories in each serving.

## CHICKEN AND POTATO CASSEROLE

2 tablespoons butter or margarine
1 5-pound roasting chicken, disjointed
3 onions, chopped
2 cups canned tomatoes
2½ teaspoons salt
1 teaspoon pepper
½ teaspoon nutmeg
4 potatoes, peeled and grated
½ cup orange juice

Melt the butter in a saucepan; brown the chicken in it over low heat. Add the onions and let brown 5 minutes, stirring frequently. Pour off any fat. Stir in the tomatoes, salt, pepper and nutmeg. Cover and cook over low heat 1½ hours or until chicken is tender. Remove chicken and cut meat from the bones.

Combine ¾ cup of the sauce with the potatoes and orange juice. Line a 1½ quart casserole with ⅔ of the potato mixture. Return the chicken to the remaining sauce and pour into the casserole; cover with the remaining potato mixture.

Bake in a 375° oven 1 hour or until potatoes are tender.

Serves 6—250 calories in each serving.

## CHICKEN PAPRIKA ❋

- 2 2½-pound fryers, disjointed
- 2 teaspoons salt
- ¾ teaspoon pepper
- 1 tablespoon butter or margarine
- 6 onions, peeled and sliced thin
- 1½ tablespoons paprika
- ½ cup chicken broth, fresh or canned
- 3 tablespoons sour cream

Wash and dry the chicken; sprinkle with the salt and pepper.

Melt the butter in a heavy saucepan. Add the chicken; cover the pan and cook over medium heat until browned. Watch carefully to avoid burning. Add the onions and paprika and continue to brown. Stir in the broth; cover and cook over low heat 30 minutes or until chicken is tender. Stir in the sour cream, taste for seasoning and cook 5 minutes longer.

Serves 6—260 calories in each serving.

## CHICKEN SAUTÉ WITH HERBS ❋

- 2 2-pound chickens, disjointed
- 3 tablespoons lemon juice
- 2 teaspoons salt
- ½ teaspoon pepper
- 2 tablespoons butter
- ½ cup dry white wine
- 2 tablespoons chopped parsley
- 2 tablespoons chopped chives or scallions
- ½ teaspoon dried tarragon
- ¼ teaspoon dried thyme

Wash and dry the chicken. Rub the skin with the lemon juice and then with the salt and pepper.

Melt the butter in a deep skillet; brown the chicken in it over low heat. Add the wine, parsley, chives, tarragon and thyme. Cover tightly and cook over low heat 35 minutes or until tender.

Serves 6—175 calories in each serving.

## CHICKEN, SPANISH STYLE ❋

- 2 tablespoons olive oil
- 2 2½-pound chickens, disjointed
- 3 teaspoons salt
- 1 teaspoon pepper
- ½ pound mushrooms
- 2 green peppers, sliced
- 6 small white onions
- 1 small eggplant, peeled and diced
- 1 cup canned tomatoes
- 2 cloves garlic, minced
- ½ teaspoon dried thyme
- ½ teaspoon dried basil
- 1 bay leaf
- ¾ cup dry white wine
- 1 pimento, chopped

Heat the oil in a skillet; sauté the chickens until browned. Transfer to a casserole or Dutch oven and sprinkle with some of the salt and pepper. Add the mushrooms, green peppers, onions and eggplant to the oil remaining in the skillet. Sauté for 10 minutes, stirring frequently. Place around the chicken with the tomatoes, garlic, thyme, basil, bay leaf, wine, and the remaining salt and pepper.

Cover and bake in a 350° oven 1 hour or until chicken is tender. Taste for seasoning, garnish with the pimento and serve.

A complete dish.

Serves 6—215 calories in each serving.

## STUFFED POACHED CHICKEN

- 1 4-pound pullet
- 2 tablespoons gin
- 2 tablespoons cognac
- 1 slice white bread
- 2 tablespoons milk
- 3 chicken livers
- ¼ pound mushrooms
- 1 tablespoon chopped chives or green onions
- 1 tablespoon chopped parsley
- 1 teaspoon salt
- ¼ teaspoon pepper
- ⅛ teaspoon thyme
- 2 egg yolks
- 2 egg whites, stiffly beaten
- 2 quarts water
- 2 cloves
- 1 onion
- 2 leeks
- 1 stalk celery
- 2 carrots
- 3 sprigs parsley
- 2 teaspoons coarse salt

Wash and dry the chicken. Rub it with the gin and cognac inside and out.

Sprinkle the bread with the milk, then mash the bread. Chop together the livers, mushrooms, chives, parsley, salt, pepper, thyme, egg yolks and bread. Fold in the egg whites. Stuff the chicken and sew up the opening.

Place the chicken in a deep saucepan with the water. Bring to a boil and skim the top. Stick the cloves in the onion and add to the saucepan with the leeks, celery, carrots, parsley, and the coarse salt. Cover and cook over low heat 2 hours or until chicken is tender. Carefully remove chicken to a heated platter and garnish with crisp watercress. Reserve the broth for future use, or serve before the chicken (after removing the fat).

Serves 6—165 calories in each serving.

## CHICKEN IN WHITE WINE, ITALIAN STYLE

- 2 teaspoons salt
- 1 teaspoon pepper
- 1 tablespoon flour
- 2 2½-pound fryers, disjointed
- 2 tablespoons olive oil
- 2 onions, chopped
- 1 cup dry white wine
- 1 tablespoon tomato paste
- ½ cup chicken broth, fresh or canned
- ½ cup wine vinegar
- 3 anchovies
- 2 cloves garlic, minced
- 1 tablespoon capers
- 2 tablespoons chopped sweet pickles or pickle relish
- 2 tablespoons chopped parsley

Mix the salt, pepper and flour together; rub into the chicken pieces.

Heat the oil in a skillet or casserole; sauté the onions 5 minutes. Add the chicken and brown on all sides. Stir in the wine, tomato paste and broth. Cover and cook over medium heat 45 minutes or until chicken is tender. Skim the fat (see Fat Skimming).

In a separate saucepan, bring the vinegar to a boil. Mash the anchovies and add with the garlic, capers, pickles and parsley. Pour over the chicken and serve directly from the skillet.

Serves 6—260 calories in each serving.

## COQ AU VIN ❋

- 2 tablespoons butter or margarine
- 1 4-pound roasting chicken, disjointed
- 2½ teaspoons salt
- ½ teaspoon pepper
- 1 slice bacon, diced
- 6 small white onions
- ½ pound mushrooms, sliced
- 1 stalk celery
- 2 sprigs parsley
- 1 bay leaf
- 2 cups dry red wine
- 1 cup chicken broth, fresh or canned
- 2 teaspoons cornstarch
- 2 tablespoons cold water

Melt the butter in a saucepan; brown the chicken in it on all sides. Transfer to a casserole; sprinkle with half the salt and pepper. Cover and roast in a 350° oven 1 hour or until the chicken is tender. Prepare the sauce while the chicken is roasting.

Cook the bacon in a saucepan; pour off the fat. Add the onions to the bacon; brown. Add the mushrooms, celery, parsley, bay leaf, wine, broth and remaining salt and pepper. Cook over low heat 1 hour, stirring occasionally.

Mix the cornstarch and water until smooth; stir into the sauce. Cook, mixing steadily until thickened. Taste for seasoning and skim the fat. Pour over the chicken and serve.

Serves 6—175 calories in each serving.

## CHICKEN TETRAZZINI

- 2 2-pound chickens, quartered
- 5 cups water
- 1 onion
- 2½ teaspoons salt
- 1 tablespoon butter or margarine
- ½ pound mushrooms, sliced
- 1½ tablespoons cornstarch
- ½ cup milk
- 2 tablespoons sherry
- ¼ teaspoon white pepper
- ⅛ teaspoon nutmeg
- ½ pound fine egg noodles, cooked and drained
- 3 tablespoons grated Parmesan cheese

Clean the chickens carefully and combine in a saucepan with the water, onion and salt. Bring to a boil; cover and cook over medium heat 45 minutes, or until tender. Cut the chicken off the bones; skin, and slice into strips. Strain and measure 2 cups stock.

Melt the butter in a skillet; sauté the mushrooms for 10 minutes, stirring frequently.

Mix the cornstarch with a little milk until smooth in a saucepan. Add the remaining milk and the stock and cook over low heat, stirring steadily until the boiling point. Add the sherry, pepper and nutmeg; cook over low heat 5 minutes.

Combine half the sauce with the mushrooms and egg noodles; pour into a 2-quart casserole. Mix the remaining sauce with the chicken and pour it over the noodles; sprinkle with the cheese.

Bake in a 375° oven 20 minutes or until browned. Serve directly from the casserole.

Serves 6—250 calories in each serving.

## CHICKEN À LA KING ✻

- 1 6-pound fowl, disjointed
- 8 cups water
- 1 onion, chopped
- 2 carrots, sliced
- 3 stalks celery, sliced
- 4 sprigs parsley
- 2 bay leaves
- ½ teaspoon thyme
- 1 tablespoon salt
- 1 tablespoon butter or margarine
- ½ pound mushrooms, sliced
- 2 green peppers, diced
- 3 pimentos, sliced
- 2 tablespoons cornstarch
- 2 egg yolks
- 2 tablespoons sherry
- 6 slices toast

Combine the fowl, water, onion, carrots, celery, parsley, bay leaves, thyme and salt in a deep saucepan. Bring to a boil and cook over low heat 2½ hours or until chicken is tender. Strain the stock and measure 3 cups of it (reserve the balance for future use).

Discard the skin and bones of the chicken, and cut the meat into cubes.

Melt the butter in a skillet; sauté the mushrooms, green peppers and pimentos for 5 minutes. Add the chicken and keep warm while preparing the sauce.

Mix the cornstarch with a little stock in a saucepan. Gradually add the balance of the stock. Cook over low heat, stirring constantly until the boiling point. Continue to cook over low heat 5 minutes.

Beat the egg yolks and sherry in a bowl; gradually add the sauce, stirring constantly to prevent curdling. Return to the saucepan and stir in the chicken mixture. Taste for seasoning. Heat, but do not let boil. Serve on the toast.

Serves 6—270 calories in each serving.

## CHICKEN CHOW MEIN

- 2 tablespoons peanut or salad oil
- 2 onions, sliced
- 2 cups sliced celery
- ¾ pound mushrooms, sliced
- 1½ cups chicken broth, fresh or canned
- 1 cup water chestnuts, sliced
- 1 cup bean sprouts
- ½ cup bamboo shoots, sliced
- 1 tablespoon cornstarch
- 3 tablespoons soy sauce
- 3 cups sliced cooked chicken (or turkey)
- 3 cups cooked fine egg noodles

Heat the oil in a skillet; sauté the onions 10 minutes, stirring frequently. Add the celery, mushrooms and broth. Cook over low heat 5 minutes. Stir in the water chestnuts, bean sprouts and bamboo shoots. Cook 3 minutes.

Mix the cornstarch and soy sauce to a smooth paste. Stir into the skillet, and stir constantly until thickened. Add the chicken; taste for seasoning and serve when chicken is hot. Serve on the noodles.

Serves 6—220 calories in each serving.

*Note:* An excellent way to utilize leftover chicken or turkey.

## SMOTHERED SQUABS ❋

3 squabs or 1¼-pound broilers, split
2 teaspoons salt
½ teaspoon pepper
1 tablespoon butter or margarine
2 cloves
6 small white onions
4 tablespoons chopped parsley
6 peppercorns
1 bay leaf
½ teaspoon thyme
2 teaspoons cornstarch
¾ cup chicken broth, fresh or canned
1 package frozen green peas, defrosted
⅛ teaspoon nutmeg
½ teaspoon sugar

Wash and dry the squabs. Season with the salt and pepper. Melt the butter in a casserole; arrange the squabs in it. Stick the cloves in one of the onions and add to the casserole with the remaining onions, parsley, peppercorns, bay leaf and thyme. Cover and roast in a 350° oven 35 minutes. Pour off any fat. Mix the cornstarch with a little broth until smooth, then add to the casserole with the remaining broth, the peas, nutmeg and sugar. Cover again and roast 35 minutes longer. Taste for seasoning and serve directly from the casserole.

Serves 6—230 calories in each serving.

## COLD MARINATED BREAST OF CHICKEN

4 onions, sliced thin
6 breasts of chicken
2 cloves garlic, minced
2 pimentos, sliced thin
1 stalk celery, chopped
3 tablespoons chopped parsley
⅓ cup tarragon vinegar
¾ cup dry white wine
2 tablespoons olive or salad oil
2 teaspoons salt
½ teaspoon pepper
⅛ teaspoon dried ground red peppers
2 bay leaves

Place half the onions in an earthenware or other heatproof casserole (not metal). Arrange the chicken over them and cover with the remaining onions, garlic, pimentos, celery and parsley.

Combine the vinegar, wine, oil, salt, pepper, red pepper and bay leaves. Add to the casserole. Bring to a boil, cover and cook over medium heat 35 minutes, or until chicken is tender.

Chill for 24 hours and serve cold.

Serves 6—250 calories in each serving.

## DEEP DISH CHICKEN PIE

2 boiled potatoes, peeled
½ cup hot milk
1 tablespoon melted butter
1½ teaspoons salt
¼ teaspoon pepper
⅛ teaspoon nutmeg
3 cups diced cooked chicken
2 eggs, beaten
¼ cup dry white wine
¼ cup chicken broth, fresh or canned
2 hard-cooked eggs coarsely chopped

Turn oven on and set at 375°.

Mash the potatoes and beat until light and fluffy with the milk, butter, salt, pepper and nutmeg.

Mix the chicken, eggs, wine, broth and chopped eggs in a bowl. Taste for seasoning. Turn into a deep 9-inch pie plate. Cover with the potatoes.

Bake 30 minutes, or until browned.

Serves 6—200 calories in each serving.

## CHICKEN DIVAN

2 packages frozen broccoli
2 tablespoons cornstarch
2 cups chicken broth, fresh or canned
½ cup milk
⅓ cup grated Parmesan cheese
18 thin slices cooked chicken

Cook the broccoli 2 minutes less than the package suggests. Drain and place in a shallow baking dish.

Mix the cornstarch with a little broth in a saucepan, then gradually add the balance of the broth. Cook over low heat, stirring constantly to the boiling point. Cook 5 minutes longer. Stir in the milk and cheese. Taste for seasoning and pour half the sauce over the broccoli. Arrange the chicken over it and cover with the remaining sauce.

Bake in a 475° oven 10 minutes or until delicately browned.

Serves 6—230 calories in each serving.

## BAKED FRIED CHICKEN ❊

2 2-pound chickens, disjointed
4 tablespoons flour
2 teaspoons salt
½ teaspoon pepper
3 tablespoons shortening, oil, butter or margarine

Wash and dry the chicken. Combine the flour, salt and pepper in a paper bag or on a piece of waxed paper. Shake the chicken in it to coat it.

Heat the fat in a skillet; brown the chicken in it, then transfer the pieces to a baking pan. Bake in a 350° oven 30 minutes or until tender. Turn the pieces over once.

Serves 6—200 calories in each serving.

## CHICKEN LIVERS EN BROCHETTE

24 mushroom caps
18 chicken livers
6 slices bacon, half-cooked and cut in thirds
½ teaspoon salt
½ teaspoon pepper
1 tablespoon melted butter or olive oil
6 tablespoons chili sauce

You'll need 6 skewers for this dish. Arrange the mushrooms, livers and bacon on the skewers, starting and ending with the mushrooms. Sprinkle the livers and mushrooms with salt and pepper, and the melted butter or oil.

Place on a rack and broil in a hot broiler, turning them frequently, until browned.

Heat the chili sauce and serve with the brochettes.

Serves 6—165 calories in each serving.

*Note:* Delicious prepared over a charcoal fire, too.

## CHICKEN CROQUETTES ✻

2 tablespoons butter or margarine
1 tablespoon flour
1 cup chicken broth, fresh or canned
2 cups chopped cooked chicken (or turkey)
1 tablespoon grated onion
1 tablespoon finely chopped parsley
2 tablespoons chopped walnuts
2 teaspoons lemon juice
¼ teaspoon white pepper
2 eggs, beaten

Melt 1 tablespoon butter in a saucepan; blend in the flour. Gradually add the broth, stirring constantly to the boiling point. Stir in the chicken, onion, parsley, walnuts, lemon juice and pepper. Taste for seasoning.

Remove from the heat and cool 10 minutes. Beat in the eggs. Chill for ½ hour. Form the mixture into 12 croquettes and chill for 2 hours.

Melt the remaining butter in a baking pan. Place the croquettes in it. Bake in a 450° oven 15 minutes or until browned on both sides. Turn the croquettes once.

Serves 6—150 calories in each serving.

## CHICKEN HASH

2 tablespoons butter or margarine
½ cup chopped onions
½ cup chopped green pepper
2 potatoes, peeled and cut in julienne strips
2 cups diced cooked chicken
1½ teaspoons salt
¼ teaspoon pepper
¼ cup chicken broth, fresh or canned
2 tablespoons chopped parsley

Melt the butter in a skillet; sauté onion, green pepper and potato 10 minutes. Stir in the chicken, salt and pepper. Add the broth and cook over low heat 10 minutes. Taste for seasoning. Sprinkle with the parsley and serve.

Serves 6—145 calories in each serving.

## SWEET AND PUNGENT SQUAB

3 squabs, split
1½ teaspoons salt
½ teaspoon garlic powder
1 tablespoon peanut oil
1 tablespoon cornstarch
1 tablespoon sugar
½ teaspoon liquid Sucaryl
½ cup vinegar
½ cup water
2 tablespoons soy sauce
½ teaspoon pepper
2 onions, sliced thin
2 green peppers, diced
3 tomatoes, cut in eighths
6 coriander seeds

Wash and dry the squabs; sprinkle with the salt and garlic powder. Grease a baking pan with the oil and arrange the squabs in it. Broil in a hot broiler 10 minutes on each side, or until squabs are tender. While they are broiling prepare the sauce.

In a saucepan, mix the cornstarch, sugar, Sucaryl and vinegar until smooth. Cook over low heat, stirring constantly until the boiling point. Add the water; stir in the soy sauce, onion, green peppers, tomatoes and coriander seeds. Cook over low heat 10 minutes. Pour over the squabs and serve.

Serves 6—130 calories in each serving.

## ROCK CORNISH HEN VERONIQUE

- 2 teaspoons salt
- ½ teaspoon pepper
- 3 Rock Cornish hens (1½ pounds each) or squabs
- 2 tablespoons butter or margarine
- ½ cup dry white wine
- 2 tablespoons Madeira or sweet sherry
- ¾ cup chicken broth, fresh or canned
- 2 teaspoons Kitchen Bouquet
- ½ cup seedless grapes, cut in half

Rub the salt and pepper into the hens.

Melt the butter in a casserole; arrange the hens in it breast side down. Roast in a 450° oven 30 minutes, turning them breast side up after 10 minutes. Then reduce the heat to 350° and roast 25 minutes longer, basting frequently. Remove the hens and keep warm.

Add the Madeira, broth and Kitchen Bouquet to the juices in the casserole. Cook over high heat until the volume is reduced to half. Skim any fat. Taste for seasoning. Add the grapes and cook 1 minute.

Cut the hens in half and serve with the sauce.

Serves 6—210 calories in each serving.

## CHICKEN LIVER AND MUSHROOM SAUTÉ

- 2 tablespoons butter or margarine
- ½ pound mushrooms, sliced
- 18 chicken livers
- 2 tablespoons chopped scallion (green onion) or onion
- 2 tablespoons chopped parsley
- 2 teaspoons flour
- ¼ cup dry white wine
- 1 teaspoon salt
- ¼ teaspoon pepper
- ⅛ teaspoon thyme
- 3 slices toast, cut in half (triangles)

Melt 1 tablespoon butter in a skillet; sauté the mushrooms 5 minutes. Remove the mushrooms. Melt the remaining tablespoon of butter in the skillet; brown the livers on both sides. Return the mushrooms to the skillet and add the scallions and parsley. Cook 2 minutes. Stir in the flour and let it brown. Add the wine, salt, pepper and thyme. Cover and cook over low heat 5 minutes. Taste for seasoning. Serve on a triangle of toast.

Serves 6—220 calories in each serving.

## CHICKEN LIVER PAPRIKA

- 2 tablespoons butter
- 3 onions, thinly sliced
- 1 pound chicken livers
- 1 teaspoon salt
- 1 tablespoon paprika
- 2 egg yolks
- 3 tablespoons sour cream
- 3 slices toast, cut in half

Melt the butter in a skillet; sauté the onions 5 minutes. Add the livers and sauté 7 minutes, turning them once or twice. Sprinkle with the salt and paprika.

Beat the egg yolks and sour cream in a saucepan; cook over low heat, stirring steadily until the mixture thickens. Combine with the livers and serve on a half piece of toast.

Serves 6—210 calories in each serving.

## BREAST OF CHICKEN AU GRATIN

- 6 breasts of chicken
- 3 tablespoons cognac
- 2 teaspoons salt
- ½ teaspoon pepper
- ½ teaspoon dried marjoram
- 2 tablespoons butter or margarine
- ⅓ cup sherry
- 1 cup chicken broth, fresh or canned
- 2 egg yolks
- ⅛ teaspoon nutmeg
- 3 tablespoons grated Swiss cheese

Sponge the chicken with the cognac and set aside for 15 minutes. Rub the salt, pepper and marjoram into the chicken.

Melt the butter in a skillet; brown the chicken over low heat on all sides. Transfer the chicken to a baking dish and keep warm while preparing the sauce.

Add the sherry and broth to the butter remaining in the skillet. Bring to a boil. Beat the egg yolks and nutmeg in a bowl. Gradually add the wine sauce, stirring constantly to prevent curdling. Taste for seasoning. Pour over the chicken and sprinkle with the cheese.

Bake in a 475° oven 10 minutes or until browned.

Serves 6—190 calories in each serving.

## DUCK WITH ORANGE SAUCE ❄

- 1 5-pound duck
- 2 teaspoons salt
- ¾ teaspoon pepper
- 1 tablespoon sugar
- 1 tablespoon vinegar
- 1 tablespoon cornstarch
- 1 cup chicken broth, fresh or canned
- ¾ cup orange juice
- 2 tablespoons lemon juice
- 2 tablespoons cognac
- 2 tablespoons grated orange rind

Wash the duck carefully and remove as much fat as possible. Rub the duck with the salt and pepper, inside and out. Place the duck on a rack in a shallow roasting pan. Roast in a 425° oven 20 minutes. Reduce the heat to 350° and roast 2 hours longer, or until duck is tender and browned. Pour off the fat several times.

In a small saucepan, combine the sugar and vinegar. Cook over low heat until it caramelizes (about 2 minutes).

Mix the cornstarch and broth in another saucepan, and cook over low heat stirring constantly until the boiling point. Add the orange juice and lemon juice. Cook over low heat 10 minutes. Stir in the caramel, cognac and orange rind. Carve the duck and serve with the sauce.

Serves 6—425 calories in each serving.

## ROAST STUFFED GOOSE ✻

10-12 pound goose
1 tablespoon salt
¾ teaspoon pepper
2 teaspoons paprika
½ teaspoon garlic powder
apple-onion stuffing (see recipe)

Remove as much fat from the goose as possible. Loosen the skin with a knife and carefully pull the fat out without breaking through the skin. Be sure all the fat is out of the inside. Mix together the salt, pepper, paprika and garlic powder; rub into the goose. (This is best done the day before it is to be roasted, but don't stuff it until just before roasting.)

Stuff the goose, truss it and place on a rack in a shallow roasting pan. Roast in a 425° oven 30 minutes. Pour off all the fat and prick the skin with a fork. Reduce the heat to 350° and roast 2¾ hours longer, or until goose is tender. Pour off the fat as it accumulates.

Carve the goose and serve 3 slices (4 ounces) and 2 tablespoons stuffing for each serving.

—375 calories in each serving.

### Goose Gravy

Goose gizzard
Goose neck
1 onion
1 stalk celery
2½ cups water
1 teaspoon salt
¼ teaspoon pepper
Goose liver
1 tablespoon cornstarch
2 teaspoons Kitchen Bouquet
1 tablespoon cognac

Combine the gizzard, neck, onion, celery, water, salt and pepper in a saucepan. Bring to a boil. Cover and cook over medium heat 1 hour. Add the liver and cook 30 minutes longer. Strain the mixture and chop the gizzard and liver.

Mix the cornstarch and Kitchen Bouquet with a little water. Add to the strained stock and cook over low heat, stirring constantly to the boiling point. Add the chopped giblets and the cognac. Cook 5 minutes longer and serve 2 tablespoons for each serving.

—60 calories in each serving.

### Apple-Onion Stuffing

- 3 cups chopped apples
- 1 cup chopped onions
- 2 cups chopped celery
- ½ cup chopped parsley
- 4 slices bread, diced small
- 2 tablespoons rendered goose fat or butter
- ½ cup chicken broth
- 1 teaspoon salt
- ¼ teaspoon pepper
- ½ teaspoon mace
- ¼ teaspoon nutmeg

Mix all the ingredients together and stuff the goose.

—45 calories in 3 tablespoons of stuffing.

*Note:* The stuffing is very good for chicken, duck or pork, too.

## DUCK WITH SAUERKRAUT

- 1 5-pound duck
- 2 teaspoons salt
- ¾ teaspoon pepper
- 1 teaspoon paprika
- ½ teaspoon garlic powder
- 2 teaspoons salad oil
- 1 onion, chopped
- 1 apple, peeled and finely chopped
- 2 cups sauerkraut, drained
- 1 teaspoon caraway seeds

Wash the duck carefully and remove as much fat as possible. Rub the duck with the salt, pepper, paprika and garlic powder.

Heat the oil in a skillet; sauté the onion and apple for 5 minutes, stirring frequently. Add the sauerkraut and caraway seeds. Mix well and taste for seasoning. Stuff the duck and close the opening with skewers, thread or aluminum foil.

Place the duck on a rack in a shallow roasting pan. Roast in a 425° oven 20 minutes. Reduce heat to 350° and roast 2 hours longer, or until duck is tender and browned. Pour off fat frequently. Carve and serve with the stuffing.

Serves 6—375 calories in each serving.

## CHINESE DUCK

- 1 5-pound duck
- 1 cup soy sauce
- 3 tablespoons powdered ginger

Clean the duck carefully and remove as much fat as possible. The duck may be prepared whole or disjointed. Combine in a saucepan the duck, soy sauce, ginger, and enough water to cover. Bring to a boil and cook over low heat 1 hour. Drain the duck, discarding the liquid.

Place the duck on a rack in a shallow roasting pan. Roast in a 425° oven 45 minutes or until duck is crisp and tender.

Serves 6—325 calories in each serving.

## ROAST TURKEY ✻

Buy a young turkey without too much fat. Remove as much fat as possible from the turkey. For the seasoning to flavor the meat close to the bone, it is advisable to season it the day before it is to be roasted. For a 12-pound turkey use:

- 1 tablespoon salt
- ¾ teaspoon pepper
- 2 teaspoons paprika
- 2 cloves garlic, minced, or ¾ teaspoon garlic powder (optional)

The garlic is marked optional, but adds a great deal of flavor so use it by all means, if you don't object to garlic.

Combine the seasoning and rub the turkey with it, inside and out. If you are stuffing it, do it just before roasting, as a stuffed uncooked turkey deteriorates quickly. Close the opening with thread, skewers or aluminum foil. The latter is easiest—just pack the foil into the opening. Truss the turkey and place in a shallow open roasting pan.

Roast in a 350° oven, about 3 hours. It is not necessary to baste the bird. Plan the roasting time so the turkey can be removed from the oven 20 minutes before serving time. This makes carving easier.

Serve 3 slices (about 4 ounces) and 2 tablespoons stuffing for each serving.

—350 calories in each serving.

## TURKEY FRICASSEE ✻

- 5 pound turkey, disjointed
- 3 onions, chopped
- 1 clove garlic, minced
- 2½ teaspoons salt
- ¾ teaspoon pepper
- 1 teaspoon paprika
- ½ cup chicken broth, fresh or canned
- 2 stalks celery, sliced
- 2 carrots, sliced
- 1 bay leaf
- ½ teaspoon thyme

Wash and dry the turkey (and the giblets). Remove as much fat as possible. Rub a heavy, hot saucepan with a small piece of fat. (Use a fork to hold the fat.) Place the turkey in the saucepan and brown over low heat. Turn the turkey; add the onions and garlic and continue browning. Pour off any fat. Add the salt, pepper, paprika, stock, celery, carrots, bay leaf and thyme. Cover and cook over low heat 1½ hours or until tender. Taste for seasoning, skim the fat and serve.

Serves 6—350 calories in each serving.

# MEATS

The symbol ✲ indicates dishes that can be frozen.

Meat is our finest source of protein, so essential to health. Most dieters are under the false impression that meat may be consumed freely; this is part of the folklore of the fat. Many men starve themselves all day only to consume an enormous steak with a baked potato and a green salad at dinnertime,—the total caloric count of this one meal often running higher than three normal meals. Eat meat by all means, but observe the size of the portions carefully. Trim as much fat from the meat before cooking as you possibly can, and then skim the fat from the gravy before serving (see the instructions for fat skimming in the soup section) . At the table, trim away any additional fat showing on your portion.

Beef is graded by standards set by the U.S. Department of Agriculture, and will be stamped with one of the following markings:

U.S.D.A. Prime: This is the finest grade and is not always available to retail consumers except in choice specialty meat shops, usually being reserved for restaurants and hotels. Prime beef has the most fat.

U.S.D.A. Choice: Almost as good as prime, and customarily available in good retail shops. The meat is bright red with veins (marbling) of white fat. Slightly lower in calories than prime.

U.S.D.A. Good: The meat is a darker red than choice, with somewhat less marbling and external fat. It is a few calories less per pound than choice.

U.S.D.A. Commercial and Utility: Has much less fat than any of the above, but is too tough for anything but stews and pot roasts.

Purchase the cuts of meats suggested in the recipes as cooking times are specified for the type to be used. Keep meats well refrigerated. Frozen meats should be kept solidly frozen until ready to thaw for cooking. You can prepare larger quantities than you require for one meal and freeze the excess for future servings (see freezing instructions).

## RIB ROAST OF BEEF

The safest way to time roast beef is with a thermometer, as the shape, amount of bone and fat all affect the cooking time. The weight will give you approximate and fairly close time, but your best bet is the thermometer. Insert a skewer in the fleshy part of the meat, being sure it does not touch the bone. Withdraw the skewer, and insert the thermometer. When it has a reading of 140° it is rare, 160°, medium and 170° well done.

There are 2 methods of roasting beef and you must decide which you prefer.

Searing the beef in a hot oven results in a browned crisp outside and a juicy inside. The one drawback is shrinkage. Allow 16 minutes per pound for rare, 20 for medium, and 25 for well done. Roasting in a one-temperature moderate oven, 325°, causes little shrinkage, but the exterior is not crisp or very browned. Allow 20 minutes per pound for rare, 25 for medium and 30 for well done.

It is not necessary to season or baste roast beef. Place on a rack in a shallow roasting pan, fat side up, and roast according to the method you prefer.

You usually buy a roast larger than the quantity required for one meal.

Serve 2 ¼-inch slices—375 calories in each serving.

## MARINATED ROAST BEEF ❊

2 teaspoons salt
¾ teaspoon pepper
1 teaspoon paprika
2 cloves garlic, minced
3 pounds sirloin of beef
½ cup dry red wine
¼ cup wine vinegar
3 onions, chopped
3 tomatoes, peeled and chopped
2 green peppers, chopped
1 bay leaf
¼ pound mushrooms, sliced

Combine the salt, pepper, paprika and garlic; rub into the meat thoroughly. Mix the wine and vinegar together and pour over the meat in a bowl. Marinate in the refrigerator overnight, basting and turning the meat a few times.

Remove the meat from the refrigerator 3 hours before it is to be roasted. Drain the meat, reserving the marinade. Place the meat on a rack in a shallow roasting pan.

Roast in a 475° oven 20 minutes; pour off the fat. Reduce the heat to 350° and add the onions, tomatoes, green pepper, bay leaf, mushrooms and marinade. Roast an additional 35 minutes for rare, 40 medium and 50 for well done.

Discard the bay leaf, skim the fat and force the gravy and vegetables through a sieve or purée in a blender.

Serve 2 slices ¼-inch thick and 2 tablespoons gravy—400 calories in each serving.

## ROAST FILLET OF BEEF

A fillet of beef is an extremely tender cut, and usually weighs 4-5 pounds. Roast it in a 450° oven 45-55 minutes, depending on its size.

Serve 2 ½-inch slices or 1 1-inch slice—350 calories in each serving.

## LONDON BROIL

1½ pounds flank steak
4 tablespoons wine vinegar
1 tablespoon salad oil
½ teaspoon garlic powder

Ask the butcher for a very tender flank steak; it should be trimmed and scored.

Mix the vinegar, oil and garlic together; marinate the meat 2 hours. Drain; place the meat on a rack 2 inches below the heat. Broil 4 minutes on each side for rare, 5 for medium and 7 for well done.

Transfer to a heated platter and cut diagonally into very thin slices.

Serve with mushroom sauce (see recipe).

Serves 6—350 calories in each serving.

## FILLET OF BEEF IN WINE SAUCE

- 2½ teaspoons salt
- ¾ teaspoon pepper
- ¼ teaspoon thyme
- 3-pound fillet of beef
- 2 onions, chopped
- 1 carrot, sliced
- 1 tablespoon flour
- 1 cup beef broth, fresh or canned
- 1 cup medium sherry
- 2 tablespoons chopped parsley

Combine the salt, pepper and thyme; rub into the meat thoroughly. Brown the meat in a Dutch oven or heavy saucepan; add the onions and carrot and brown lightly. Sprinkle with the flour, then the broth, mixing until well blended.

Roast in a 350° oven 30 minutes; stir in the wine and roast 20 minutes longer for rare, 25 for medium and 30 for well done. Baste occasionally.

Transfer the beef to a hot platter; force the gravy through a sieve and skim the fat thoroughly. Sprinkle with the parsley. Serve 2 slices, ¼-inch thick and 2 tablespoons gravy—300 calories in each serving.

## BROILED STEAK

Select the cut of your choice; shell, porterhouse, sirloin or fillet. For 2 people a shell steak is best, as you can have it cut thick, but a sirloin is good for larger numbers. A steak should be cut 2 inches (or more) thick.

Broil 3 inches below the heat in a hot broiler, and turn the steak only once. A 2-inch steak usually requires 8 minutes on each side for rare, 10 for medium and 13 for well done. Season the steak, slice and serve.

Serve 3 slices, ½-inch thick—400 calories in each serving.

## PAN BROILED STEAK

Use a steak 1 inch thick for pan broiling. Cut a piece of fat from the steak, and rub a hot skillet with it. Place the steak in it and brown over high heat. Turn, season with salt and pepper, and brown other side.

Serve 4 ½-inch thick slices—375 calories in each serving.

## POT ROAST ❋

3 pounds beef (eye round, chuck or similar cut)
2 onions, chopped
2 teaspoons salt
½ teaspoon pepper
¼ teaspoon thyme
1 bay leaf
½ teaspoon garlic powder (optional)
1 cup beef broth, fresh or canned

Heat a Dutch oven or heavy saucepan; rub it with a little piece of beef fat. Place the meat in it; cover and cook over medium heat until meat is browned on all sides. Watch carefully to avoid burning. Add the onions and brown them, stirring frequently. Sprinkle with the salt, pepper, thyme, and add the bay leaf, garlic powder and broth. Cover and cook over low heat 2¼ hours, or until tender. Taste for seasoning and skim the fat.

Serve 2 slices, ¼-inch thick, and 2 tablespoons gravy—400 calories in each serving.

## BEEFSTEAK, FLEMISH STYLE ❋

1 tablespoon butter or margarine
4 onions, sliced
2 pounds beef (chuck, top or bottom round) cut in 12 pieces
2 teaspoons flour
1 cup beer
2 teaspoons vinegar
1½ teaspoons salt
½ teaspoon pepper
½ teaspoon sugar
2 bay leaves
½ teaspoon thyme
3 tablespoons chopped parsley

Melt the butter in a heavy saucepan or casserole; sauté the onions 10 minutes, stirring frequently. Remove the onions. Brown the beef on all sides; sprinkle with the flour, stirring until well blended. Return the onions to the pan and add the beer, vinegar, salt, pepper, sugar, bay leaves, thyme and parsley. Cover and cook over low heat 2 hours. Stir occasionally and add a little water if necessary. Skim the fat and serve.

Serves 6—375 calories in each serving.

## BEEF STEW ❋

2 pounds beef (chuck or cross rib)
1½ teaspoons sugar
1 teaspoon flour
2 tomatoes, chopped
1 green pepper, sliced
1 cup beef broth, fresh or canned
1½ teaspoons salt
½ teaspoon pepper
¼ teaspoon thyme

Cut the beef into 1½-inch cubes and trim the fat. Heat a Dutch oven or heavy saucepan and rub it with a piece of fat. Place the meat in it; cover and brown the meat on all sides over medium heat. Watch carefully to prevent burning. Sprinkle the meat with the sugar and flour, and brown it well. Add the tomatoes, green pepper, broth, salt, pepper and thyme. Cover and cook over low heat 1½ hours, or until very tender. Taste for seasoning, skim any fat and serve.

Serves 6—385 calories in each serving.

## BEEF ROULADES ✻

- 6 minute steaks, 4 ounces each
- ½ pound mushrooms, chopped
- 2 tablespoons chopped parsley
- 3 tablespoons chopped onion
- ¼ teaspoon garlic powder
- 1½ teaspoons salt
- ½ teaspoon pepper
- 1 tablespoon salad oil
- 1 tablespoon cornstarch
- 1 cup dry red wine
- 1½ tablespoons tomato paste
- 6 stuffed green olives, sliced

Have the butcher pound the steak thin or do it yourself with a mallet.

Mix together the mushrooms, parsley, onion, garlic powder, ½ teaspoon salt and ¼ teaspoon pepper. Spread some of the mixture on each steak and roll up. Tie each end with white thread or fasten with toothpicks.

Heat the oil in a heavy skillet or casserole; brown the rolls in it. Mix the cornstarch, wine and tomato paste together; add to the rolls with the remaining salt and pepper. Cover and cook over low heat ¾ hour. Add the olives and cook 15 minutes longer. Taste for seasoning.

Serves 6—360 calories in each serving.

## HUNGARIAN GOULASH ✻

- 1 tablespoon butter or margarine
- 5 onions, chopped
- 2 tablespoons paprika
- 2 pounds beef (chuck or cross rib) cut in 1½-inch cubes
- 2 teaspoons salt
- ½ teaspoon pepper
- 1 can (8 ounces) tomato sauce
- 2 tablespoons sour cream

Melt the butter in a Dutch oven or heavy saucepan; sauté the onions over very low heat until soft. Stir frequently. Sprinkle with the paprika, and add the beef. Brown the beef on all sides, then add the salt, pepper and tomato sauce. Cover and cook over low heat 2 hours, or until meat is tender.

Taste for seasoning and skim the fat. Stir in the sour cream and serve.

Serves 6—430 calories in each serving.

## BEEF FRICASSEE ✻

- 2 pounds beef (rump or chuck)
- 2 teaspoons salt
- ½ teaspoon pepper
- ½ teaspoon dried thyme
- ⅛ teaspoon nutmeg
- 1 tablespoon butter or margarine
- 2 onions, chopped
- 2 carrots, chopped
- 2 stalks celery, sliced
- 1 bay leaf
- 2 cloves
- 1½ cups dry white wine
- 2 tablespoons sweet sherry

Pound the beef with the salt, pepper, thyme and nutmeg. Cut into 6 pieces. Heat the butter in a casserole or heavy skillet; brown the beef on both sides. Add the onions, carrots, celery, bay leaf, cloves and white wine. Cover and bake in a 375° oven 1 hour. Turn the meat after ½ hour cooking and add the sherry. Serve directly from the casserole.

Serves 6—400 calories in each serving.

## BOEUF BOURGIGNON ❋

- 2 pounds beef (top or bottom round)
- 2 tablespoons flour
- 1½ teaspoon salt
- ½ teaspoon pepper
- 1 tablespoon butter or margarine
- 2 onions, chopped
- 1 carrot, chopped
- 1 clove garlic, minced
- 2 tablespoons cognac
- 3 sprigs parsley
- 1 bay leaf
- ¼ teaspoon marjoram
- 2 cups dry red wine

Cut the beef into 1½-inch cubes and trim the fat. Mix the flour, salt and pepper together; lightly roll the meat in the mixture.

Melt the butter in a skillet; brown the meat very well. Transfer to a casserole. Add the onions, carrots and garlic to the fat remaining in the skillet and brown, stirring frequently.

Heat the cognac in a ladle, set it aflame and pour it over the beef. When the flame dies, add the browned vegetables, the parsley, bay leaf, marjoram and wine. Cover and bake in a 350° oven for 2½ hours. Taste for seasoning; discard the bay leaf and parsley, skim the fat and serve directly from the casserole.

Serves 6—425 calories in each serving.

## CURRIED BEEF PIE ❋

- 1 tablespoon butter or margarine
- 2 onions, chopped
- 1 slice white bread, crumbled
- ½ cup skim milk
- 1¼ pounds ground lean beef
- 2 eggs
- 1 tablespoon curry powder
- 1 teaspoon salt
- 1 tablespoon lemon juice
- 2 tablespoons ground almonds

Melt the butter in a skillet; sauté the onions 10 minutes, stirring frequently.

Soak the bread in the milk, then squeeze dry, reserving the milk. Combine the bread with the beef, sautéed onions, 1 egg, the curry powder, salt, lemon juice and almonds. Mix well.

Pack the meat into a 9-inch pie plate. Beat the remaining egg with the reserved milk and pour over the meat.

Bake in a 350° oven 1 hour. Serve directly from the pie plate.

Serves 6—370 calories in each serving.

## MEAT LOAF ❋

- 1¼ pounds ground lean beef
- 1 egg, beaten
- 2 tablespoons ice water
- 3 tablespoons ketchup
- 1½ teaspoons salt
- ¼ teaspoon pepper
- 3 tablespoons grated onion
- 1 tablespoon bread crumbs
- 1 teaspoon salad oil
- 3 tablespoons chili sauce

Mix together the beef, egg, ice water, ketchup, salt, pepper, onion and bread crumbs. Shape into a loaf and place on a lightly oiled baking pan or pack into a lightly oiled 8-inch loaf pan.

Bake in a 375° oven 30 minutes; spread the chili sauce on top and bake 30 minutes longer. Slice and serve.

Serves 6—290 calories in each serving.

## BEEF STROGANOFF ✻

- 2 pounds sirloin steak, ¼-inch thick
- 1 tablespoon butter or margarine
- 3 tablespoons grated onion
- ¾ pound mushrooms, sliced
- 1½ teaspoons salt
- ½ teaspoon pepper
- ¼ teaspoon basil
- 2 tablespoons sour cream
- ¼ cup yogurt

Pound the steak with a mallet, then cut into strips ¼-inch wide by 2 inches long.

Melt the butter in a skillet; sauté the onion and beef for 5 minutes over medium heat. Turn beef to brown both sides. Remove the beef and keep warm. Sauté the mushrooms for 5 minutes in the same skillet; return beef to the skillet and season with the salt, pepper and basil. Mix the sour cream and yogurt together and pour over the meat. Heat but do not let boil.

Serves 6—415 calories in each serving.

## BOILED BEEF ✻

- 2 cloves
- 1 onion
- 2 quarts water
- 4 pounds first-cut brisket of beef, trimmed
- 2 stalks celery and leaves
- 2 carrots
- 3 sprigs parsley
- 1 bay leaf
- 3 peppercorns
- 1 tablespoon salt

Stick the cloves in the onion. Bring the water to a boil in a deep saucepan; add the onion, beef, celery, carrots, parsley, bay leaf and peppercorns. Bring to a boil again and add the salt; cover and cook over low heat 2½ hours, or until meat is tender. Transfer the beef to a heated platter. Strain the stock for future use.

You'll have leftovers, but serve 2 slices ½-inch thick—250 calories in each serving.

*Note:* Vinaigrette sauce (see recipe) or horseradish are good accompaniments.

## NEW ENGLAND BOILED DINNER

- 4 pounds corned brisket of beef (first cut)
- 6 carrots, scraped
- 6 small white onions
- 3 potatoes, cut in half
- 6 small parsnips
- 1 head cabbage, cut in 6

Cover the beef with water, bring to a boil and drain. Add fresh boiling water to cover; bring to a boil again, then cook over low heat 3 hours, or until meat is almost tender.

Skim the fat; add the carrots, onions, potatoes and parsnips. Cook 10 minutes, then add the cabbage and cook 10 minutes longer. Drain carefully.

You'll have meat left over, but serve 2 slices beef, ½-inch thick, and the vegetables evenly divided.

—300 calories in each serving.

## BEEF AND EGGPLANT CASSEROLE

1½ tablespoons olive or salad oil
1½ pounds lean beef, cut in ½-inch cubes
1 eggplant, peeled and sliced thin
2 onions, sliced thin
4 tomatoes, cubed
2 green peppers, diced
2 teaspoons salt
¾ teaspoon pepper
½ teaspoon oregano

Heat 1 tablespoon oil in a skillet; brown the beef in it over high heat.

Grease a casserole with the remaining oil. Arrange successive layers of the eggplant, beef, onions, tomatoes and green peppers, seasoning each layer with a mixture of the salt, pepper and oregano. Cover the casserole.

Bake in a 350° oven 1 hour. Remove the cover and bake 15 minutes longer.

Serves 6—290 calories in each serving.

## CHINESE STEAK

2 tablespoons peanut oil
3 cups finely shredded cabbage
1 cup chicken broth, fresh or canned
2 teaspoons cornstarch
¼ teaspoon garlic powder
4 tablespoons soy sauce
1¼ pounds steak, ¼-inch thick, cut in 2-inch strips

Heat 1 tablespoon oil in a saucepan; stir in the cabbage and cook over low heat 10 minutes, stirring frequently. Add ¼ cup broth; cover and cook over low heat 5 minutes, then drain.

Mix the cornstarch, garlic powder and soy sauce in a saucepan until smooth. Add the remaining broth and cook over low heat, stirring constantly to the boiling point. Cook 5 minutes longer.

Heat the remaining oil in a skillet; brown the meat in it over high heat. Add the sauce. Arrange the cabbage on a heated platter and pour the steak and sauce over it.

Serves 6—325 calories in each serving.

## BEEF-POTATO PIE

1 tablespoon butter or margarine
2 onions, chopped
3 cups diced cooked beef
¾ cup beef broth, fresh or canned
1 bay leaf
½ teaspoon pepper
⅛ teaspoon ground cloves
2 teaspoons salt
3 large potatoes, cooked and drained
½ cup hot milk
¼ teaspoon nutmeg

Melt the butter in a skillet; sauté the onions 10 minutes, stirring frequently. Stir in the beef, broth, bay leaf, pepper, cloves and 1 teaspoon salt; cover and cook over low heat 15 minutes. Discard the bay leaf.

Mash the potatoes, and beat in the milk, nutmeg and remaining salt. Spread ⅔ of the potatoes on the bottom and sides of a 9-inch-deep pie plate. Turn the meat mixture into it and cover with the remaining potatoes.

Bake in a 425° oven 20 minutes, or until browned on top.

Serves 6—285 calories in each serving.

## SUKIYAKI

- 1 tablespoon peanut or salad oil
- 1½ pounds sirloin steak, ¼-inch thick, cut into strips ½-inch x 2 inches
- ½ cup soy sauce
- 1 tablespoon sugar
- ¼ teaspoon liquid Sucaryl
- 1 tablespoon sherry
- ½ cup beef broth
- 3 onions, sliced thin
- 1 cup sliced celery
- 1 cup sliced bamboo shoots
- ½ pound mushrooms, sliced thin
- 4 scallions (green onions), sliced

Heat the oil in a large skillet (if you want to prepare the dish at the table, use an electric frying pan or chafing dish). Brown the meat over high heat, then push it to one side. Combine the soy sauce, sugar, Sucaryl, sherry and broth. Pour half the mixture over the meat.

Cook the onions and celery in the skillet for 3 minutes, then push them to one side and add the remaining soy-sauce mixture, bamboo shoots, mushrooms and scallions. Cook 4 minutes. Don't overcook, as everything should be crisp.

Serve directly from the skillet with ½ cup fine egg noodles for each serving.

Serves 6—405 calories in each serving.

## STUFFED CABBAGE

- 1 large head cabbage
- 3 onions
- Veal knuckles or bones
- 1 can (#2½) tomatoes
- 1 pound ground lean beef
- 3 teaspoons salt
- ¼ teaspoon black pepper
- ½ cup rice, half-cooked and drained
- 1 egg, beaten
- 2 tablespoons cold water
- 4 tablespoons lemon juice
- 1 tablespoon brown sugar
- ½ teaspoon liquid Sucaryl

Cover the cabbage with water; bring to a boil and cook 10 minutes. Drain. Carefully separate 12 leaves.

Slice 2 onions and combine in a heavy saucepan with the bones and tomatoes. Cook over medium heat while preparing the cabbage rolls.

Grate the remaining onion and combine with the beef, 1½ teaspoons salt, the pepper, rice, egg and water. Mix well. Place a heaping tablespoon of the mixture on each leaf. Turn two opposite sides in and carefully roll up the cabbage. They should stay rolled up, but if not, fasten with toothpicks or tie with thread.

Arrange in the tomato mixture (if there is any meat mixture left, form into balls and add). Add the remaining salt. Cover and cook over low heat 1 hour. Stir in the lemon juice, sugar and Sucaryl. Cook uncovered 30 minutes. Taste for seasoning; it should be both sweet and sour. Skim the fat.

Serves 6—280 calories in each serving.

## SAUERBRATEN ❋

- 2 cups vinegar
- 2 teaspoons salt
- 10 peppercorns
- 3 cloves
- 2 bay leaves
- 2 onions, chopped
- 2 carrots, sliced
- 4 pounds beef (chuck, brisket, top round)
- ¾ cup boiling water

Bring to a boil the vinegar, salt, pepper, cloves, bay leaves, onions and carrots.

Place the meat in a bowl and pour the marinade over it. Refrigerate for 3 days, turning the meat frequently. Drain the meat, reserving the marinade.

Brown the meat over low heat in a heavy saucepan or Dutch oven. Add the marinade and water. Cover and cook over low heat 3 hours, or until meat is tender. Skim the fat.

Serve 2 slices, ¼-inch thick—300 calories in each serving. Leftovers are delicious reheated.

*Note:* For special occasions, add 4 tablespoons sour cream to the sauce, but add 35 calories to each serving.

## STUFFED PEPPERS ❋

- 6 large, uniform green peppers
- 3 onions
- ¾ pound lean ground beef
- 2 tablespoons uncooked rice
- 2½ teaspoons salt
- ½ teaspoon black pepper
- 1 egg, beaten
- 2 tablespoons cold water
- 1 tablespoon butter or margarine
- 1 can (#2½) tomatoes
- 4 tablespoons lemon juice
- 1 tablespoon brown sugar
- 1 teaspoon liquid Sucaryl

When buying the beef, ask the butcher for a beef bone.

Wash the peppers. Cut a 1-inch piece from the stem ends and reserve; carefully scoop out the seeds and fibers.

Grate 1 onion and mix with the beef, rice, 1¼ teaspoons salt, ¼ teaspoon pepper, the egg and water. Stuff the peppers and replace the tops firmly.

Slice the remaining onions. Melt the butter in a Dutch oven or heavy saucepan; sauté the onions 5 minutes. Add the tomatoes, bone, and remaining salt and pepper. Arrange the peppers in an upright position. Cover and cook over low heat 1¼ hours. Stir in the lemon juice, brown sugar and Sucaryl. Cook 15 minutes longer, or until peppers are tender. Taste for seasoning; the sauce should have both a sweet and sour flavor. Skim the fat and serve.

Serves 6—295 calories in each serving.

## NORWEGIAN HAMBURGERS ❋

- 1 slice bread, crumbled
- ¼ cup skim milk
- 1 tablespoon butter or margarine
- 4 tablespoons finely chopped onion
- 1 pound ground lean beef
- 1 egg, beaten
- 3 tablespoons ice water
- 1 teaspoon salt
- ¼ teaspoon pepper
- ⅛ teaspoon nutmeg
- ¼ cup dry white wine
- 1 tablespoon chopped parsley

Soak the bread in the milk. Melt 1 teaspoon butter in a skillet and sauté the onion for 5 minutes. Combine the soaked bread, onions, meat, egg, water, salt, pepper and nutmeg. Mix well and chill 1 hour.

Form into 6 patties. Melt the remaining butter in a heavy skillet; place the patties in it. Cover and cook over medium heat 8 minutes on each side. Transfer to a hot platter. Pour the wine and parsley into the skillet; bring to a vigorous boil and pour over the patties.

Serves 6—285 calories in each serving.

## FRANKFURTER GOULASH

- 1 tablespoon salad oil
- 2 onions, minced
- 1 clove garlic, minced
- 3 green peppers, diced
- 1 can (#2½) tomatoes
- 1 teaspoon salt
- ½ teaspoon black pepper
- 1 teaspoon paprika
- 1 bay leaf
- 12 beef frankfurters

Heat the oil in a casserole or Dutch oven. Sauté the onions and garlic 5 minutes. Add the green peppers and sauté 5 minutes. Stir in the tomatoes, salt, pepper, paprika and bay leaf. Cover and cook over low heat 1 hour. Cut the frankfurters into 2-inch pieces. Cook in the sauce 30 minutes. Skim the fat, taste for seasoning and serve.

Serves 6—310 calories in each serving.

## MEATBALLS IN MUSHROOM SAUCE ❋

- 1¼ pounds ground lean beef
- 1 onion, grated
- 2 teaspoons salt
- ¼ teaspoon pepper
- 3 tablespoons cold water
- 1 egg, beaten
- 1 tablespoon butter or margarine
- 1 pound mushrooms
- 2 egg yolks
- 2 tablespoons lemon juice
- 2 tablespoons chopped parsley

Mix the beef, onion, 1 teaspoon salt, pepper, water and egg. Shape into 1-inch balls.

Melt the butter in a skillet; fry the meatballs in it to desired degree of rareness. Remove and keep warm.

Sauté the mushrooms 5 minutes in the fat remaining in the skillet. Beat the egg yolks, lemon juice and remaining salt together, and add to the mushrooms, stirring constantly to prevent curdling. Add the meatballs and parsley. Cook over low heat 5 minutes, but do not let boil.

Serves 6—335 calories in each serving.

## BEEF RAGOUT ⁂

- 2 pounds beef (chuck or cross rib)
- 1 cup dry red wine
- 1 teaspoon salt
- 1 bay leaf
- 2 cloves
- 1 clove garlic, minced
- 4 crushed peppercorns
- 1 slice bacon, cut in small pieces
- 1 cup beef broth
- 2 stalks celery
- 3 sprigs parsley
- 4 carrots, sliced
- 6 small white onions
- 12 mushroom caps
- 1 cup shelled green peas

Cut the beef into 1½-inch cubes and trim the fat. Combine the wine, salt, bay leaf, cloves, garlic and peppercorns in a bowl; add the meat and let marinate 2 hours.

Brown the bacon in a Dutch oven or heavy saucepan; pour off the fat. Drain the meat, but reserve the marinade. Brown the meat in the saucepan until dark brown on all sides. Add the marinade, broth, celery and parsley. Cover and cook over low heat 1 hour. Add the carrots, onions, mushrooms and peas; cover and cook 1 hour longer or until tender.

Taste for seasoning; discard the bay leaf, celery and parsley, skim the fat and serve.

Serves 6—405 calories in each serving.

## BROILED LIVER

- 1½ pounds calf's liver, sliced ¼-inch thick
- 2 tablespoons melted butter or margarine
- 1 teaspoon salt
- ⅛ teaspoon pepper
- 1 tablespoon lemon juice
- 2 teaspoons chopped parsley

Turn broiler on 10 minutes before you will need it.

Wash and dry the liver. Grease a broiling pan with a little of the melted butter. Arrange the liver in it side by side. Sprinkle with the remaining butter.

Broil about 3 inches under the heat, 2 minutes on each side for rare, 3 medium, and 4 well done. Season with the salt, pepper, lemon juice and parsley.

Serves 6—180 calories in each serving.

## SAUTÉED LIVER

- 1½ pounds calf's liver, sliced ¼-inch thick
- 2 tablespoons flour
- 1¼ teaspoons salt
- ¼ teaspoon pepper
- ½ teaspoon paprika
- 2 tablespoons butter or margarine
- 1 onion, minced
- ⅓ cup dry white wine

Wash and dry the liver; sprinkle with the mixed flour, salt, pepper and paprika. Melt the butter in a skillet; sauté the liver about 3 minutes on each side. Transfer to a heated platter and keep warm.

Stir the onion into the butter remaining in the skillet; cook 2 minutes. Add the wine and cook over high heat 2 minutes. Pour over the liver.

Serves 6—190 calories in each serving.

## SWEETBREADS IN WINE

- 3 pairs sweetbreads
- 3 cups water
- 1 tablespoon vinegar
- 2 teaspoons salt
- 1½ tablespoons butter
- 1 onion, chopped
- ¼ teaspoon pepper
- ⅛ teaspoon thyme
- ⅓ cup sweet sherry

Wash the sweetbreads and soak in cold water 20 minutes. Drain and combine with the 3 cups water, vinegar and 1 teaspoon salt. Bring to a boil; cover and cook over low heat 15 minutes. Let cool in the liquid 15 minutes. Drain. Remove the membranes and cube the sweetbreads.

Melt the butter in a skillet; sauté the onion and sweetbreads 5 minutes. Add the pepper, thyme, sherry and remaining salt; cook over low heat 5 minutes.

Serves 6—150 calories in each serving.

## BAKED TONGUE

- 5-pound pickled tongue
- 3 onions, sliced
- 2 cups canned tomatoes
- 1 bay leaf
- 2 cloves

Cover the tongue with water in a deep saucepan. Bring to a boil and drain. Cover with fresh boiling water and cook over medium heat 2 hours. Drain, reserving 1 cup of the stock. Peel and trim the tongue.

Place the tongue in a roasting pan; add the onions, tomatoes, bay leaf, cloves and reserved stock.

Bake in a 350° oven 1 hour or until tender. Baste frequently. Serve 3 slices, ¼-inch thick, and 3 tablespoons gravy.

Serves 10-12—210 calories in each serving.

## BAKED BRAINS AND EGGS

- 2 pair brains
- 2 cups water
- 1 tablespoon vinegar
- 1 teaspoon salt
- 1 bay leaf
- 4 tomatoes, peeled and diced
- 1 tablespoon olive oil
- 2 tablespoons chopped onion
- 2 teaspoons chopped parsley
- 6 eggs

Wash the brains thoroughly and soak in cold water 10 minutes. Drain and combine with the 2 cups water, the vinegar, salt and bay leaf. Bring to a boil; cover and cook over low heat 15 minutes. Drain and cool. Remove the membranes and dice the brains. Divide among 6 individual baking dishes. Mix the tomatoes, oil, onion and parsley, and spread over the brains. Break an egg carefully into each dish. Season with salt and pepper.

Bake in a 325° oven 10 minutes or until the eggs are set.

Serves 6—160 calories in each serving.

## SALISBURY STEAK ❋

- 1½ pounds ground lean beef
- 3 tablespoons grated onion
- 1 clove garlic, minced
- 2 tablespoons finely chopped green pepper
- 2 tablespoons finely chopped parsley
- 1½ teaspoons salt
- ½ teaspoon pepper
- Pinch thyme
- 3 tablespoons ice water
- 1 teaspoon salad oil
- ⅓ cup ketchup
- 1 tablespoon sherry
- 1 teaspoon Worcestershire sauce
- 1 teaspoon prepared mustard
- 1 teaspoon prepared horseradish

Mix together the beef, onion, garlic, green pepper, parsley, salt, pepper, thyme and water. Shape into 6 patties. Place on a lightly oiled broiling pan.

Broil in a hot broiler, about 3 inches below the heat, 4 minutes on each side for rare, 5 medium and 7 well done. While the steaks are broiling prepare the sauce.

Combine the ketchup, sherry, Worcestershire sauce, mustard and horseradish in a saucepan; bring to a boil. Serve with the steak.

Serves 6—385 calories in each serving.

## VEAL PARMIGIANA

- 6 veal cutlets (1½ pounds)
- 1 cup canned tomato sauce
- 1 onion, chopped
- ¼ teaspoon basil
- 1 egg
- 1 teaspoon salt
- ¼ teaspoon pepper
- ⅓ cup dry bread crumbs
- 4 tablespoons grated Parmesan cheese
- 1 tablespoon olive oil
- 3 thin slices Mozzarella cheese, cut in half

Have the butcher pound the veal very thin, or do it yourself. Cook the tomato sauce, onion and basil over low heat for 15 minutes. Taste for seasoning.

Beat the egg, salt and pepper together in a flat dish. Mix the bread crumbs and cheese on a piece of waxed paper. Dip the veal first in the egg mixture and then in the cheese mixture.

Heat the olive oil in a skillet and brown the veal on both sides. Transfer to a baking pan and cover with the tomato sauce and Mozzarella cheese. Bake in a 375° oven 15 minutes.

Serves 6—345 calories in each serving.

## VEAL PAPRIKA ❋

- 1 teaspoon salt
- ¼ teaspoon pepper
- 1¾ pounds veal, cut in 1-inch cubes
- 2 tablespoons butter or margarine
- 2 onions, finely chopped
- 1 tablespoon paprika
- 1 cup chicken broth, fresh or canned
- ¼ cup yogurt

Sprinkle the salt and pepper on the veal. Melt the butter in a heavy saucepan; brown the veal in it on all sides. Add the onions and brown them. Sprinkle with the paprika and mix well. Add the broth. Cover and cook over low heat 1 hour, or until veal is tender. Stir in the yogurt; heat but do not let boil. Taste for seasoning.

Serves 6—310 calories in each serving.

## VEAL SCALLOPINI

- 1½ pounds veal, loin or round
- 4 tablespoons flour
- 1½ teaspoons salt
- ¼ teaspoon pepper
- 2 tablespoons butter or margarine
- ¼ cup beef broth, fresh or canned
- 2 tablespoons sweet sherry

Buy thinly cut veal; if you tell the butcher you want it for scallopini he'll cut it and pound it for you. Have it cut in 6 pieces.

Mix together the flour, salt and pepper; lightly dip the veal in it. Melt the butter in a skillet; brown the veal in it on both sides. Transfer to a hot platter.

Stir the broth and sherry into the skillet, and cook over high heat 1 minute, stirring steadily. Pour over the veal and serve.

Serves 6—290 calories in each serving.

## VEAL GOULASH ❊

- 1 tablespoon butter or margarine
- 3 onions, finely chopped
- 2 pounds leg of veal, cut in 1-inch cubes
- 1½ teaspoons salt
- 1 tablespoon paprika
- 2 tomatoes, chopped
- 1 green pepper, diced
- ½ cup hot water
- 2 tablespoons capers
- 2 tablespoons sour cream

Melt the butter in a Dutch oven or heavy saucepan; sauté the onions over low heat until soft and lightly browned. Add the veal, salt and paprika. Cook over low heat until meat browns, stirring frequently. Stir in the tomatoes, green pepper and water. Cover and cook over low heat 45 minutes or until the veal is tender. Stir in the capers and sour cream; heat but do not let boil.

Serves 6—355 calories in each serving.

## STUFFED BREAST OF VEAL ❊

- 1 tablespoon butter or margarine
- 2 onions, minced
- 2 green peppers, diced
- ½ pound mushrooms
- 1 cup shredded cabbage
- 1 slice white bread, trimmed and cubed
- 3 teaspoons salt
- ½ teaspoon pepper
- 1 teaspoon paprika
- 1 breast of veal (with pocket for stuffing)
- ½ cup canned tomato sauce

Melt the butter in a skillet; sauté the onions, green pepper, mushrooms and cabbage 10 minutes. Mix in the bread, 1 teaspoon salt and ¼ teaspoon pepper.

Combine the remaining salt, pepper and the paprika; rub into the veal. Stuff the veal; close the opening with skewers, toothpicks or thread. Place in a roasting pan.

Roast in a 375° oven 30 minutes. Reduce the heat to 350°; add the tomato sauce and roast 2 hours longer, or until tender. Baste frequently and add a little water if pan becomes dry. Serve 2 ribs and 4 tablespoons stuffing.

—300 calories in each serving.

## VEAL RAGOUT ❋

- 1½ pounds shoulder of veal
- 1 tablespoon butter or margarine
- 1 clove garlic, minced
- 1 tablespoon flour
- 1½ teaspoons salt
- ¼ teaspoon pepper
- 1½ cups boiling water
- 2 carrots, sliced
- 3 stalks celery, sliced
- 2 potatoes, peeled and cubed
- 3 sprigs parsley
- 1 cup shelled green peas
- ½ teaspoon marjoram

Cut the veal in 2-inch cubes. Melt the butter in a Dutch oven or casserole; sauté the veal and garlic until browned on all sides. Sprinkle with the flour, salt and pepper, then add the water, stirring constantly to the boiling point. Cover and cook over low heat 1¼ hours.

Add the carrots, celery, potatoes, parsley, peas, marjoram and a little more water if necessary. Cover and cook over low heat 30 minutes. Taste for seasoning, skim the fat, and serve.

Serves 6—310 calories in each serving.

## VEAL, HUNTER'S STYLE

- 2 pounds leg of veal, sliced ½-inch thick
- 3 tablespoons flour
- 1½ teaspoon salt
- ¼ teaspoon pepper
- 1 tablespoon olive oil
- ¼ pound mushrooms, sliced
- 3 tablespoons chopped onion
- ¼ cup dry white wine
- ½ cup canned tomatoes, drained

Have the butcher pound the veal very thin and cut into 12 pieces. Sprinkle with a mixture of the flour, salt and pepper. Heat the oil in a skillet; sauté the veal over low heat until browned on both sides. Transfer to a serving dish and keep warm while preparing the sauce.

Cook the mushrooms and onions for 5 minutes in the oil remaining in the skillet. Add the wine and tomatoes. Cook over medium heat 5 minutes. Correct the seasoning, pour over the veal and serve.

Serves 6—340 calories in each serving.

## BAKED VEAL LOAF ❋

- 1 tablespoon butter or margarine
- 2 onions, chopped
- 1¼ pounds ground lean veal
- 2 tablespoons chopped pimento
- 1 green pepper, finely chopped
- 2 tablespoons milk
- 1 tablespoon lemon juice
- 1 egg, beaten
- 1½ teaspoons salt
- ½ teaspoon black pepper
- 1 teaspoon paprika
- 2 tablespoons cracker meal
- ½ cup beef broth, fresh or canned

Melt the butter in a skillet; sauté the onions 10 minutes, stirring frequently. Combine with the veal, pimento, green pepper, milk, lemon juice, egg, salt, pepper, paprika and cracker meal. Mix lightly and shape into a loaf. Place in a baking pan.

Bake in a 325° oven 2 hours. Add the broth after the first half hour and baste frequently.

Serves 6—295 calories in each serving.

## SWEETBREADS AND MUSHROOMS

3 pairs sweetbreads
3 cups water
1 tablespoon vinegar
2 teaspoons salt
1 tablespoon butter or margarine
2 onions, chopped
½ pound mushrooms, sliced
1 tablespoon flour
¼ teaspoon black pepper
1 cup cooked or canned peas
2 tablespoons chopped parsley

Wash the sweetbreads and soak in cold water 20 minutes. Drain and combine with the 3 cups water, the vinegar and 1 teaspoon salt. Bring to a boil; cover and cook over low heat 20 minutes. Let cool in the liquid 20 minutes. Drain, reserving 1 cup of the stock. Remove the membranes and dice the sweetbreads.

Melt the butter in a skillet; sauté the onion 5 minutes. Add the mushrooms and sauté 5 minutes longer. Sprinkle with the flour, then blend in the stock, stirring constantly to the boiling point. Add the pepper, peas, parsley, and remaining salt. Cover and cook over low heat 10 minutes.

Serves 6—155 calories in each serving.

## SMOKED BEEF TONGUE

5-pound smoked tongue
2 cloves
1 onion
1 clove garlic
1 bay leaf
3 sprigs parsley

Soak the tongue overnight in water to cover. Drain. Stick the cloves in the onion and combine in a deep saucepan with the garlic, bay leaf, parsley, tongue and cold water to cover. Bring to a boil and cook over low heat 3 hours, or until tongue is tender. Let cool in the stock for 30 minutes, then drain. Pull off the skin and cut off the fat and connective tissue. Slice diagonally.

If you want to serve the tongue cold, let it cool in the stock for 30 minutes, then plunge into very cold water. Serve 4 slices, ¼-inch thick.

Serves 8-10—250 calories in each serving.

## TONGUE EN PAPILLOTE

- 1 tablespoon butter or margarine
- ¼ pound mushrooms, chopped
- 3 tablespoons chopped onion
- 2 tablespoons chopped parsley
- 1 cup ground cooked tongue
- 1 tablespoon cognac
- 2 tablespoons sherry
- 1 tablespoon tomato paste
- ½ teaspoon salt
- ¼ teaspoon pepper
- 12 slices tongue, ¼-inch thick

Melt the butter in a skillet; sauté the mushrooms, onion and parsley 5 minutes. Add the chopped tongue and cook over low heat 5 minutes, stirring frequently. Blend in the cognac, sherry, tomato paste, salt and pepper.

Cut 6 pieces of aluminum foil large enough to completely cover the tongue slices. Spread 6 slices of tongue heavily with the mixture. Cover with the remaining slices of tongue. Wrap each sandwich securely in the foil. Place on a baking pan.

Bake in a 375° oven 15 minutes. Turn the packages and bake 20 minutes longer. Slit the package, drain any fat and serve in the foil.

Serves 6—225 calories in each serving.

## BROILED SWEETBREADS

- 3 pairs sweetbreads
- 3 cups water
- 1 tablespoon vinegar
- 1½ teaspoons salt
- 3 tablespoons bread crumbs
- 1½ tablespoons butter or margarine

Wash the sweetbreads and soak in cold water 20 minutes. Drain and combine with the 3 cups water, vinegar and salt. Bring to a boil; cover and cook over low heat 20 minutes. Drain and cover with cold water for 20 minutes. Drain again. Remove the membranes and split the sweetbreads.

Dip lightly into the bread crumbs. Melt the butter in a baking pan and place the sweetbreads in it.

Broil in a hot broiler about 3 inches under the heat until browned on both sides. Serve with lemon wedges.

Serves 6—130 calories in each serving.

## OXTAIL CASSEROLE ✲

- 2 oxtails (about 3 pounds), cut up
- 2½ teaspoons salt
- ¾ teaspoon pepper
- ½ teaspoon garlic powder
- 1 tablespoon salad oil
- 3 cloves
- 12 small white onions
- 3 potatoes, peeled and quartered
- 4 carrots, cut in 2-inch pieces
- ½ pound whole mushrooms
- 1 bay leaf
- 4 sprigs parsley
- ½ teaspoon savory
- 2 cups beef broth, fresh or canned
- 1½ cups dry red wine

Wash and dry the oxtails. Sprinkle with the salt and pepper and garlic powder. Heat the oil in a skillet; brown the pieces in it. Drain all the fat.

Stick the cloves in an onion and add to the oxtail with all the onions, the potatoes, carrots, mushrooms, bay leaf, parsley, savory, broth and wine. Cover tightly.

Bake in a 300° oven 3½ hours. Skim the fat and taste for seasoning. Serve directly from the casserole.

Serves 6—320 calories in each serving.

## KIDNEY SAUTÉ

- 6 veal kidneys
- 1 tablespoon butter or margarine
- ½ cup beef broth, fresh or canned
- ¼ cup dry white wine
- ¼ pound mushrooms, sliced
- 2 teaspoons cornstarch
- ¾ teaspoon salt
- ¼ teaspoon pepper
- 2 tablespoons cold water
- 2 tablespoons chopped parsley

Remove the outer skin of the kidneys; soak in cold water 2 hours. Drain; split and remove the cores, then slice the kidneys.

Melt the butter in a skillet; cook the kidneys over high heat about 2 minutes on each side. Transfer to a hot platter and keep warm.

Stir in the broth, wine and mushrooms to the butter remaining in the skillet. Cover and cook over medium heat 5 minutes. Mix the cornstarch, salt, pepper and water until smooth; blend into the mushroom mixture, stirring constantly to the boiling point. Cook 2 minutes, then return the kidneys to it with the parsley. Cook 1 minute; but do not let boil.

Serves 6—150 calories in each serving.

## TRIPE À LA MODE DE CAEN

- 2 pounds honeycomb tripe
- 1 slice bacon, chopped
- 2 onions, diced
- 2 carrots, sliced
- 1 green pepper, finely chopped
- 2 stalks celery, sliced
- 1 veal knuckle, chopped
- 1½ teaspoons salt
- ½ teaspoon pepper
- ¼ teaspoon marjoram
- ¼ teaspoon thyme
- 2 bay leaves
- 2 cups beef broth, fresh or canned
- 2 cups white wine
- 3 tablespoons tomato paste
- 2 tablespoons cognac

Wash the tripe thoroughly and soak in cold water for one hour, changing the water twice. Spread the bacon, onions, carrots, green pepper and celery on the bottom of a Dutch oven or heavy casserole. Place the tripe and veal knuckle over them. Add the salt, pepper, marjoram, thyme, bay leaves, broth and wine. Cover tightly.

Bake in a 300° oven 6 hours (you can do this overnight if you prefer). Stir in the tomato paste and cognac. Bake 1 hour longer. Skim the fat and serve directly from the casserole.

Serves 6—285 calories in each serving.

## BRAISED LOIN OF VEAL ✻

- 3-pound loin of veal
- Veal knuckle
- 1½ teaspoons salt
- ¼ teaspoon pepper
- 2 onions, sliced
- 2 carrots, sliced
- 2 stalks celery
- 2 sprigs parsley
- 1 bay leaf
- ¼ teaspoon thyme
- 2 cups beef broth, fresh or canned

Trim the veal and rub the salt and pepper into it. Spread the onions, carrots, celery, parsley, bay leaf and thyme on the bottom of a Dutch oven or casserole. Place the veal knuckle and veal over it.

Roast in a 425° oven 25 minutes; stir in the broth. Roast 30 minutes, basting frequently, then cover the pan. Reduce the heat to 350° and roast 2 hours longer, or until tender. Baste occasionally.

Discard the celery, parsley, bay leaf and veal knuckle. Transfer the veal to a serving platter and force the gravy through a sieve. Serve 3 ¼-inch thick slices and 2 tablespoons of gravy.

—295 calories in each serving.

## VEAL CHOP CASSEROLE

- 2 teaspoons salt
- ½ teaspoon pepper
- ¼ teaspoon dried thyme
- 1 tablespoon butter or margarine
- 6 veal chops, 2-inches thick
- ¼ cup dry bread crumbs
- 2 cloves
- 1 onion
- 1 cup dry white wine
- ½ cup beef broth, fresh or canned
- ¼ teaspoon garlic powder
- 1 bay leaf
- 3 sprigs parsley
- ¼ cup chopped scallions (green onions)

Mix the salt, pepper and thyme; season the chops with the mixture. Melt the butter in a casserole and sauté the chops until browned on both sides. Stir in the bread crumbs and let them brown lightly. Stick the cloves in the onion and add to the casserole with the wine, broth, garlic powder, bay leaf, parsley and scallions. Cover the casserole.

Bake in a 375° oven 45 minutes. Remove the cover and bake 15 minutes longer or until tender. Skim the fat and serve directly from the casserole.

Serves 6—235 calories in each serving.

## OSSO BUCO

- 3 pounds veal knuckle
- 1 tablespoon olive or salad oil
- 1 clove garlic, minced
- 2 teaspoons salt
- ½ teaspoon pepper
- 1 carrot, sliced
- 1 tablespoon grated lemon rind
- 1 cup dry white wine
- 1 cup beef broth, fresh or canned
- 1 tablespoon tomato paste
- 2 tablespoons chopped parsley

Have the veal knuckle sawed into 2-inch pieces. Melt the butter in a deep skillet; brown the pieces in it very well, then add the garlic, salt, pepper, carrot, lemon rind, wine, broth and tomato paste. Cover and cook over low heat 1 hour or until the meat is tender. Taste for seasoning, sprinkle with parsley, and serve with ½ cup boiled rice.

Serves 6—325 calories in each serving.

## SPRING LAMB STEW ❋

- 1½ pounds lamb, neck or shoulder
- 1 clove garlic, minced
- 2 onions, diced
- 1½ teaspoons salt
- ½ teaspoon pepper
- 2 teaspoons paprika
- 2 green peppers, diced
- 2 carrots, sliced
- 1 cup canned tomato sauce
- 2 potatoes, peeled and cubed
- ½ pound green beans, cut in thirds
- ½ pound green squash, peeled and sliced thin (optional)

Trim the lamb of all fat. Cut in 1-inch cubes. Heat a Dutch oven or heavy saucepan and rub it with a small piece of fat. Brown the lamb in it, then add the garlic and onions. Continue browning, but watch carefully to avoid burning. Stir in the salt, pepper, paprika, green peppers, carrots and tomato sauce. Cover and cook over low heat 1 hour. Add the potatoes, green beans and squash. Cook 30 minutes, adding a little water if necessary. Taste for seasoning.

Serves 6—365 calories in each serving.

## CROWN ROAST OF LAMB ❋

This is definitely a dinner-party dish, as you can serve at least 8. Buy a whole loin of spring lamb (about 16 ribs) and ask the butcher to make the crown, french the bones and cut them off short. Have the scraps ground for the stuffing. The rib bones will now be outside. It is advisable to put a cube of potato on each bone end or wrap in aluminum foil to keep them from charring. Fill the center of the crown with the following:

1 pound mushrooms, chopped
1 onion, finely chopped
½ cup chopped celery
Ground lamb (from the bones)
1 teaspoon salt
¼ teaspoon pepper
¼ teaspoon basil
1 egg beaten

Place the crown in a baking pan. Mix all the ingredients together and place in the center.

Roast in a 450° oven for 25 minutes. Pour off the fat. Reduce the heat to 350° and roast 2½ hours longer, or to desired degree of rareness (make a small slit near the bone to test).

Remove the potatoes or aluminum foil and replace with paper frills or broiled mushroom caps. Carve into individual ribs. Serve 2 ribs and 3 tablespoons stuffing for each serving.

—350 calories in each serving.

## ROAST LEG OF LAMB ❋

5-pound leg of lamb
½ lemon
2 cloves garlic, minced
1 tablespoon salt
1 teaspoon pepper
1 teaspoon paprika
1 onion, sliced
1 carrot, sliced
1 bay leaf
½ cup water

Sponge the lamb with a damp cloth. It is not necessary to remove the outer skin (fell). Rub the lamb with the cut lemon. Mix the garlic, salt and paprika together and rub it into the lamb. Place in a shallow roasting pan.

Roast in a 425° oven 30 minutes. Pour off the fat. Add the onion, carrot, bay leaf and water. Reduce the heat to 350° and roast 1¼ hours longer or until the lamb is tender. Baste occasionally. Serve 3 slices ¼-inch thick, 4 inches x 4 inches for each serving.

—300 calories in each serving.

## LEG OF LAMB WITH BARBECUE SAUCE ❋

- 2 teaspoons salt
- ½ teaspoon pepper
- 5-pound leg of lamb
- 1 cup beef broth, fresh or canned
- 3 tablespoons chili sauce
- 1 tablespoon vinegar
- 2 tablespoons Worcestershire sauce
- ¼ teaspoon thyme
- 2 onions, grated
- ¼ teaspoon garlic powder

Rub the salt and pepper into the lamb; place in a shallow roasting pan. Roast in a 425° oven 30 minutes. Pour off the fat.

Mix the broth, chili sauce, vinegar, Worcestershire sauce, thyme, onions and garlic. Bring to a boil and pour over the lamb. Reduce the heat to 350° and roast 1½ hours, or until the lamb is tender. Skim the fat from the sauce. Serve 3 slices, ¼-inch thick, 4 inches x 4 inches, and 2 tablespoons sauce.

—330 calories in each serving.

## LAMB AND RICE CASSEROLE

- 2 cups beef broth, fresh or canned
- 1 cup canned tomatoes
- 1 onion, grated
- 2 cups diced cooked lamb (leftover leg of lamb is good for this)
- 1 teaspoon salt
- ¼ teaspoon pepper
- 1 tablespoon butter or margarine
- ½ cup uncooked rice
- 2 tablespoons Worcestershire sauce

Combine the broth, tomatoes, onion, lamb, salt and pepper in a casserole. Place in a 350° oven for 10 minutes.

Melt the butter in a skillet; add the rice and stir constantly until lightly browned. Add to the casserole with the Worcestershire sauce. Continue baking for 35 minutes or until the rice is tender. Serve directly from the casserole.

Serves 6—165 calories in each serving.

## LAMB PILAU

- 6 shoulder lamb chops
- 2 onions, chopped
- 2 teaspoons salt
- ½ teaspoon pepper
- 1 bay leaf
- 2 carrots, sliced
- 2 stalks celery, sliced
- 3 cups boiling water
- ¾ cup uncooked rice
- ¼ pound mushrooms, chopped
- 1 egg yolk, beaten

Trim as much fat as possible from the chops. Brown on both sides in a skillet; pour off the fat. Add the onions and continue browning. Add the salt, pepper, bay leaf, carrots, celery, and 1½ cups boiling water. Cover and cook over low heat 40 minutes.

While the lamb is cooking prepare the rice. Add the rice and mushrooms to the remaining boiling water. Cover and cook over low heat 20 minutes. Place in a casserole, and add the sauce from the lamb. Stir in the egg yolk and taste for seasoning; arrange the chops on top.

Bake in a 375° oven 10 minutes. Serve directly from the casserole.

Serves 6—305 calories in each serving.

## ROAST LOIN OF PORK ✻

6-rib loin of pork (center cut)
¼ pound mushrooms, sliced
2 teaspoons salt
½ teaspoon pepper
1 teaspoon paprika
¼ teaspoon garlic powder

Have the butcher crack the bones for easier carving. Make small slits about ½ inch apart near the rib end, and place a slice of mushroom in each. Combine the salt, pepper, paprika and garlic powder; rub into the pork.

Place the pork on a rack in a shallow roasting pan. Roast in a 350° oven 2 hours, or until browned and the meat is white. Serve 2 ¼-inch slices.

Serves 10—350 calories in each serving.

## LAMB CHOPS, COUNTRY STYLE

6 double rib-lamb chops
1½ teaspoons salt
½ teaspoon pepper
1 tablespoon flour
½ cup beef broth, fresh or canned
6 small white onions
6 large mushroom caps
6 pitted black olives
1 clove garlic, minced
¼ teaspoon marjoram
2 stalks celery
2 sprigs parsley
1 bay leaf
1 cup half-cooked green peas
2 tablespoons sherry

Trim the chops of as much fat as possible; season with the salt and pepper. Brown the chops on both sides in a skillet or casserole; pour off any fat. Sprinkle with the flour and brown it. Add the broth, onions, mushrooms, olives, garlic, marjoram, celery, parsley and bay leaf.

Bake in a 350° oven 20 minutes. Add the peas and sherry. Cover and bake 15 minutes longer. Taste for seasoning, discard the celery, parsley and bay leaf.

Serves 6—375 calories in each serving.

## LAMB CURRY ✻

1½ pounds lamb, shoulder or neck
3 onions, chopped
1 clove garlic, crushed
1 bay leaf
¼ teaspoon thyme
1½ tablespoons curry
3 cups beef broth, fresh or canned
1 tablespoon tomato paste
2 teaspoons cornstarch
2 tablespoons water
2 tablespoons shredded chopped coconut

Trim the fat and cut the lamb into ½-inch cubes. Heat a heavy saucepan and rub it with a piece of fat. Brown the lamb and onions in it; watch carefully to prevent burning. Add the garlic, bay leaf, thyme, curry, broth and tomato paste. Cover and cook over low heat 1¼ hours. Mix the cornstarch and water and stir into the saucepan. Add the coconut. Cook 5 minutes. Skim the fat and serve with ½ cup cooked rice.

Serves 6—430 calories in each serving.

## SHISH KEBOB

1½ pounds lamb shoulder or leg
½ cup lemon juice
3 tablespoons grated onion
1 clove garlic, minced
2 teaspoons salt
¼ teaspoon diced ground red peppers
1 teaspoon powdered ginger
¼ teaspoon ground coriander
½ teaspoon turmeric
Tomatoes
Onions
Green peppers
Mushrooms
1 tablespoon olive oil

Trim the lamb of all fat; cut into 1-inch cubes. Mix together the lemon juice, onion, garlic, salt, red peppers, ginger, coriander and turmeric. Place the lamb in it and let marinate for 2 hours, basting and turning the meat frequently.

Cut the tomatoes, onions and green peppers in pieces similar in size to the lamb. Thread the lamb and vegetables onto 6 individual skewers (no amount of vegetables is specified because the pieces of lamb will vary in number).

Place on an oiled broiling pan and broil in a hot broiler until browned on all sides. Turn the skewers frequently.

Serves 6—330 calories in each serving.

*Note:* The kebobs are delicious broiled over an open fire.

## CROWN ROAST OF PORK ✳

Buy a loin of pork, and ask the butcher to form it into a crown. Ask the trimmed weight. Cover each rib bone with a cube of potato or a piece of aluminum foil to prevent charring.

2½ teaspoons salt
¾ teaspoon pepper
2 tablespoons flour
1 tablespoon butter or margarine
2 onions, chopped
1 cup sliced celery
3 apples, peeled and sliced
2 teaspoons liquid Sucaryl
¼ teaspoon thyme
¼ teaspoon nutmeg
⅛ teaspoon cinnamon
2 slices white toast, crumbled
2 tablespoons chopped parsley
3 tablespoons boiling water

Mix the salt, pepper and flour together and rub into the pork.

Melt the butter in a skillet; sauté the onions and celery for 5 minutes. Add the apples, Sucaryl, thyme, nutmeg and cinnamon; cook over low heat 10 minutes. Stir in the crumbled toast, parsley and water. Fill the crown with the mixture.

Place on a rack in a shallow roasting pan and roast in a 350° oven 30 minutes per pound. Remove the potatoes or foil and replace with paper frills. Serve 1 rib and 2 tablespoons stuffing for each serving.

Serves 8-10 people—375 calories in each serving.

## PORK CHOPS AND APPLE CASSEROLE

- 6 pork chops, ⅓-inch thick
- 1½ teaspoons salt
- ¼ teaspoon pepper
- 6 small white onions
- 3 apples, cut in thirds
- 2 tablespoons seedless raisins
- 1 tablespoon brown sugar
- ¾ cup beef broth, fresh or canned
- ¼ teaspoon nutmeg
- ¼ teaspoon thyme
- 1 bay leaf
- 2 sprigs parsley

Broil the chops on a broiling rack 15 minutes, turning them once. Transfer to a casserole and sprinkle with the salt and pepper. Arrange the onions, apples and raisins over them; add the sugar, broth, nutmeg, thyme, bay leaf and parsley. Cover and bake in a 375° oven 1¼ hours. Skim the fat, discard the bay leaf and parsley. Serve directly from the casserole.

Serves 6—350 calories in each serving.

## BARBECUED SPARERIBS

- 1 sheet spareribs
- ½ cup ketchup
- ½ teaspoon salt
- ¼ teaspoon pepper
- 1 teaspoon dry mustard
- 1 teaspoon Worcestershire sauce
- ¼ cup water

Have the spareribs cut into 6 pieces (about 2 ribs for each). Trim all the fat.

Combine the ketchup, salt, pepper, mustard, Worcestershire sauce and water. Marinate the ribs in it for 2 hours. Drain, but reserve the marinade.

Place the ribs on a rack in a shallow roasting pan. Roast in a 350° oven 30 minutes. Pour off the fat and add the marinade. Roast 30 minutes longer, basting frequently.

Serves 6—300 calories in each serving.

## SPARERIBS WITH SAUERKRAUT

- 1 sheet spareribs (about 2 pounds)
- 1 teaspoon salt
- ½ teaspoon pepper
- 2 pounds sauerkraut, undrained
- 2 onions, finely chopped
- 2 potatoes, peeled and grated
- 2 cloves
- 1 bay leaf

Have the butcher cut the spareribs into 6 pieces (about 2 ribs each). Remove as much fat as possible. Season with the salt and pepper.

Broil the ribs 10 minutes on each side; drain well.

Combine the sauerkraut, onions, potatoes, cloves and bay leaf in a casserole. Arrange the ribs over them. Bake in a 350° oven 1 hour, basting frequently. Serve directly from the casserole.

Serves 6—400 calories in each serving.

## CHINESE PORK TENDERLOIN

- 1 pork tenderloin (about ¾ pound)
- 4 tablespoons soy sauce
- 1 tablespoon sherry
- 2 teaspoons sugar
- ¼ teaspoon liquid Sucaryl
- ¼ teaspoon garlic powder
- 1 teaspoon ginger

Wash and dry the tenderloin. Mix the soy sauce, sherry, sugar, Sucaryl, garlic powder and ginger together. Place the tenderloin in it and let marinate 2 hours.

Broil the pork in a medium broiler 45 minutes, turning it frequently to brown on all sides. Cut into diagonal ¼-inch thick slices.

Serves 6—180 calories in each serving.

## BAKED CANADIAN-STYLE BACON

- 2-pound piece Canadian-style bacon
- Cloves
- ½ cup crushed pineapple

Slit the casing of the bacon and slip it off under cold running water. Place on a rack, fat side up. Insert meat thermometer into the center.

Bake in a 375° oven 1½ hours, or until thermometer registers 170°.

Score the fat and stud with the cloves. Spread the pineapple over it. Bake 25 minutes longer.

Serves 8—325 calories in each serving.

## ROAST FRESH HAM ❊

You can buy a whole or half fresh ham, depending on the number of people you want to serve or the amount of leftovers desired. Cold ham is delicious. Have the butcher remove the skin. Season the ham with salt and pepper an hour before roasting time.

- 4 cloves
- 2 onions
- 2 carrots, sliced
- 2 stalks celery
- 2 cups dry white wine
- 1 tablespoon flour
- 1 cup chicken broth, fresh or canned
- 1 tablespoon cognac

Place the ham on a rack in a shallow roasting pan. Roast in a 425° oven 30 minutes. Pour off the fat; reduce the heat to 350°. Stick the cloves in the onions and add with the carrots, celery and wine. Roast 25 minutes per pound, basting frequently. Transfer to a heated serving dish. Skim all the fat from the gravy.

Mix the flour with the broth in a small saucepan; stir in the cognac and skimmed gravy. Cook over low heat, stirring steadily until the boiling point. Cook 5 minutes. Serve 2 slices ⅛ inch thick, 4 inches x 4 inches and 1 tablespoon gravy.

—375 calories in each serving.

## BAKED HAM

Smoked hams are sold precooked and uncooked. An uncooked ham requires cooking for 25 minutes a pound before it is to be baked. Then drain it, and strip off the skin. A processed ham is cooked, but follow the instructions on the wrapping for the length of time required to bake it. Both types of ham may be prepared in the same manner from this point. Score the fat—with a sharp knife make diagonal cuts, ¾ inch apart, ⅛ inch deep.

- ¼ cup brown sugar
- ½ teaspoon dry mustard
- Cloves
- 2 tablespoons grated orange rind
- 2 cups low-calorie ginger ale

Rub the sugar and mustard into the ham; stick the cloves into it in any design you choose to follow; sprinkle the orange rind over the top. Bake in a 425° oven 45 minutes. Drain all the fat. Pour the ginger ale over the ham, reduce the heat to 350° and bake 1 hour longer, basting frequently. Remove ham and let it stand at room temperature for ½ hour before carving. Serve 2 slices, ¼ inch thick, 3 x 4 inches.

You can serve 8-20 people depending on the size of ham bought—425 calories in each serving.

## BAKED HAM SLICE

- 1 tablespoon butter or margarine
- 1 onion, minced
- ¼ cup minced celery
- 1 green pepper, minced
- ⅛ teaspoon salt
- ⅛ teaspoon pepper
- ½ cup canned corn kernels, drained
- ¼ cup crushed cornflakes
- 2 slices cooked ham, ½-inch thick (about 1¼ pounds)

Melt the butter in a skillet; sauté the onion 5 minutes. Add the celery and green pepper. Cook over low heat 5 minutes, stirring frequently. Stir in the salt, pepper, corn and cornflakes.

Place the ham in a baking dish. Bake in a 350° oven 10 minutes. Drain the fat and turn the ham. Cover with the corn mixture. Bake 25 minutes longer.

Serves 6—450 calories in each serving.

## HAM IN COFFEE SAUCE

- 6 slices cooked ham, ¼-inch thick (about 4 ounces each)
- ¾ cup brewed coffee
- 1 teaspoon cornstarch
- ¼ cup milk

Brown the ham slices on both sides. Drain the fat thoroughly. Add the coffee and cook over low heat 10 minutes. Mix the cornstarch and milk until smooth. Stir into the pan, mixing steadily until the boiling point.

Serves 6—410 calories in each serving.

The symbol ❋ indicates dishes that can be frozen.

The downfall of many dieters is often brought about by meals lacking in bulk. Getting up from the dinner table with that "empty" feeling inevitably leads to late-evening high-calorie snacks. Therefore it is essential that most meals be high in bulky foods to give the diner a sense of having finished a large, filling meal. More than almost all foods, green vegetables supply the desired effect of high bulk and low caloric count.

Don't serve the same vegetables night after night or your family will grow bored with them. Try a different vegetable every evening and capture their interest. A combination of several vegetable recipes—your own selection—makes a delectable vegetable plate, just perfect for a complete lunch.

Refrigerated railroad cars, air freight and quick freezing have made almost every vegetable available the entire year round, completely disregarding the seasons. Variety in vegetables is particularly important to the homemaker who wants her family to eat the proper foods. Take full advantage of the wide choice of vegetables offered to you in your local store.

*Fresh vegetables:* When buying, be sure they are really fresh, as there is a substantial loss of flavor and vitamin content if kept too long. Beans and peas can be tested by breaking the shell—they should snap; older specimens are limp. Greens (such as spinach) should be crisp and without brown spots. Refrigerate all vegetables until needed, in the vegetable crisper of your refrigerator. If paring is required, use a vegetable parer so as to remove as thin a layer as possible. Don't soak vegetables before cooking as it results in a vitamin loss.

*Frozen vegetables:* These deteriorate quickly if not kept solidly frozen. Be sure the package is firm when buying it, and then rush it to your freezer. Once the package has softened, it should be used and not refrozen. Follow the directions and cooking times specified on the package. You'll find some variation as various processors use different methods.

## ASPARAGUS

There are various types of asparagus cookers. One is an oblong kettle with a rack which allows the asparagus to remain above the water level. The other popular type is the unright boiler which allows the stalk ends (they require longer cooking than the tips) to cook, while the tips are just steamed. You may also use a double boiler. Tie the asparagus in individual servings. Place upright in the bottom of the double boiler half full of boiling salted water. Cover with the inverted top of the double boiler. Cook about 15 minutes or until tender. Drain.

- 2 pounds asparagus
- ⅔ cup special hollandaise sauce (see recipe)

Wash and scrub the asparagus. Cut off the stem ends. Cook as directed above. Drain and serve with 2 tablespoons hollandaise sauce.

Serves 6—55 calories in each serving.

## SAUTÉED ARTICHOKE HEARTS

- 1 package frozen artichoke hearts
- 2 tablespoons flour
- 1 teaspoon salt
- ¼ teaspoon pepper
- 2 tablespoons butter or margarine

Partially defrost the artichokes. Combine the flour, salt and pepper; dust the artichokes with the mixture.

Melt the butter in a skillet; sauté the artichokes over low heat 8 minutes turning them once.

Serves 6—60 calories in each serving.

## ASPARAGUS WITH EGG SAUCE

2 pounds asparagus
2 tablespoons butter or margarine
1 slice white bread, trimmed and crumbled fine
2 hard-cooked eggs, grated
1 teaspoon salt
¼ teaspoon pepper
1 tablespoon finely chopped parsley

Cut most of the ends off the asparagus. Cook as directed; drain, but reserve ¼ cup of the liquid.

Melt the butter in a skillet; brown the bread crumbs in it. Stir in the asparagus liquid, the eggs, salt, pepper and parsley.

Arrange the asparagus on individual plates and pour the sauce over them.

Serves 6—105 calories in each serving.

## STEAMED ARTICHOKES

6 artichokes
2 teaspoons salt
1 clove garlic, minced (optional)
2 tablespoons lemon juice
Vinaigrette sauce or special mayonnaise (see recipes)

Wash the artichokes and soak in cold salted water, stem up, for 30 minutes. Drain and cut off the stem.

Arrange in a saucepan, stem end down, and add about 2 inches of water, the salt, garlic and lemon juice. Cover and cook over medium heat 45 minutes, or until a leaf pulls out easily.

Drain and serve hot with 2 tablespoons of either vinaigrette sauce or mayonnaise.

Serves 6—50 calories in each serving.

## STUFFED ARTICHOKES

6 artichokes
1 cup crushed cornflakes
¼ cup finely chopped onion
3 tablespoons chopped parsley
6 anchovy fillets, minced
½ teaspoon paprika
2 tablespoons olive oil
1 cup chicken broth, fresh or canned

Wash and soak the artichokes in cold salted water, stem up for 30 minutes. Drain; cut off the stem and force the leaves apart gently. Insert a knife or grapefruit corer and cut out the choke (the hairy looking section).

Mix together the cornflakes, onion, parsley, anchovies and paprika. Stuff the artichokes and brush with the olive oil. Arrange in a baking dish, stem end down. Pour the broth into it. Bake in 350° oven 1 hour, basting frequently. Serve hot or cold.

Serves 6—70 calories in each serving.

## GREEN BEANS

There are several names for the green beans, depending on the section of the country; snap, string or green. Wax beans (yellow) may also be prepared in any of the following ways:

### STEAMED GREEN BEANS

- 2 pounds green beans or 2 packages frozen
- 1 cup water
- ¾ teaspoon salt
- ½ teaspoon monosodium glutamate
- 2 tablespoons melted butter or margarine

If fresh beans are used, cut off the ends and cut into thirds, halves, or leave whole. Bring the water, salt and monosodium glutamate to a boil; drop the beans into it. Cover and cook over low heat and cook about 15 minutes or until just tender. Drain and toss with the butter.

If frozen beans are used, follow the time given by the individual packer.

Serves 6—70 calories in each serving.

### GREEN BEANS IN TOMATO SAUCE

- 1 tablespoon olive oil
- 2 onions, diced
- 1 clove garlic, minced
- 1 can (#2½) tomatoes
- 1 teaspoon salt
- ¼ teaspoon pepper
- ¼ teaspoon oregano
- 1 bay leaf
- 2 pounds green beans, cut in half, or 2 packages frozen

Heat the oil in a heavy saucepan. Sauté the onion and garlic 5 minutes. Stir in the tomatoes, salt, pepper, oregano and bay leaf. Bring to a boil and drop the beans into it. Cover and cook over low heat 1½ hours.

Serves 6—75 calories in each serving.

### CHINESE GREEN BEANS

- 1 tablespoon peanut or salad oil
- 1 clove garlic, minced
- ½ pound raw lean beef, diced as small as possible
- 2 onions, sliced
- 2 pounds green beans, cut in half, or 2 packages frozen
- 1½ cups beef broth, fresh or canned
- ½ teaspoon pepper
- 1 bay leaf
- 1 teaspoon powdered ginger
- 2 tablespoons soy sauce

Heat the oil in a heavy saucepan; brown the garlic and meat over high heat, stirring almost constantly. Add the onions, beans, broth, pepper, bay leaf, ginger and soy sauce. Mix well. Cook over low heat 30 minutes stirring occasionally. Taste for seasoning.

Good as a luncheon or supper dish, or as an accompaniment to broiled meat.

Serves 6—180 calories in each serving.

## MARINATED GREEN BEANS

- 3 tablespoons cider vinegar
- 2 tablespoons water
- 1½ tablespoons salad oil
- 1 teaspoon salt
- ⅛ teaspoon pepper
- 1 teaspoon chopped dill or parsley
- 3 cups cooked green beans

Combine the vinegar, water, oil, salt, pepper and dill or parsley. Pour over the beans; let marinate 1 hour. Serve cold, on lettuce leaves.

Serves 6—50 calories per serving.

## SAUTÉED GREEN BEANS

- 2 pounds green beans or 2 packages frozen, partially defrosted
- 2 tablespoons butter or margarine
- 2 tablespoons water
- ¾ teaspoon salt
- ½ teaspoon monosodium glutamate
- 1 tablespoon finely chopped parsley

Prepare the beans as directed and cut in thirds.

Heat the butter, water, salt and monosodium glutamate in a saucepan; drop the beans into it; cover tightly and cook over low heat 15 minutes (if frozen, the time package suggests) or until just tender. Shake the pan frequently to avoid burning. Sprinkle with the parsley and serve.

Serves 6—70 calories in each serving.

## BOSTON BAKED BEANS

- 2 cups navy or pea beans
- 2 slices bacon, diced
- 2 tablespoons molasses
- 2 teaspoons liquid Sucaryl
- 1 teaspoon dry mustard
- 2 teaspoons salt
- ¼ cup grated onion
- 1½ cups chicken broth, fresh or canned

Wash the beans thoroughly and discard any imperfect ones. Cover with cold water and let soak overnight. Drain and add fresh water to cover. Cover and cook over low heat 1½ hours. Drain.

Spread half the bacon on the bottom of an earthenware pot. Turn the beans into it. Mix together the molasses, Sucaryl, mustard, salt, onion, and ½ cup broth. Pour over the beans and lift them carefully with a spoon to allow the seasoning to run under. Sprinkle the remaining bacon on top. Cover the pot.

Bake in a 300° oven 5 hours. Remove the cover every hour and add a little broth if too dry, and turn them carefully. Remove the cover for the last ¾ hour.

Serves 8—190 calories in each serving.

## STEAMED LIMA BEANS

In some parts of the country lima beans are called butter beans.

- 2 pounds fresh lima beans or 1 package frozen
- 1 tablespoon butter or margarine
- ½ cup water
- ¼ teaspoon salt
- ¼ teaspoon monosodium glutamate

Shell (hull) the lima beans by cutting a thin strip along the pod side of the shell. Open and pop the beans out.

Combine the butter, water, salt and monosodium glutamate. Bring to a boil and drop the beans into it. Cover and cook over low heat about 12 minutes or until the beans are tender. (If frozen beans, cook as long as package suggests.) Drain.

Serves 6—85 calories in each serving.

## LIMA BEANS AND PEARL ONIONS

- 1 tablespoon butter or margarine
- 12 small white onions, peeled
- 1 tablespoon cornstarch
- 1 cup chicken broth, fresh or canned
- 2 pounds fresh lima beans, shelled or 1 package frozen
- ½ teaspoon salt
- 1 tablespoon chopped parsley

Melt the butter in a saucepan; sauté the onions over low heat 10 minutes. Shake the pan frequently.

Mix the cornstarch with the broth and add to the onions stirring constantly to the boiling point. Add the beans, salt and parsley. Cook about 15 minutes or until tender.

Serves 6—105 calories in each serving.

## LIMA BEANS IN YOGURT

- 2 pounds fresh lima beans or 1 package frozen
- ½ cup water
- 1 teaspoon salt
- 1 tablespoon butter or margarine
- ¼ cup finely chopped onion
- 1 pimento, minced
- ½ cup yogurt

Shell the beans if fresh are used. Bring the water and salt to a boil and drop the beans into it. Cover and cook over low heat 12 minutes or until tender (if frozen beans are used, cook as long as package suggests). Drain.

While the beans are cooking, melt the butter in a skillet; sauté the onion and pimento 5 minutes. Add the beans and yogurt. Heat but do not let boil. Taste for seasoning.

Serves 6—90 calories in each serving.

## BOILED BEETS

Canned beets are delicious, especially when used in recipes. Fresh beets take a while to cook, but young, fresh beets are worth the trouble. To retain all the flavor and vitamins they may be cooked unpeeled.

6 beets
Water
1 teaspoon salt

Scrub the beets well and remove the stems. If cooked whole, don't peel until after they are cooked. Plunge into boiling salted water; cover and cook 1 hour or until tender. Drain; hold under running water and slip skins off.

Or peel and dice the beets. Cook in boiling salted water 20 minutes, or until tender. Drain and use in recipes or serve with 2 tablespoons melted butter.

Serves 6—65 calories in each serving.

## SAVORY BEETS AND CABBAGE

2 tablespoons butter or margarine
3 beets, pared and grated on the medium grater
2 cups cabbage, finely shredded
1 onion, chopped
½ teaspoon salt
⅛ teaspoon pepper
2 tablespoons vinegar
2 tablespoons water
¼ teaspoon liquid Sucaryl or 2 tablets

Melt the butter in a deep skillet. Add the beets, cabbage and onion. Cover and cook over low heat 5 minutes. Stir in the salt, pepper, vinegar, water and Sucaryl. Cover and cook 15 minutes. Taste for seasoning.

Serves 6—65 calories in each serving.

## BROCCOLI AMANDINE

2 bunches broccoli or 2 packages frozen
2 tablespoons butter or margarine
3 tablespoons lemon juice
3 tablespoons chopped almonds

Wash the fresh broccoli thoroughly and soak in cold salted water 10 minutes. Drain well and discard the large leaves and lower parts of the stalks. Cook in boiling salted water to cover 15 minutes, or until tender (a piece of bread in the water keeps the odor from spreading). Drain well. (If frozen broccoli is used, cook as the packer suggests.)

Melt the butter in a skillet; add the lemon juice and almonds. Heat and pour over the broccoli.

Serves 6—85 calories in each serving.

## BUTTERED BEETS

- 2 tablespoons butter or margarine
- 6 beets, pared and grated on medium grater
- ½ teaspoon salt
- ⅛ teaspoon pepper
- ¼ teaspoon monosodium glutamate
- ⅛ teaspoon onion salt
- 2 tablespoons water

Melt the butter in a skillet; add the beets, salt, pepper, monosodium glutamate, onion salt and water. Cover and cook over low heat 20 minutes or until tender. Shake the pan frequently.

Serves 6—65 calories in each serving.

## HARVARD BEETS

- 1 tablespoon cornstarch
- ½ cup vinegar
- 1 tablespoon brown sugar
- 2 teaspoons liquid Sucaryl or 18 tablets
- 1 tablespoon butter or margarine
- 4 cups sliced or diced cooked or canned beets

Mix the cornstarch and vinegar until smooth in a saucepan. Stir in the brown sugar and Sucaryl. Cook over low heat, stirring constantly, until thick, about 5 minutes. Add the butter and beets. Heat and serve.

Serves 6—75 calories in each serving.

## BRAISED BROCCOLI

- ½ cup grated carrots
- ½ cup chopped onions
- 2 bunches fresh or 2 packages frozen broccoli
- 2 cups chicken broth, fresh or canned
- ¼ teaspoon pepper

Mix the carrots and onions in a saucepan or casserole. Arrange the broccoli over them and add the broth and pepper. Cover and cook over low heat about 15 minutes, or until tender. (If frozen broccoli is used, cook the time the package suggests.) Taste for seasoning and serve.

Serves 6—55 calories in each serving.

## BRUSSELS SPROUTS

- 1½ pounds Brussels sprouts
- Water
- 1 teaspoon salt
- 2 tablespoons melted butter or margarine
- 1 tablespoon lemon juice
- 1 tablespoon chopped parsley

Wash the sprouts thoroughly; pull off any wilted outside leaves and cut off the stems. Soak in cold salted water 10 minutes. Drain. Drop into boiling salted water to cover. Cook about 10 minutes, or until tender. *Don't* overcook and you won't have strong-tasting sprouts. Drain.

Mix the butter, lemon juice and parsley together and pour over the sprouts.

Serves 6—60 calories in each serving.

## STEAMED CABBAGE

- 2 heads cabbage (about 2 pounds each)
- 1 cup water
- 1 teaspoon salt
- 2 tablespoons melted butter

Buy young green heads of cabbage. Wash thoroughly and remove the coarse outer leaves. Cut each head into 4 wedges.

Bring the water and salt to a boil; drop the cabbage into it. Cover and cook over low heat about 8 minutes, or until tender but firm. *Don't overcook.* Drain. Toss the cabbage with the butter.

Serves 6—50 calories in each serving.

## SWEET AND SOUR RED CABBAGE

- 4 pounds red cabbage
- ¼ cup water
- ½ apple, peeled and cubed
- 1 tablespoon flour
- ¼ cup cider vinegar
- 1 teaspoon brown sugar
- 1 teaspoon liquid Sucaryl
- 1 teaspoon salt

Wash the cabbage thoroughly. Shred medium fine and combine with the water and apple in a saucepan. Cover and cook over low heat 10 minutes, mixing occasionally.

Mix the flour, sugar, Sucaryl and salt together. Pour over the cabbage, stirring constantly until the boiling point. Cover and cook over low heat 30 minutes. Taste for seasoning.

Serves 6—35 calories in each serving.

## CAULIFLOWER WITH MUSHROOM SAUCE

- 1 large head cauliflower or 2 packages frozen
- 1 tablespoon butter or margarine
- ½ pound mushrooms, sliced
- 2 teaspoons flour
- 1 teaspoon salt
- ⅛ teaspoon pepper
- ½ cup milk

If fresh cauliflower is used, remove the leaves. Soak in cold salted water 15 minutes. Drain. Separate into flowerets; cook in boiling salted water about 10 minutes, or until tender but firm. If frozen cauliflower is used, follow the instructions on the package. Drain.

While the cauliflower is cooking, melt the butter in a skillet. Sauté the mushrooms 5 minutes. Sprinkle with the flour, salt and pepper, then stir in milk. Cook over low heat, stirring constantly until the boiling point; cook 5 minutes longer.

Pour over the cauliflower and serve.

Serves 6—60 calories in each serving.

## BRUSSELS SPROUTS AND CHESTNUTS

½ pound chestnuts
1 pound Brussels sprouts
½ teaspoon salt
⅛ teaspoon pepper
½ cup chicken broth, fresh or canned

Make two crisscross gashes on the flat side of the chestnut with a pointed knife. Bake in a 350° oven for about 15 minutes, or until the shells can be removed easily. Shell and remove the skin.

Wash and soak the Brussels sprouts. Drain. Arrange alternate layers of the sprouts and chestnuts, sprinkled with salt and pepper. Pour the broth over all.

Bake in a 350° oven 30 minutes, or until tender.

Serves 6—80 calories in each serving.

## CREOLE CABBAGE

1 tablespoon butter or margarine
1 onion, chopped
¼ cup minced green pepper
3 pounds cabbage, shredded
1½ cups canned tomatoes
1 teaspoon salt
¼ teaspoon pepper
1 bay leaf
1 teaspoon sugar

Melt the butter in a saucepan; sauté the onion and green pepper 5 minutes. Add the cabbage, tomatoes, salt, pepper, bay leaf and sugar. Cook over low heat 25 minutes. Stir frequently. Taste for seasoning.

Serves 6—45 calories in each serving.

## SAUTÉED CABBAGE

4 pounds cabbage
2 tablespoons melted butter or margarine
¾ teaspoon salt
¼ teaspoon freshly ground black pepper
1 teaspoon sugar

Wash and drain the cabbage. Grate on the coarse grater, or shred it. Melt the butter in a skillet; sauté the cabbage, sprinkled with the salt, pepper and sugar for 10 minutes, or until tender. Mix frequently, and add a tablespoon or two of water to avoid burning.

Serves 6—50 calories in each serving.

## BAKED CARROTS

9 carrots
1 onion, finely chopped
¼ cup water
1 teaspoon salt
¼ teaspoon powdered ginger
1 tablespoon butter or margarine

Scrape the carrots and cut lengthwise into 4 pieces. Arrange in a baking dish or casserole. Sprinkle with the onion, water, salt and ginger; dot with the butter. Cover.

Bake in a 375° oven 35 minutes or until tender.

Serves 6—50 calories in each serving.

## CREAMED CARROTS

1 tablespoon butter or margarine
9 carrots, grated
1 teaspoon salt
¼ teaspoon liquid Sucaryl or 2 tablets
1 teaspoon cornstarch
¼ cup milk

Melt the butter in a saucepan; stir in the carrots, salt and Sucaryl. Cover and cook over low heat 5 minutes. Watch carefully to avoid burning. Mix the cornstarch and milk together and mix into the carrots. Cover and cook over low heat 5 minutes longer.

Serves 6—60 calories in each serving.

## CARROTS AND APPLES

1 tablespoon fine barley
9 carrots, grated
2 apples, peeled and grated
1 teaspoon salt
2 tablespoons water
⅓ teaspoon liquid Sucaryl or 3 tablets
1 tablespoon butter or margarine

Soak the barley for 1 hour; drain and combine in a saucepan with the carrots, apples, salt and water. Cover and cook over low heat 30 minutes. Stir occasionally. Add the Sucaryl and butter. Cook 15 minutes longer.

Serves 6—85 calories in each serving.

## BRAISED CELERY

3 bunches celery
2 tablespoons butter or margarine
1 cup beef broth, fresh or canned
½ teaspoon Worcestershire sauce

Remove the leaves of the celery and cut each bunch in quarters, lengthwise.

Melt the butter in a skillet; sauté the celery until lightly browned. Add the broth and Worcestershire sauce. Cook over medium heat 10 minutes, or until celery is tender but still crisp.

Serves 6—45 calories in each serving.

## CELERY AND TOMATOES

1 tablespoon butter or margarine
3 cups celery, cut into 1 inch pieces
1 onion, grated
2 cups canned tomatoes, drained
1 teaspoon salt
¼ teaspoon pepper

Melt the butter in a skillet; sauté the celery and onion 5 minutes, stirring frequently. Add the tomatoes, salt and pepper. Cover and cook over low heat 10 minutes.

Serves 6—40 calories in each serving.

## CORN ON THE COB

When buying corn be sure it is fresh; test by pricking a kernel with your nail. Milk should run out; if it doesn't, don't buy it.

- 6 ears of corn
- 2 cups water
- 2 teaspoons sugar
- 6 teaspoons butter

Remove the husk and silk just before cooking; earlier removal toughens the corn.

Bring the water and sugar to a boil and drop the corn into it. Cover and cook over high heat about 6 minutes, or until corn is tender. Drain and serve each corn with a teaspoon of butter. It should be seasoned at the table with salt and pepper.

Serves 6—120 calories in each serving.

## CORN SAUTÉ

- 6 ears of corn
- 1 tablespoon butter
- 1 teaspoon sugar
- ¼ cup milk
- ½ teaspoon salt
- ⅛ teaspoon pepper

Husk the corn. With a sharp knife, cut the kernels from the corn.

Melt the butter in a skillet; sauté the corn 1 minute, stirring almost constantly. Add the sugar, milk, salt and pepper. Cover and cook over low heat 5 minutes.

Serves 6—110 calories in each serving.

## CREOLE STYLE CORN

- 1 tablespoon butter or margarine
- 2 cups corn kernels, fresh or canned
- 1 onion, chopped
- 1 small green pepper, diced
- ½ cup canned tomatoes
- 1 teaspoon salt
- ¼ teaspoon pepper
- ½ teaspoon chili powder

Melt the butter in a saucepan; sauté the corn, onion and green pepper 5 minutes, stirring frequently. Add the tomatoes, salt, pepper and chili powder. Cook over low heat 5 minutes.

Serves 6—70 calories in each serving.

## BRAISED CUCUMBERS

- 4 cucumbers
- 2 teaspoons salt
- 3 slices bacon, diced
- 1 teaspoon sugar
- ¼ teaspoon liquid Sucaryl
- ⅛ teaspoon pepper
- 1 tablespoon cider vinegar

Peel the cucumbers and slice thinly into a bowl. Sprinkle with the salt and set aside for 30 minutes. Drain them thoroughly.

Fry the bacon until browned but not crisp. Drain well. Add the cucumbers, sugar, Sucaryl, pepper and vinegar to the bacon. Mix well; cover and cook over low heat 15 minutes.

Serves 6—40 calories in each serving.

## EGGPLANT PARMIGIANA

- 1 large eggplant
- 1 tablespoon olive oil
- ½ cup dry bread crumbs
- 3 tablespoons grated Parmesan cheese
- ½ teaspoon salt
- ¼ teaspoon pepper
- ½ teaspoon garlic powder
- 1 cup canned tomato sauce
- 3 thin slices Mozzarella or white American cheese

Peel the eggplant and slice ¼ inch thick. Pour boiling water over the slices and let soak 5 minutes; drain and dry.

Heat the oil in a skillet; brown the eggplant slices on both sides.

Mix together the bread crumbs, cheese, salt, pepper and garlic powder. In a baking dish arrange layers of eggplant, bread crumb mixture and the tomato sauce. Cover with the cheese.

Bake in a 325° oven 25 minutes.

Serves 6—120 calories in each serving.

## BAKED STUFFED EGGPLANT

- 1 medium eggplant
- 1 tablespoon olive oil
- 1 onion, minced
- 1 green pepper, diced
- ¼ pound mushrooms, sliced
- 2 tomatoes, chopped
- 1½ teaspoons salt
- ¼ teaspoon freshly ground black pepper
- ½ teaspoon basil

Wash and dry the eggplant. Cut it in half lengthwise; scoop out the pulp carefully and dice it.

Heat the olive oil in a skillet; sauté the onion, green pepper, mushrooms and eggplant pulp for 10 minutes, stirring frequently. Add the tomatoes, salt, pepper and basil. Cook 5 minutes.

Stuff the shells and place in a baking pan containing ½ inch of water. Bake in a 375° oven 20 minutes. Cut each half in three.

Serves 6—55 calories in each serving.

## FRENCH FRIED ONIONS

- 2 large sweet onions (Bermuda type)
- ½ cup milk
- ⅓ cup sifted flour
- 1 teaspoon salt
- 4 tablespoons shortening or oil (for frying)

Peel the onions and slice ¼ inch thick. Separate into rings and soak in the milk for 1 hour. Drain. Combine the flour and salt on a piece of waxed paper or in a bag. Roll or shake the onions until lightly coated.

Heat the shortening in a deep skillet. Drop the onion rings into it, but don't crowd the skillet. Fry until browned on both sides. Drain well and keep warm while preparing the remaining rings.

Serves 6—100 calories in each serving.

## BAKED LETTUCE

- 2 heads lettuce
- 1 tablespoon cornstarch
- ¼ cup milk
- 1 cup chicken broth, fresh or canned
- 1 teaspoon salt
- 1 tablespoon butter or margarine
- 2 tablespoons coarsely chopped nuts
- 2 tablespoons dry bread crumbs

Wash the lettuce and remove any bruised leaves. Pour boiling water over it, let soak 1 minute, then drain. Cook in water to cover 5 minutes; drain very well. Cut each head in 3. Place in a casserole.

Mix the cornstarch and milk until smooth in a saucepan. Stir in the broth, salt and butter. Cook over low heat, stirring constantly until the boiling point. Pour over the lettuce and sprinkle with the bread crumbs and nuts.

Bakes in a 425° oven 15 minutes or until browned.

Serves 6—55 calories in each serving.

## BROILED STUFFED MUSHROOMS

- 24 mushrooms
- 1 onion
- 2 tablespoons butter or margarine
- ½ teaspoon salt
- ⅛ teaspoon pepper
- 3 tablespoons cottage cheese
- 2 tablespoons dry bread crumbs

Try to have the mushrooms all one size. Wash and dry them. Remove the stems and chop fine with the onion. Melt 1 tablespoon butter in a skillet; sauté the onion mixture 5 minutes, stirring frequently. Add the salt, pepper, cheese and bread crumbs. Mix well. Stuff the mushrooms with the mixture.

Melt the remaining butter in a baking pan and place the mushrooms in it. Cook over direct heat 3 minutes, then broil in a hot broiler for 3 minutes, or until browned.

Serves 6—60 calories in each serving.

## MUSHROOM SAUTÉ WITH SOUR CREAM

- 1 tablespoon butter or margarine
- 1 onion, chopped
- 1 pound mushrooms, sliced
- 1 teaspoon salt
- ¼ teaspoon pepper
- 1 teaspoon paprika
- 2 tablespoons sour cream

Melt the butter in a skillet; sauté the onion 5 minutes stirring frequently. Add the mushrooms and sauté 5 minutes. Season with salt, pepper and paprika; stir in the sour cream. Heat but do not let boil.

Serves 6—45 calories in each serving.

## ONION SAUTÉ

4 medium sweet onions (Bermuda type)
1 tablespoon butter or margarine
1 tablespoon olive oil
1 teaspoon salt
¼ teaspoon pepper
½ teaspoon marjoram

Peel the onions and slice very thin. Heat the butter and olive oil in a large heavy skillet. Add the onions; sprinkle with the salt, pepper and marjoram. Cook over low heat, stirring constantly for 2 minutes. Cover and cook 10 minutes, or until onions are golden and tender.

Serves 6—40 calories in each serving.

## GLAZED ONIONS

18 small white onions, peeled
2 tablespoons butter or margarine
1 cup chicken broth, fresh or canned
1 tablespoon brown sugar
½ teaspoon Worcestershire sauce
½ teaspoon salt

Combine all the ingredients in a saucepan. Cook over low heat 20 minutes or until the onions are tender and sauce almost absorbed. Stir occasionally.

Serves 6—40 calories in each serving.

## BELGIAN STYLE ENDIVE

6 stalks endive
2 tablespoons lemon juice
½ cup chicken broth, fresh or canned
2 tablespoons melted butter or margarine
1 teaspoon salt
½ teaspoon freshly ground black pepper
1 teaspoon sugar

Wash the endive and cut in half lengthwise. Arrange in a shallow baking dish. Sprinkle with the lemon juice and add the broth, butter, salt, pepper and sugar. Cover the dish with aluminum foil.

Bake in a 350° oven 35 minutes. Remove the foil and bake 10 minutes longer.

Serves 6—40 calories in each serving.

## PARSNIPS IN CHEESE SAUCE

6 parsnips
1 tablespoon butter or margarine
1 tablespoon flour
1 teaspoon salt
1 cup skim milk
3 tablespoons grated American cheese

Scrub the parsnips and cook in boiling water 20 minutes or until tender. Drain and peel. Slice thin, crosswise, into a shallow baking dish.

Melt the butter in a saucepan; stir in the flour and salt. Gradually add the milk, stirring constantly to the boiling point. Cook 5 minutes; remove from the heat and add the cheese, stirring until melted. Pour over the parsnips.

Bake in a 475° oven 10 minutes or until browned.

Serves 6—65 calories in each serving.

## PEAS, FRENCH STYLE

1 tablespoon butter or margarine
6 lettuce leaves, shredded
3 scallions (green onions) sliced or 1 onion, sliced
2 pounds green peas, shelled or 1 package, frozen
¾ teaspoon salt
2 teaspoons sugar
2 tablespoons water

If frozen peas are used, defrost them for 2 hours before using.

Melt the butter and arrange the lettuce over it. Add the scallions, peas, salt, sugar and water. Cover and cook over low heat 25 minutes. Watch carefully to avoid burning. Mix carefully and serve.

Serves 6—80 calories in each serving.

## GREEN PEA AND POTATO CASSEROLE

2 potatoes, peeled and diced
1 pound green peas, shelled or ½ package frozen, defrosted
1¼ teaspoons salt
¼ teaspoon pepper
⅛ teaspoon thyme
⅛ teaspoon chervil
2 tablespoons chopped parsley
½ cup skim milk
1 tablespoon butter or margarine

In a small heat proof casserole, combine the potatoes, peas, salt, pepper, thyme, chervil and parsley. Mix well. Pour the milk over it and cover the casserole. Cook over low heat 25 minutes, shaking the casserole frequently. Add the butter and stir carefully until it melts.

Serves 6—90 calories in each serving.

## ITALIAN-STYLE PEPPER SAUTÉ

1 tablespoon olive oil
2 onions, sliced
3 green peppers, sliced
½ pound mushrooms, sliced
1 teaspoon salt
⅛ teaspoon crushed dried red peppers
⅛ teaspoon oregano

Heat the oil in a skillet; sauté the onion 5 minutes. Add the peppers; sauté 3 minutes, stirring frequently. Add the mushrooms, salt, red pepper and oregano. Cook over medium heat 5 minutes, stirring frequently.

Serves 6—40 calories in each serving.

## MASHED POTATOES ❊

4 large potatoes, pared and quartered
¾ teaspoon salt
1 tablespoon butter
⅓ cup dry nonfat dry milk
3 tablespoons cold water

Cook the potatoes until tender; drain. Mash with a potato masher, put through a ricer, or mash in an electric mixer. Add the salt and butter. Mix the dry milk and water, heat, and beat into the potatoes until fluffy.

Serves 6—95 calories in each serving.

## POTATO PANCAKES ❋

- 3 potatoes (1 pound)
- 1 egg
- 1 egg yolk
- 1 teaspoon salt
- ¼ teaspoon pepper
- 1 tablespoon grated onion
- 2 teaspoons potato starch or 1 tablespoon flour
- 2 tablespoons butter, margarine or shortening

Pare the potatoes and grate on the medium grater into a bowl of cold water. Or you can cut them into small pieces and run in the electric blender. In either case, drain all the water.

Mix the potatoes with the egg, egg yolk, salt, pepper, onion and potato starch or flour.

Heat half the fat in a skillet and drop the potato mixture into it by the tablespoon. Sauté over low heat until browned on both sides. Keep hot while preparing the balance and add the remaining shortening as needed.

Serves 6—110 calories in each serving.

## SAVOYARD POTATOES

- 3 large potatoes, peeled
- 1 tablespoon butter or margarine
- 1 teaspoon salt
- ½ teaspoon freshly ground black pepper
- 1 teaspoon paprika
- 2 tablespoons grated Parmesan cheese
- 1 onion, thinly sliced
- ½ cup chicken broth, fresh or canned
- 3 tablespoons milk

Slice the potatoes paper thin. Grease an 11-inch pie plate with 1 teaspoon butter.

Mix the salt, pepper, paprika and cheese together. Arrange layers of the potatoes and onions, sprinkled with the cheese mixture and dotted with the remaining butter. Mix the broth and milk together and pour over all.

Bake in a 375° oven 50 minutes or until browned and tender. Serve directly from the pie plate.

Serves 6—105 calories in each serving.

## POTATOES AU GRATIN

- 3 large potatoes, peeled
- ¾ cup skim milk, scalded
- 1 egg, beaten
- 1¼ teaspoons salt
- 3 tablespoons grated onion
- 1 clove garlic
- 2 tablespoons grated Gruyere cheese

Slice the potatoes as thin as possible. Add the milk, egg, salt and onion. Mix well.

Rub a shallow baking dish with the garlic (or use 6 individual dishes). Turn the mixture into it and sprinkle with the cheese.

Bake in a 350° oven 45 minutes for the large dish or 35 for the individual dishes.

Serves 6—100 calories in each serving.

## BAKED STUFFED POTATOES ⁂

3 large Idaho potatoes
½ cup cottage cheese
1 egg yolk
1½ teaspoons salt
2 tablespoons chopped chives or onions

Wash, scrub and dry the potatoes. Bake in a 375° oven 50 minutes or until tender when pricked with a fork. Cut in half lengthwise and scoop out the pulp carefully. Reserve the shells.

Mash the potatoes and beat in the cheese, egg yolk, salt and chives. Stuff the shells. Place on a baking sheet and bake in a 425° oven 10 minutes or until delicately browned.

Serves 6—90 calories in each serving.

## POTATO SOUFFLÉ

4 potatoes, peeled and cooked
¾ cup skim milk
1 teaspoon salt
⅛ teaspoon white pepper
⅛ teaspoon nutmeg
1 tablespoon grated Parmesan cheese
2 egg yolks
4 egg whites, stiffly beaten

Turn oven on and set at 375°.

Mash the potatoes and measure two cups. Beat the milk, salt, pepper, nutmeg and cheese into it. Cool 10 minutes. Add the egg yolks and mix well. Fold the egg whites into it.

Turn into a 1½ quart soufflé dish or casserole. Bake 30 minutes or until browned and set. Serve at once.

Serves 6—125 calories in each serving.

## FRENCH FRIED POTATOES ⁂

2 large Idaho potatoes, peeled
Fat for deep frying
Salt

Peel the potatoes and cut into strips ¼ inch thick, ¼ inch wide and 2 inches long. Soak in cold water for 1 hour. Drain and dry.

Heat the fat (about 5 inches deep) to 375° and drop the potatoes into it, but don't crowd the basket or pan. Fry 7 minutes. Remove and drain on paper towels. (This part may be done early in the day.) When ready to serve, heat the fat to 400° and return the potatoes to it. Fry 2 minutes, or until browned and crisp. Drain. Sprinkle with salt and serve.

Serves 6—125 calories in each serving.

*Note:* For Shoestring Potatoes, cut the potatoes into matchlike strips and fry only once, in 375° fat until crisp and brown, about 5 minutes.

## POTATOES IN SOUR CREAM

- 1 tablespoon shortening, butter or margarine
- 3 potatoes (about 1 pound) peeled and sliced thin
- 1 onion, chopped
- 1 teaspoon salt
- 1 teaspoon paprika
- 2 tablespoons water
- 2 tablespoons sour cream

Melt the shortening in a skillet; add the potatoes and onion; sauté 2 minutes, stirring constantly. Sprinkle with the salt, paprika and water. Cover and cook over low heat 10 minutes, turning them occasionally. Add the sour cream and cook 3 minutes longer or until tender.

Serves 6—90 calories in each serving.

## SWISS POTATOES

- 2 large Idaho potatoes (about 1½ pounds)
- 1 tablespoon butter or margarine
- 1 teaspoon salt
- ¼ teaspoon pepper

Peel the potatoes. Grate on a medium grater into a bowl of cold water. Drain well.

Melt the butter in a 9-11 inch skillet. Turn the potatoes into it. Cover the skillet and cook over low heat until the underside is browned. Turn carefully in one piece, and brown the other side, uncovered. Sprinkle with salt and pepper. Cut into pie shaped wedges.

Serves 6—85 calories in each serving.

## CREAMED SPINACH

- 3 pounds spinach or 2 packages frozen
- 1 tablespoon butter or margarine
- 2 tablespoons grated onion
- 1 teaspoon salt
- ⅛ teaspoon pepper
- ⅛ teaspoon nutmeg
- 1 tablespoon flour
- ½ cup skim milk

If fresh spinach is used, wash thoroughly in several changes of water. Remove the tough stems and chop the spinach. If frozen spinach is used, defrost it for 2 hours.

Melt the butter in a saucepan; sauté the onion 3 minutes. Add the spinach, salt, pepper and nutmeg. Cover and cook over medium heat 5 minutes, or until the spinach is tender. Mix a few times.

Drain if any water remains. Mix the flour and milk together and pour over the spinach. Cook over low heat, mixing lightly with a fork until the boiling point. Cook 3 minutes and serve. For a smooth creamed spinach purée in the blender or put through a food mill.

Serves 6—60 calories in each serving.

## BAKED MASHED SWEET POTATOES ❄

- 2 sweet potatoes (about 1½ pounds)
- ½ cup skim milk, scalded
- 1 egg yolk
- 2 tablespoons cognac
- ½ teaspoon salt
- ⅛ teaspoon nutmeg
- 1 egg white, stiffly beaten

Wash, scrub and dry the potatoes. Bake in a 375° oven 50 minutes (prick the potatoes in several places after 15 minutes baking time to prevent bursting) or until tender. Cut in half and scoop out the pulp.

Mash and beat in the milk, egg yolk, cognac, salt and nutmeg. Fold in the egg white. Turn into a 1 quart soufflé dish or casserole.

Bake in a 400° oven 25 minutes.

Serves 6—70 calories in each serving.

## SWEET POTATO AND APPLE CASSEROLE

- 2 large sweet potatoes (about 1½ pounds)
- 2 apples
- 1 teaspoon butter
- 2 tablespoons brown sugar
- ½ cup orange juice
- 1 teaspoon liquid Sucaryl
- Cinnamon or nutmeg

Wash and scrub the potatoes. Cook in water to cover 20 minutes. Drain, peel and slice ¼ inch thick.

Peel the apples and slice thin. In a baking dish arrange alternate layers of potatoes and apples, sprinkled with the brown sugar. Mix the orange juice and Sucaryl together and pour over all. Sprinkle with the cinnamon or nutmeg.

Bake in a 375° oven 45 minutes, or until tender and browned.

Serves 6—100 calories in each serving.

## BAKED ACORN SQUASH

- 3 small acorn squash
- 1 teaspoon salt
- ⅛ teaspoon pepper
- ½ teaspoon ginger
- 2 tablespoons melted butter
- 1 teaspoon liquid Sucaryl

Scrub, wash and dry the squash. Cut in half lengthwise and remove the seeds and fibers. Sprinkle with a mixture of the salt, pepper and ginger. Mix the butter and Sucaryl together and divide among the squash.

Set in a shallow baking pan with 1 inch of water on the bottom. Cover the pan with a piece of aluminum foil.

Bake in a 350° oven 1 hour, removing the foil after 40 minutes of baking time. Hubbard squash may be prepared in the same manner.

Serves 6—60 calories in each serving.

## CANDIED SWEET POTATOES

3 sweet potatoes
1 teaspoon salt
2 tablespoons brown sugar
1 teaspoon liquid Sucaryl
1 tablespoon melted butter or margarine
¼ cup orange juice

Wash and scrub the potatoes. Cook in water to cover for 30 minutes. Drain and peel. Cut lengthwise into 6 pieces and arrange in a shallow baking dish. Sprinkle with the brown sugar. Mix the Sucaryl, butter and orange juice together and pour over the potatoes.

Bake in a 375° oven 25 minutes or until browned and glazed. Baste occasionally.

Serves 6—85 calories in each serving.

## SUMMER SQUASH

4 pounds summer (yellow) squash
1½ teaspoons salt
¾ teaspoon liquid Sucaryl
1 tablespoon raw rice
½ cup milk

Peel the squash lightly and slice thin. Combine in a saucepan with the salt and Sucaryl. Cover and cook over very low heat 10 minutes. Add the rice, cover and cook over low heat 30 minutes, stirring frequently to prevent burning. Mash smooth and stir in the milk. Taste for seasoning; it should have a slightly sweet flavor.

Serves 6—40 calories in each serving.

## HUNGARIAN STYLE SAUERKRAUT

2 pounds sauerkraut
1 tablespoon butter or margarine
1 potato, peeled and grated
2 onions, grated
2 cloves
1 bay leaf
¾ teaspoon salt
½ teaspoon freshly ground black pepper
½ cup yogurt

Wash and drain the sauerkraut. Melt the butter in a saucepan. Add the sauerkraut, potato, onions, cloves, bay leaf, salt and pepper. Cover and cook over low heat 1 hour, stirring frequently. Stir in the yogurt and cook 5 minutes longer. Taste for seasoning.

Serves 6—45 calories in each serving.

## TOMATOES AND OKRA

1 pound okra or 1 package frozen
1 tablespoon butter or margarine
1 onion, chopped
1 can (#2) tomatoes
1½ teaspoons salt
½ teaspoon pepper
¼ teaspoon basil

If fresh okra is used, wash and slice in 1 inch pieces, or let the frozen oka defrost sufficiently to be able to slice.

Melt the butter in a saucepan; sauté the onion 5 minutes. Add the okra and sauté 5 minutes. Stir in the tomatoes, salt, pepper and basil. Cook over low heat 15 minutes.

Serves 6—45 calories in each serving.

## SAUERKRAUT IN WHITE WINE

1½ pounds sauerkraut
2 cups dry white wine or leftover champagne
1 jar puréed apricots (baby food)

Wash the sauerkraut very well and drain thoroughly. Combine in a heavy saucepan with the wine and apricots. Cover and cook over low heat 2 hours, stirring frequently.

Serves 6—35 calories in each serving.

## SUCCOTASH

1 tablespoon butter or margarine
1 cup cooked fresh or frozen lima beans
1½ cups cooked fresh or canned corn kernels
¾ teaspoon salt
⅛ teaspoon pepper

Melt the butter in a saucepan; stir in the lima beans and corn. Cook over low heat 2 minutes, or until thoroughly heated. Season with the salt and pepper.

Serves 6—85 calories in each serving.

## DEVILED TOMATOES

6 medium tomatoes
1½ teaspoons salt
¼ teaspoon pepper
2 tablespoons dry bread crumbs
1 tablespoon butter
2 hard-cooked eggs
¾ teaspoon prepared mustard
2 teaspoons Worcestershire sauce
1 tablespoon wine vinegar
½ teaspoon sugar

Cut the tomatoes in half and place in a baking dish. Mix together the salt, pepper and bread crumbs. Spread on the cut tomatoes and dot with butter.

Bake in a 400° oven 10 minutes. While the tomatoes are baking, grate the eggs. Add the mustard, Worcestershire sauce, vinegar and sugar. At the end of 10 minutes baking time, spread a little of the mixture on the tomatoes. Bake 5 minutes longer.

Serves 6—75 calories in each serving.

## STUFFED TOMATOES, PARISIENNE

6 medium tomatoes
1 tablespoon butter or margarine
½ pound mushrooms, chopped
1 onion, chopped
1 teaspoon salt
⅛ teaspoon pepper
1 tablespoon chopped parsley
¼ cup chicken broth, fresh or canned

Buy even-sized tomatoes. Cut a 1-inch piece from the stem end of the tomatoes. Carefully scoop out the pulp (save it for other dishes).

Melt the butter in a skillet; sauté the mushrooms and onion 5 minutes. Add the salt, pepper and parsley. Stuff the tomatoes.

Pour the broth into a shallow baking dish. Arrange the tomatoes in it. Bake in a 375° oven 30 minutes, or until the tomatoes are browned and tender.

Serves 6—50 calories in each serving.

## BAKED STUFFED TOMATOES

- 6 tomatoes
- 1½ cups cottage cheese
- 1 teaspoon salt
- ⅛ teaspoon pepper
- 3 tablespoons grated onion

Cut a 1-inch piece from the stem end of the tomatoes. Carefully scoop out; chop the pulp coarsely and combine with the cottage cheese, salt, pepper and onion. Stuff tomatoes; place on a baking pan.

Bake in a 350° oven 20 minutes or until tender.

Serves 6—55 calories in each serving.

## ZUCCHINI PROVENÇALE

- 2 tablespoons olive oil
- 1 onion, chopped
- 1 clove garlic, minced
- 2 pounds small zucchini (green squash), sliced thin
- 1 green pepper, diced
- 2 tomatoes, diced
- 1½ teaspoons salt
- ½ teaspoon pepper
- ¼ teaspoon oregano

Heat the olive oil in a skillet or casserole; sauté the onion and garlic 5 minutes, stirring frequently. Add the zucchini and sauté 10 minutes, turning the slices when delicately browned on one side. Add the green pepper, tomatoes, salt, pepper and oregano. Cover and cook over low heat 20 minutes. Mix occasionally.

Serves 6—65 calories in each serving.

## MIXED-VEGETABLE CASSEROLE

- 1 tablespoon butter or margarine
- 3 tomatoes, diced
- 3 tablespoons minced onion
- 2 packages frozen mixed vegetables
- 1 teaspoon salt
- ¼ teaspoon pepper
- 2 tablespoons chopped parsley

Melt the butter in a casserole. Sauté the tomatoes and onion 3 minutes. Add the vegetables, salt and pepper. Cover and cook over low heat 15 minutes, stirring occasionally.

Sprinkle with the parsley and serve.

Serves 8—65 calories in each serving.

There is nothing more tempting than a crisp salad with its crunchy texture spiced with a piquant dressing. Low in calories, salad ingredients are colorful and eye-catching as well as being high in vitamins and minerals. Most important of all, they provide much-needed bulk for the diet. Beware of commercially prepared dressings, however, for you can waste hundreds of calories needlessly with packaged French dressing or mayonnaise. Make your own, using the recipes in the Sauces and Dressings section.

Buy firm, green salad greens. Wash very thoroughly, discarding any bruised leaves. Dry and store in the vegetable crisper or hydrator of your refrigerator, or wrap in Saran, aluminum foil or a moist kitchen towel.

Tear, don't cut, the greens when preparing a salad. Shake, and then pat the leaves until completely dry, as water dilutes the dressing. Add tomatoes just before serving (if you're using them) as their juice tends to thin the dressing, too.

Place any combination of vegetables in a large bowl (wooden, if possible). Chill until ready to serve, and then, *not before*, add the dressing. Toss with a large spoon and fork until well coated, and serve immediately.

## ANCHOVY SALAD

- 1 bunch scallions (green onions), sliced thin
- 3 green peppers, cut in julienne strips
- 3 tomatoes, diced
- 6 ripe black olives, sliced
- 12 anchovy fillets, drained
- 3 tablespoons wine vinegar
- ¼ teaspoon freshly ground black pepper

Combine the scallions, green peppers, tomatoes and olives in a bowl. Cut up the anchovies and add with the vinegar and pepper. Mix well and chill for 1 hour. Serve as a first course.

Serves 6—50 calories in each serving.

## CARROT SALAD

- 6 carrots
- 3 tablespoons raisins
- ¼ cup special mayonnaise (see recipe)

Grate the carrots on the medium grater. Mix well with the raisins and mayonnaise. Chill and form into mounds.

Serves 6—30 calories in each serving.

## CAESAR SALAD

- 3 heads romaine lettuce
- 2 slices white toast
- 2 cloves garlic, minced
- 2 tablespoons olive oil
- 1 teaspoon salt
- ½ teaspoon freshly ground black pepper
- ¼ teaspoon dry mustard
- 5 tablespoons lemon juice
- 1 egg, boiled 1 minute
- 4 anchovy fillets, shredded
- 3 tablespoons grated parmesan cheese

The crisper the lettuce the better the salad.

Wash the romaine very thoroughly and remove the large outside leaves. Dry and chill until needed.

Trim the toast and cut into small cubes. Combine half the garlic with half the oil; pour over the toast cubes and toss until well mixed.

Tear the lettuce in a salad bowl. Season with the salt, pepper, mustard and remaining garlic; toss lightly. Mix the lemon juice with the remaining oil; pour over the salad and toss.

Break the egg into the salad and toss until thoroughly mixed. Add the anchovies and cheese, tossing again. Sprinkle the bread cubes over the salad and serve immediately, as an appetizer.

Serves 6—80 calories in each serving.

## GREEN-BEAN SALAD

- 2 tablespoons olive oil
- 3 onions, chopped
- 2 pounds fresh or 2 packages frozen (defrosted) green beans
- 1 cup tomato juice
- 1 teaspoon salt
- ½ teaspoon freshly ground black pepper

Heat the oil in a saucepan; sauté the onions 10 minutes, stirring frequently. Add the beans, tomato juice, salt and pepper. Cover and cook over low heat 25 minutes. Taste for seasoning and chill.

Serves 6—90 calories in each serving.

## CELERY REMOULADE

- 3 celery roots (celairic)
- ¼ cup special French dressing (see recipe)
- ½ cup special mayonnaise (see recipe)
- 1 tablespoon prepared mustard
- 2 tablespoons finely chopped capers
- 1 tablespoon grated onion
- 1 tablespoon chopped parsley

Peel the roots and cut in julienne strips. Let marinate in the French dressing 4 hours, mixing occasionally.

Mix together the mayonnaise, mustard, capers, onion and parsley. Pour over the celery root, and mix well. Serve cold.

Serves 6—45 calories in each serving.

## CHEF'S SALAD

- 1 head lettuce
- 1 cup shredded cooked chicken
- 1 cup sliced cooked tongue
- ¼ cup sliced Swiss cheese
- 3 hard-cooked eggs, cut in half
- 1 bunch watercress
- ½ cup special French dressing (see recipe)

Shred the lettuce into a bowl, or onto 6 individual plates. The chicken, tongue and cheese should all be cut in julienne strips. Arrange over the lettuce and garnish with the eggs and watercress. Serve with the French dressing.

Serves 6—165 calories in each serving.

## CHIFFONNADE SALAD

- 1 head romaine lettuce
- 1 bunch chicory
- 1 head Boston or Simpson lettuce
- 3 stalks celery
- 1 bunch watercress
- 2 tomatoes, peeled and cut in thirds
- 4 canned beets, chopped
- 3 hard-cooked eggs, chopped
- ⅓ cup vinaigrette sauce (see recipe)

Wash and dry the romaine, chicory, Boston lettuce, celery and watercress (if large heads use only half). Shred finely and combine with the tomatoes, beets and eggs. Mix lightly, then add the vinaigrette sauce, tossing until well blended.

Serves 6—60 calories in each serving.

## COLESLAW WITH SOUR CREAM

- 1 head cabbage (about 3 pounds)
- 4 tablespoons yogurt
- ½ cup special mayonnaise (see recipe)
- 2 tablespoons sour cream
- 1 teaspoon liquid Sucaryl
- 1½ tablespoons cider vinegar
- 1 teaspoon salt
- ¼ teaspoon freshly ground black pepper

Wash the cabbage thoroughly and soak in ice water 1 hour. Drain thoroughly and shred finely into a bowl.

Mix together the yogurt, mayonnaise, sour cream, Sucaryl, vinegar, salt and pepper. Pour over the cabbage and toss until well blended. Chill for 1 hour before serving.

Serves 6—60 calories in each serving.

## RED COLESLAW

- 1 head red cabbage (about 2 pounds)
- 1 onion
- 1 green pepper
- 1 carrot
- 1½ teaspoons salt
- ¼ teaspoon pepper
- ⅛ teaspoon garlic powder
- ½ cup yogurt
- 3 tablespoons lemon juice
- 2 tablespoons chopped parsley

Soak the washed cabbage in ice water for 1 hour. Drain well; shred finely. Grate the onion, green pepper and carrot. Combine with the cabbage in a bowl. Add the salt, pepper and garlic powder, tossing lightly.

Mix together the yogurt, lemon juice and parsley. Pour over the vegetables, tossing well. Let stand 15 minutes before serving.

Serves 6—25 calories in each serving.

## CUCUMBER SALAD

- 4 cucumbers, peeled and sliced thin
- 3 tablespoons cider vinegar
- 2 tablespoons sour cream
- ¼ cup yogurt
- ½ teaspoon salt
- 1 tablespoon chopped dill

Soak the cucumbers in ice water for 30 minutes. Drain well. Mix together the vinegar, sour cream, yogurt and salt. Pour over the cucumbers and mix well. Sprinkle with the dill. Chill 30 minutes.

Serves 6—35 calories in each serving.

## ENDIVE SALAD

- 1 clove garlic, minced
- 3 tablespoons grated onion
- 2 tablespoons finely chopped capers
- 1 tablespoon chopped parsley
- ½ teaspoon sugar
- 2 tablespoons olive oil
- 2 tablespoons tarragon vinegar
- 1 teaspoon salt
- ½ teaspoon freshly ground black pepper
- 6 endive, washed and chilled

Combine the garlic, onion, capers, parsley, sugar, oil, vinegar, salt and pepper in a salad bowl. Mix well. Separate the endive into individual leaves and add. Toss lightly and chill 1 hour. Toss again before serving.

Serves 6—55 calories in each serving.

## SALAD À LA GRECQUE

2 tablespoons olive oil
2 tablespoons wine vinegar
1 teaspoon salt
½ teaspoon freshly ground black pepper
1 clove garlic
1 bay leaf
¼ teaspoon thyme
2 cups chicken broth, fresh or canned
2 small zucchini, sliced thin
12 small white onions
1 small eggplant, peeled and cut in julienne strips
½ cup green beans

Any combination of vegetables (except potatoes) may be prepared in this manner. Mushrooms, artichokes and cauliflower are particularly good in addition to the ones listed.

Combine everything in a saucepan and cook over low heat 10 minutes. Remove the vegetables, strain the liquid and cook over high heat until reduced to half its quantity. Pour over the vegetables and serve very cold.

Serves 6—60 calories in each serving.

## GREEK SALAD

2 fillets of salt herring
1 onion, sliced thin
1 green pepper, diced
1 cup shredded cabbage
2 tomatoes, cubed
6 radishes, sliced thin
¼ cup cider vinegar
¼ teaspoon freshly ground black pepper
¼ teaspoon liquid Sucaryl

Soak the herring in cold water 1 hour. Drain. Cut in 1 inch slices. Combine in a glass or wooden bowl the herring, onions, green pepper, cabbage, tomatoes and radishes.

Mix the vinegar, pepper and Sucaryl together and pour over the herring mixture. Toss lightly and chill 1 hour.

Serves 6—50 calories in each serving.

## ITALIAN GREEN SALAD

1 green pepper
1 red pepper
2 tomatoes
2 sprigs parsley
6 radishes
2 scallions (green onions)
½ teaspoon salt
½ teaspoon freshly ground black pepper
4 anchovies, shredded
2 tablespoons capers
3 tablespoons wine vinegar
2 tablespoons water
2 tablespoons olive oil

Chop together the green pepper, red pepper, tomatoes, parsley and radishes. Sprinkle with the salt and pepper, tossing lightly. Add the anchovies, capers, vinegar, water and olive oil. Mix well. Chill and serve on lettuce leaves, if desired.

Serves 6—55 calories in each serving.

## MIXED SALAD WITH COTTAGE CHEESE

2 cups shredded spinach
2 cups shredded cabbage
1 teaspoon salt
¼ teaspoon celery seed
3 tablespoons grated onion
1 cup cottage cheese
¼ cup special French dressing (see recipe)

Combine the spinach, cabbage, salt, celery seed and onion in a bowl. Mix thoroughly. Add the cheese and dressing; toss lightly.

Serves 6—55 calories in each serving.

## ORANGE AND ONION SALAD

3 oranges
1 large, sweet onion, thinly sliced
⅓ cup special French dressing (see recipe)

Peel the oranges and separate into sections. Arrange the orange sections and onion slices alternately on 6 individual plates. Pour 1 tablespoon dressing over each.

Serves 6—70 calories in each serving.

## RICE SALAD

1½ cups cooked rice
2 green peppers, thinly sliced
3 tomatoes, peeled and cubed
2 pimentos, diced
3 tablespoons chopped scallions (green onions)
2 tablespoons chopped parsley
1 clove garlic, minced
⅓ cup wine vinegar
2 tablespoons olive oil
1 teaspoon salt
¼ teaspoon freshly ground black pepper

Combine the rice, green peppers, tomatoes, pimentos, scallions, parsley and garlic in a bowl. Toss lightly with 2 forks.

Beat together the vinegar, oil, salt and pepper. Pour over the rice mixture. Toss again. Chill.

Serves 6—95 calories in each serving.

## ROAST-PEPPER SALAD

4 green peppers
2 cucumbers, peeled and sliced
2 onions (red, if available), sliced
3 tomatoes, sliced
3 tablespoons cider vinegar
2 tablespoons water
2 tablespoons olive oil
1 teaspoon salt
¼ teaspoon freshly ground black pepper

Wash and dry the peppers. Place each on a long fork and hold over a flame until skin browns and crinkles. Peel the peppers or cut in 1-inch strips. Cool 1 hour.

Combine the peppers, cucumbers, onions and tomatoes in a salad bowl. Mix the vinegar, water, oil, salt and pepper together. Pour over the vegetables. Mix lightly and chill 1 hour.

Serves 6—60 calories in each serving.

## GREEN-PEPPER SALAD

- 8 green peppers
- 3 tablespoons cider vinegar
- 3 tablespoons water
- 2 tablespoons olive oil
- ¾ teaspoon salt
- 2 teaspoons sugar
- 2 teaspoons prepared mustard

Cut the peppers in quarters; cover with water and cook over medium heat 20 minutes. Drain.

Beat together the vinegar, water, oil, salt, sugar and mustard. Pour over the peppers and let marinate in the refrigerator 3 hours.

Serves 6—50 calories in each serving.

## POTATO SALAD

- 6 small potatoes (about 1½ pounds)
- 1 teaspoon salt
- ¼ teaspoon freshly ground black pepper
- 3 tablespoons finely chopped onion
- 2 tablespoons white wine vinegar
- ½ cup special mayonnaise (see recipe)

Boil the potatoes in their skins until tender but firm. Drain and peel while hot. Slice them into a bowl and sprinkle with the salt, pepper and onion. Toss lightly. Add the vinegar and mayonnaise. Blend well. Serve at room temperature.

Serves 6—90 calories in each serving.

## HOT GERMAN POTATO SALAD

- 6 small potatoes (about 1½ pounds)
- 2 slices bacon, diced
- 3 tablespoons chopped onion
- ½ teaspoon salt
- ½ teaspoon freshly ground black pepper
- ¼ cup beef broth, fresh or canned
- ¼ cup cider vinegar

Boil the potatoes in their skins until tender but firm. Drain and peel while hot. Slice them into a bowl.

While the potatoes are cooking fry the bacon. Drain, but leave the bacon in the pan. Add the onion and cook 3 minutes, stirring frequently. Stir in the salt, pepper, broth and vinegar. Bring to a boil and pour over the potatoes. Toss lightly and serve hot.

Serves 6—80 calories in each serving.

## RUSSIAN SALAD

- 2 potatoes, pared
- 1 pound green beans
- 1 cup green peas
- 3 canned beets
- 1 cup sliced cooked tongue
- ¼ cup special French dressing (see recipe)
- ¼ cup special mayonnaise (see recipe)

Cook the potatoes, green beans and green peas separately until tender but firm. Dice the potatoes and cut the beans in ½-inch lengths. Dice the beets. Combine the vegetables, tongue and French dressing in a bowl.

Toss well and chill 1 hour. Drain and add the mayonnaise.

Serves 6—110 calories in each serving.

## SPINACH SALAD

1 pound spinach
¼ cup special French dressing (see recipe)
2 hard-cooked eggs, chopped

Buy young, fresh spinach. Wash thoroughly and dry it. Wrap in Saran wrap and chill for 1 hour.

Shred the spinach into a bowl; pour the dressing over it and toss until well blended. Sprinkle the eggs on top.

Serves 6—45 calories in each serving.

## SPRING SALAD

3 tablespoons wine vinegar
1 tablespoon salad oil
1 teaspoon salt
¼ teaspoon pepper
½ teaspoon dry mustard
1 cup cooked sliced asparagus tips
1 cup cooked green beans
1 cup cooked green peas
6 radishes, sliced
2 hard-cooked eggs, chopped
2 tablespoons chopped chives or scallions (green onions)
1 tablespoon chopped parsley
¼ cup special mayonnaise (see recipe)

In a bowl, mix the vinegar, oil, salt, pepper and mustard. Add the asparagus, green beans, green peas, radishes, eggs, chives and parsley. Toss lightly and let marinate for 20 minutes. Blend in the mayonnaise.

Serves 6—65 calories in each serving.

## TOMATO-VEGETABLE ASPIC

4 cups canned tomatoes
1 onion, sliced
2 stalks celery
½ teaspoon liquid Sucaryl
1 teaspoon salt
½ teaspoon pepper
¼ teaspoon marjoram
1 bay leaf
2 tablespoons gelatin
1 tablespoon lemon juice
2 cups cooked mixed vegetables

Combine the tomatoes, onion, celery, Sucaryl, salt, pepper, marjoram and bay leaf in a saucepan. Cook over low heat 20 minutes. Force through a sieve, then strain through cheesecloth.

Soften the gelatin in the water and stir into the hot tomato juice, mixing until dissolved. Add the lemon juice. Taste for seasoning. Cool until it begins to set.

Rinse a 1½ quart mold with cold water. Mix the vegetables into the aspic and pour into the mold. Chill until firm. Carefully unmold and serve on shredded lettuce.

Serves 6—45 calories in each serving.

## TROPICAL SALAD

- ¼ cup grated coconut, fresh or dried
- 3 cups finely shredded cabbage
- 1 cup diced fresh pineapple
- ½ cup special mayonnaise (see recipe)

If dried coconut is used, soak it in cold water for 15 minutes, then drain well.

Combine the coconut, cabbage, pineapple and mayonnaise in a bowl. Mix well and chill.

Serves 6—55 calories in each serving.

## WILTED LETTUCE SALAD

- 2 slices bacon, diced
- 4 tablespoons cider vinegar
- 2 tablespoons water
- 1 teaspoon grated onion
- 1 teaspoon salt
- 1 teaspoon sugar
- 2 heads lettuce

Fry the bacon crisp; drain well, but leave the bacon in the pan. Add the vinegar, water, onion, salt and sugar; bring to a boil.

Break the lettuce into fairly large pieces and pour the hot dressing over it. Toss well. Spinach may be served in the same manner.

Serves 6—20 calories in each serving.

## SAUERKRAUT SLAW

- 1½ pounds sauerkraut, barrel or canned
- 1 onion, grated
- 1 cup chicken broth, fresh or canned
- 1 bay leaf
- ½ cup special French dressing (see recipe)

Combine the sauerkraut, onion, broth and bay leaf in a saucepan. Cover and cook over low heat 1 hour, stirring occasionally. Drain and chill. Add the French dressing and toss until well blended. Serve very cold.

Serves 6—30 calories in each serving.

## HOME STYLE SALAD

- 2 hard-cooked egg yolks
- ¾ teaspoon salt
- ¼ teaspoon freshly ground black pepper
- 2 tablespoons wine vinegar
- 1 tablespoon salad oil
- 1 cup sliced cooked chicken
- 1 cup cooked green beans
- 1 cup cooked cauliflower flowerets
- 2 tomatoes, diced
- 1 tablespoon chopped chives or scallions (green onions)
- 1 tablespoon chopped parsley

Mash the egg yolks in a bowl; stir in the salt, pepper, vinegar and oil. Add the chicken, green beans, cauliflower and tomatoes. Toss well. Sprinkle with the chives and parsley.

Serves 6—75 calories in each serving.

## YORKSHIRE SALAD

2 heads lettuce, shredded
6 scallions (green onions) sliced
6 tablespoons vinegar
2 tablespoons water
2 tablespoons molasses
½ teaspoon liquid Sucaryl
½ teaspoon freshly ground black pepper

Combine the lettuce and scallions in a bowl. Beat together the vinegar, water, molasses, Sucaryl and pepper. Pour over the salad, tossing until well blended.

Serves 6—25 calories in each serving.

## CHICKEN-AND-CORN SALAD

3 cups diced boiled chicken
3 tomatoes, cubed
2 green peppers, finely diced
1 cup cooked or canned corn kernels
1 teaspoon salt
¼ teaspoon pepper
½ cup special mayonnaise (see recipe)
Lettuce leaves
2 hard-cooked eggs, cut in thirds

Combine the chicken, tomatoes, green peppers, corn, salt and pepper. Mix lightly. Add the mayonnaise and mix again.

Heap in mounds on the lettuce and garnish with a piece of egg on top.

Serves 6—160 calories in each serving.

## RELISH SALAD

1½ cups shredded green cabbage
1 cup shredded red cabbage
¼ cup sliced scallions (green onions)
1 cup grated raw beets
2 tablespoons lemon juice
1 tablespoon cider vinegar
⅓ cup prepared horseradish
1 teaspoon salt
¼ teaspoon freshly ground black pepper
¼ teaspoon garlic powder
½ teaspoon liquid Sucaryl
¼ cup special mayonnaise (see recipe)

Combine all the ingredients in a bowl. Mix lightly until well blended. Chill.

Serves 6—40 calories in each serving.

## WALDORF SALAD

2 cups diced celery
2 apples, peeled and diced
3 tablespoons chopped pecans
¾ cup sweet cooked salad dressing (see recipe)

Mix together all the ingredients. Serve on lettuce leaves.

Serves 6—80 calories in each serving.

## TOSSED TUNA SALAD

1 can (7¾ ounces) tuna fish
2 potatoes, cooked and cubed
2 tomatoes, cut in wedges
1 green pepper, cut in julienne strips
2 heads romaine lettuce, broken into pieces
1 bunch watercress
⅓ cup special French dressing (see recipe)

Drain the tuna fish and break it into chunks. Combine with the potatoes, tomatoes, green pepper, lettuce and watercress. Mix gently. Add the dressing and toss lightly. Serve as a luncheon salad.

Serves 6—120 calories in each serving.

Eggs, in common with champagne, may be served at any stage of a meal—as an appetizer, main dish, salad or in desserts. They are an excellent source of protein and should be served frequently.

Buy the freshest eggs possible, preferably in a shop where they are kept under refrigeration, as the quality deteriorates rapidly when stored in warm places. The color of the shell does not control the flavor or quality of the egg. Brown eggs are more expensive in some parts of the country and less expensive in others; by all means purchase the less expensive variety in your community.

In cooking, if a recipe calls for stiffly beaten whites, remove the eggs from the refrigerator one hour before they are to be used. Separate the yolks and whites immediately and let stand at room temperature for greater volume. Eggs curdle when combined with hot mixtures, so always add a little of the hot mixture to the eggs, beating steadily to avoid this. Cook eggs over very low heat to avoid toughening them.

## DOUBLE BOILER EGGS

3 eggs
¼ teaspoon salt
⅛ teaspoon pepper
2 teaspoons butter or margarine

Beat the eggs, salt and pepper until frothy. Melt the butter in the top of a double boiler. Pour the eggs into it. Cook over hot water and as the eggs begin to set, mix them lightly with a wooden spoon.

Serves 2—145 calories in each serving.

## SCRAMBLED EGGS WITH ONIONS

1 onion, chopped
¼ cup milk
3 eggs
¼ teaspoon salt
⅛ teaspoon pepper
2 teaspoons butter or margarine

Cook the onions and milk in a small skillet 5 minutes. Cool 10 minutes. Beat the eggs, salt and pepper together, then add the onion mixture.

Melt the butter in a skillet; pour the egg mixture into it. Cook over low heat mixing lightly with a wooden spoon until as firm as you like. Transfer to a heated plate and serve.

Serves 2—165 calories in each serving.

## EGGS IN NESTS

2 eggs
1 teaspoon melted butter or margarine
⅛ teaspoon salt
Dash pepper

Turn oven on and set at 350°.

Separate the eggs carefully. Beat the whites until stiff but not dry. Grease a baking dish and pile the egg whites into it. Make 2 depressions and transfer the egg yolks into them. Sprinkle with the salt and pepper.

Bake 10 minutes or until set.

Serves 1 or 2—90 calories in each egg.

## POACHED EGG

You may use a small skillet or a special egg poacher. If the egg poacher is used follow the directions of the manufacturer. Fill the skillet ⅔ full of water. Add ½ teaspoon of salt and bring to a boil, then reduce the heat. Break the egg into a saucer or cup and carefully slide it into the water. Cover and cook until set. Remove carefully with a skimmer or slotted spoon. Serve on a thin piece of toast.

1 poached egg—75 calories.

## POACHED EGGS CREOLE

- 1 tablespoon butter or margarine
- ¼ cup chopped onion
- ½ cup green pepper, cut julienne fashion
- ⅛ pound mushrooms, sliced
- 6 green olives, sliced
- 1 cup chicken broth, fresh or canned
- 1 cup canned tomatoes
- 1 teaspoon salt
- ½ teaspoon freshly ground black pepper
- 1 clove
- ⅛ teaspoon marjoram
- 6 eggs

Melt the butter in a casserole or large skillet; sauté the onion 5 minutes. Add the green pepper and sauté 2 minutes, stirring frequently. Stir in the mushrooms and olives; cook over low heat 5 minutes. Add the broth, tomatoes, salt, pepper, clove and marjoram. Cover and cook 20 minutes. Taste for seasoning.

Drop in one egg at a time and poach until the whites are set. Serve directly from the casserole. If you like, the sauce may be divided among individual casseroles or skillets before adding the eggs.

Serves 6—110 calories in each serving.

## FRIED EGGS

- 2 eggs
- 2 teaspoons butter or margarine
- 1 tablespoon water

Break the eggs into a saucer or cup very carefully.

In a small skillet, heat the butter and water over low heat until bubbles form. Carefully slide the eggs into it. Cover and cook the way you like them. With this method, if you normally like eggs turned over, it is not necessary to do it—just cook longer. Remove eggs to a heated plate and serve.

Serves 1 or 2—100 calories in each egg.

## EGGS, ARAB STYLE

- 1 tablespoon butter
- 2 onions, sliced thin
- 3 tomatoes, peeled and diced
- 2 green peppers, diced
- 1 teaspoon salt
- ⅛ teaspoon freshly ground black pepper
- ½ cup water
- 6 eggs

Melt the butter in a skillet (use one you can serve from if you have it). Sauté the onion until lightly browned. Add the tomatoes and green peppers; cook 5 minutes. Stir in the salt, pepper and water. Cook 10 minutes.

Carefully break the eggs over the vegetable mixture. Bake in a 350° oven 10 minutes, or until the eggs are set.

Serves 6—110 calories in each serving.

## EGGS BENEDICT

- 3 English muffins
- 6 thin slices ham
- 6 poached eggs
- ¾ cup special hollandaise sauce (see recipe)
- Paprika

Cut the muffins in half and toast them. Brown the ham in a skillet, drain and arrange on the muffins. Carefully place a poached egg on each and cover with the hollandaise sauce. Sprinkle with the paprika and serve at once.

Serves 6—235 calories in each serving.

## CURRIED EGGS

- 2 teaspoons butter or margarine
- 1 onion, chopped
- 1 tablespoon cornstarch
- 1 tablespoon curry powder
- ¼ cup milk
- 1½ cups chicken broth, fresh or canned
- 6 hard-cooked eggs, sliced
- 6 thin slices white toast

Melt the butter in a saucepan; sauté the onion 5 minutes. Mix the cornstarch, curry powder and milk to a smooth paste; add to the onions with the broth. Stir constantly to the boiling point. Cook over low heat 5 minutes. Add the eggs and cook 2 minutes. Serve on the toast.

Serves 6—160 calories in each serving.

## EGGS BOULANGÈRE

- 1 tablespoon butter or margarine
- 2 potatoes, pared and sliced thin
- 3 tablespoons grated Parmesan cheese
- 6 eggs
- 1 teaspoon salt
- ¼ teaspoon freshly ground black pepper
- ¼ cup milk

Melt the butter in a large skillet; brown the potatoes in it, stirring frequently. Transfer to a baking dish and spread evenly. Carefully break the eggs over the potatoes; sprinkle with the salt, pepper and milk. Bake in a 350° oven 10 minutes, or until the eggs are set. Serve directly from the dish. This makes an excellent luncheon or supper dish.

Serves 6—150 calories in each serving.

## SHIRRED EGGS

- 1 teaspoon butter
- 1 egg
- ⅛ teaspoon salt

Melt the butter in an individual ramekin or baking dish. Break the egg into it and sprinkle with the salt. Bake in a 350° oven 10 minutes, or until the egg is set. Serve in the dish.

Serves 1—110 calories.

## OMELET

3 eggs
1 tablespoon water
½ teaspoon salt
1 tablespoon butter or margarine

Devotees of the omelet set aside one pan for its use and never wash it. The pan is wiped with a dry cloth each time after use, and is not used for any other purpose. However, you may use any heavy 8-inch skillet.

Beat the eggs, water and salt until just blended; do not overbeat. Heat the butter in the skillet over low heat until it sizzles. Pour in the eggs and tilt the pan to spread them evenly. As the eggs begin to set, push them back from the sides of the pan with a fork, to permit the uncooked portion to run underneath. Quickly fold the omelet over and roll out of the skillet onto a heated plate. Do not overcook; eggs toughen with too much heat.

Serves 2—160 calories in each serving.

## CHEESE OMELET

Sprinkle 4 tablespoons grated American or Swiss cheese on the omelet before folding it.

Serves 2—210 calories in each serving.

## HERB OMELET

Sprinkle the omelet with any combination of minced parsley, chopped chives, fresh or diced chervil, fresh or dried tarragon, before folding it.

Serves 2—165 calories in each serving.

## HAM OMELET

Sprinkle the omelet with 2 tablespoons chopped ham before folding it.

Serves 2—200 calories in each serving.

## PUFFY OMELET

- 4 egg yolks
- ¼ cup milk
- ½ teaspoon salt
- 4 egg whites
- 1 tablespoon butter or margarine

Turn oven on and set at 350°.

Beat the egg yolks, milk and salt with a fork until frothy. Beat the egg whites until stiff but not dry and fold into the egg yolk mixture. Melt the butter in a 9-inch skillet; turn the mixture into it.

Bake 15 minutes or until set and delicately browned. Carefully fold it over and turn out onto a heated plate.

Serves 4—110 calories in each serving.

## CHINESE OMELET

- 3 teaspoons salad or peanut oil
- 1 onion, chopped
- 6 eggs
- ½ cup finely chopped green pepper
- ½ cup finely chopped mushrooms
- ½ cup finely chopped celery
- ¾ teaspoon salt
- ⅛ teaspoon pepper

Heat 2 teaspoons oil in a large skillet; sauté the onion 5 minutes. Beat the eggs lightly and stir in the green pepper, mushrooms, celery, salt and pepper. Add the remaining oil to the skillet and pour the egg mixture into it. Cook over low heat until firm and browned, stirring the center as it sets. Cut into pie-shaped wedges and serve at once.

Serves 6—105 calories in each serving.

## APPLE OMELET

- 1 apple, peeled and sliced
- ½ teaspoon liquid Sucaryl
- 2 tablespoons cold water
- 4 egg yolks
- ¼ cup hot water
- ½ teaspoon salt
- 4 egg whites, stiffly beaten
- 2 teaspoons butter or margarine

Combine the apple, Sucaryl and water in a saucepan. Cook over low heat about 5 minutes, or until the apples are tender but still firm.

Beat the egg yolks, water and salt together. Fold in the egg whites. Heat the butter in a skillet until it sizzles. Tilt pan to coat sides with butter. Pour the omelet into it and rotate pan to spread mixture evenly. Cook over low heat until lightly browned. Spread apples on it and fold in half. Turn out carefully onto a heated platter.

Serves 6—80 calories in each serving.

The symbol ❄ indicates dishes that can be frozen.

The perfume of baking bread is unique, and the finished product is particularly rewarding. Your first venture into bread making may seem somewhat troublesome, but you'll soon become proficient and adept. A woman kneading bread is a truly beautiful and feminine sight, a sage once remarked, but it has become something of a lost art. Nevertheless it is an art which deserves to be revived. Try one of the delicious breads in the section which follows; your family will be delighted. Fats and sugars have been controlled in these recipes to produce breads with the lowest possible calorie count.

Pancakes are one of mankind's earliest food preparations, dating back some two thousand or more years. Twenty centuries have not diminished their popularity. They are versatile, being suitable for breakfast, lunch or supper, or even as an hors d'oeuvre. Pancakes, in and of themselves, are not unwarrantedly high in calories; it is in their preparation and service that added calories make them prohibitive to the weight-conscious.

## KNEADING YEAST DOUGH

Use lightly floured hands, and press the dough firmly into a ball. Then fold the dough in half toward you. Now, with the heel of the hand, push the dough down and away from you. Turn the dough slightly and repeat until smooth and glossy.

## SHAPING LOAVES OF BREAD

Cut the dough in half with a sharp knife if you have enough for two loaves. Flatten dough and fold lengthwise. Flatten again, then stretch to lengthen it. Fold into three and press firmly together sealing the edges. Form into a roll and place in a pan, sealed edge down.

## WHITE BREAD ❋

½ cup skim milk
1 tablespoon sugar
⅛ teaspoon liquid Sucaryl
1¼ teaspoons salt
2 tablespoons butter or margarine
1 cake or package yeast
½ cup lukewarm water
3 cups sifted flour

Scald the milk with the sugar, Sucaryl, salt and butter. Let cool.

Soften the yeast in the water; stir until dissolved. Stir in the milk mixture and 1½ cups flour. Beat with a wooden spoon until smooth, then beat in remaining flour. Knead on a lightly floured surface until smooth and elastic. Place in a bowl and cover with a cloth. Let rise in a warm place until double in bulk. Punch down and shape into a loaf to fit a lightly greased 9-inch loaf pan. Cover and let rise until almost double in size.

Bake in a 400° oven 45 minutes or until browned. Cool on a cake rack.

Makes 27 slices ⅓ inch thick—60 calories in each slice.

## EGG BREAD ❋

1 cake or package yeast
1 cup lukewarm water
4 cups sifted flour
1 teaspoon salt
2 teaspoons sugar
2 eggs, beaten

Soak the yeast in the water for 5 minutes; stir until dissolved. Sift the flour, salt and sugar together, mixing until smooth. Cover with a cloth and let rise in a warm place until double in bulk, about 45 minutes. Beat in the eggs, and then the remaining flour mixture.

Knead on a lightly floured surface until smooth and elastic. Place in a bowl, cover with a cloth and let rise again until double in bulk, about 2 hours. Punch down and knead for 3 minutes. You may make two 9-inch loaves, 1 loaf and 1 twist, or 2 twists. Shape into loaves and place in lightly greased loaf pans. For twists divide the dough in two, then divide each piece into three equal parts. Roll each piece between the hands into long round strips. Fasten 3 strips together at one end and braid them. Place on a greased baking sheet. Cover and let rise for 1 hour. Brush the tops with beaten egg yolks.

Bake in a 400° oven 10 minutes. Reduce the heat to 375° and bake 35 minutes longer, or until browned on top. Remove from pans immediately and cool on a cake rack.

Makes about 40 slices, ½ inch thick—45 calories in each slice.

## BRIOCHE ✻

- 1 cake or package yeast
- ¼ cup lukewarm water
- ¼ cup skim milk, scalded and cooled
- ½ teaspoon liquid Sucaryl
- 2 tablespoons sugar
- ¼ teaspoon salt
- 2⅓ cups sifted flour
- ⅓ cup soft butter
- 2 egg yolks
- 1 egg

Soften the yeast in the water and stir until dissolved. Add the milk, Sucaryl and salt. Beat in 1 cup flour, then the butter. Beat until smooth (a wooden spoon is best for this). Add 1 egg yolk at a time, then the egg, beating after each addition. Add the remaining flour, again beating well. Cover with a cloth and let rise in a warm place until double in bulk. Remove cloth and cover bowl with waxed paper and then with the cloth wrung out in cold water. Chill overnight or for 12 hours.

Remove dough from refrigerator and on a lightly floured surface shape into 1½-inch balls. Make the same number of marble-sized balls and press into the top of each of the two-inch balls. Place in small brioche pans or muffin cups. Cover and let rise until double in size. Brush tops with milk. Bake in a 375° oven 15 minutes or until browned.

Makes about 20—55 calories in each.

## REFRIGERATOR ROLLS ❋

- 1 cup skim milk
- 6 tablespoons butter or margarine
- 1 tablespoon sugar
- ¾ teaspoon liquid Sucaryl
- 1½ teaspoons salt
- 1 cake or package yeast
- ½ cup lukewarm water
- 1 egg
- 3½ cups sifted flour

Scald the milk and stir in the butter, sugar, Sucaryl and salt. Let cool. Soften the yeast in the water; stir until dissolved. Add the egg and beat until well blended. Combine with the milk mixture and beat in half the flour. Beat well and add the remaining flour. Beat until dough blisters. Place in a bowl; cover and chill for 24 hours.

Break off the amount you want to bake, and place in greased muffin tins, filling them ⅓ full. Let rise until double in bulk.

Bake in a 425° oven 20 minutes or until browned. Remove from pans at once.

Makes about 24—90 calories in each.

The dough may be kept in the refrigerator for 1 week.

## WHOLE-WHEAT ROLLS OR BREAD ❋

- 1 cake or package yeast
- 1 teaspoon sugar
- ½ teaspoon liquid Sucaryl
- 1¼ teaspoons salt
- ½ cup lukewarm water
- 1 cup skim milk
- 1 tablespoon butter or margarine
- 2 cups sifted whole-wheat flour
- 1 cup sifted flour

Combine the yeast, sugar, Sucaryl, salt and water. Stir until yeast dissolves.

Scald the milk; add the butter and let cool. Add the yeast mixture and the flour. Beat until smooth. Knead on a lightly floured surface until smooth and elastic. Place in a greased bowl, then turn dough over. Cover and let rise in a warm place until double in bulk. Punch down.

If you don't want to bake all the dough at once, chill part of it, as it will keep 1 week.

**For Rolls**

Break off small pieces of dough, roll into balls and place 2 balls in each greased muffin cup. Cover and let rise until double in bulk.

Bake in a 400° oven 20 minutes or until browned.

Makes about 24 rolls—60 calories in each roll.

**For Bread**

Divide the dough in two, and shape each piece into loaves to fit a greased 9-inch loaf pan. Cover and let rise until double in bulk.

Bake in a 375° oven 45 minutes or until browned. Remove from pans at once and let cool on a cake rack.

Each loaf makes 27 slices ⅓-inch thick—30 calories in each slice.

## WALNUT BREAD ❊

- 2 cups sifted flour
- 1 tablespoon baking powder
- ¼ teaspoon salt
- 2 tablespoons sugar
- ½ cup coarsely chopped walnuts
- 2 eggs
- ¾ teaspoon liquid Sucaryl
- 1 cup skim milk

Turn oven on and set at 350°. Lightly grease a 9-inch loaf pan.

Sift the flour, baking powder, salt and sugar into a bowl. Stir in the nuts.

Beat the eggs until thick; stir in the milk. Add to the flour mixture, stirring just enough to blend. Turn into the pan.

Bake 40 minutes or until browned and a cake tester comes out clean. Cool on a cake rack, then carefully turn out. Cool thoroughly before slicing ¼-inch thick.

Makes 36 slices—40 calories in each slice.

## ORANGE BREAD ❊

- 1½ cups sifted flour
- 2½ teaspoons baking powder
- ½ teaspoon salt
- 2 tablespoons grated orange rind
- 2 tablespoons butter or margarine
- 2 tablespoons sugar
- 1 egg
- ¾ teaspoon liquid Sucaryl
- ¼ cup milk
- ½ cup orange juice

Turn oven on and set at 350°. Lightly grease a 9-inch loaf pan.

Sift together the flour, baking powder and salt; stir in the orange rind.

Cream the butter and sugar together. Beat in the egg and Sucaryl. Mix the milk and orange juice and add to the butter mixture alternately with the flour. Turn into the pan.

Bake 50 minutes or until browned and a cake tester comes out clean. Cool on a cake rack. Cut in ½-inch slices.

Makes 18 slices—55 calories in each slice.

## CORN BREAD

¾ cup yellow corn meal
1¼ cups sifted flour
1 tablespoon sugar
1½ tablespoons baking powder
1 teaspoon salt
1 egg
⅔ cup skim milk
¾ teaspoon liquid Sucaryl
2 tablespoons melted butter or margarine

Turn oven on and set at 425°. Lightly grease an 8-inch-square baking pan.

Sift the corn meal, flour, sugar, baking powder and salt into a bowl. Beat the egg and stir in the milk, Sucaryl and butter. Add to the corn-meal mixture. Stir with a fork only until dry mixture becomes moistened; don't worry about lumps. Turn into the pan.

Bake 30 minutes, or until browned and firm. Serve hot, cut into squares.

Serves 12—80 calories in each serving.

### Corn Sticks

Grease corn-stick pans and fill three-quarters full. Bake 20 minutes.

Makes 14—75 calories in each stick.

### Corn Muffins

Grease 12 muffin tins and fill two-thirds full. Bake 25 minutes.

—80 calories in each muffin.

## BAKING POWDER BISCUITS

- 1 cup sifted flour
- 2 teaspoons baking powder
- ½ teaspoon salt
- 3 tablespoons butter or margarine
- ⅓ cup skim milk

Turn oven on and set at 425°.

Sift the flour, baking powder and salt into a bowl. Cut in the shortening with a pastry blender or fingers until the size of peas. Add the milk all at once and stir only until a dough is formed. Roll out on a lightly floured board, fold in three, roll out again and fold in three. Roll out ½-inch thick and cut with a 1½-inch floured biscuit cutter. Transfer to an ungreased baking sheet with a spatula. Place close together for soft sides or ½ inch apart for crisp sides.

Bake 12 minutes or until browned.

Makes about 15—55 calories in each biscuit.

*Note:* The biscuit dough may be prepared early in the day. Wrap in aluminum foil and chill until ready to bake. Then roll out and bake.

### Chive Biscuits

Add 2 tablespoons freshly chopped chives before adding the milk.

Makes about 15—55 calories in each biscuit.

### Cheese Biscuits

Add 3 tablespoons grated cheddar cheese and a dash of cayenne pepper before adding skim milk.

Makes about 18—55 calories in each biscuit.

### Cinnamon Rolls

Roll biscuit dough ¼-inch thick. Sprinkle with 4 tablespoons sugar mixed with 1 teaspoon cinnamon. Roll up like a jelly roll and cut in ½-inch slices.

Makes about 24 rolls—45 calories in each roll.

### Drop Biscuits

Increase skim milk to ⅔ cup. Drop by the teaspoon onto the baking sheet.

Makes about 20—45 calories in each.

## MUFFINS

- 1 cup sifted flour
- 2 teaspoons baking powder
- 2 teaspoons sugar
- ½ teaspoon salt
- 1 egg
- ½ cup skim milk
- 2 tablespoons melted butter or margarine
- ¼ teaspoon liquid Sucaryl

Turn oven on and set at 425° Lightly grease 8 muffin cups.

Sift the flour, baking powder, sugar and salt into a bowl. Beat the egg until foamy; blend in the milk, butter and Sucaryl. Add the flour mixture all at once, stirring just until the dry ingredients are dampened. Don't worry about lumps. Fill each muffin cup a little over half-full.

Bake 20 minutes, or until browned and a cake tester comes out clean. Run a spatula around each muffin and turn out. Serve hot.

Makes 8—95 calories in each muffin.

### Blueberry Muffins

Sprinkle ½ teaspoon liquid Sucaryl on ½ cup blueberries. Add to the batter and bake as directed.

Makes 8—100 calories in each muffin.

### Orange Muffins

Substitute ¼ cup orange juice for ¼ cup skim milk. Add 2 tablespoons grated orange rind and ¾ teaspoon liquid Sucaryl and bake as directed.

Makes 8—95 calories in each muffin.

## BRAN MUFFINS

- ½ cup sifted flour
- ¼ teaspoon salt
- 1½ teaspoons baking powder
- ½ cup bran
- ½ cup skim milk
- 1 tablespoon soft shortening
- 1 tablespoon sugar
- ¼ teaspoon liquid Sucaryl
- 1 egg, beaten

Turn oven on and set at 400°. Lightly grease 6 muffin cups.

Sift together the flour, salt and baking powder. Soak the bran in the milk. Cream the shortening and sugar until light. Add the Sucaryl and egg, mixing well. Stir into the bran mixture. Add the flour mixture, stirring only until blended. Fill muffin cups ⅔ full. Bake 25 minutes or until browned.

Makes 6—85 calories in each muffin.

## POPOVERS

- 1 cup sifted flour
- ¾ teaspoon salt
- 2 eggs
- 1 cup skim milk

Turn oven on and set at 375° Lightly grease 12 muffin tins or medium custard cups.

Sift the flour and salt into a bowl. Beat the eggs with an egg beater, then blend in the milk. Add to the flour mixture, beating until smooth. Fill cups ⅓ full.

Bake 50 minutes. Cut a slit on the side of each popover and return to the oven for 5 minutes. Serve hot.

Makes 12—45 calories in each.

### Yorkshire Pudding

Grease an 11x7-inch pan with 1 tablespoon roast beef drippings or 1 tablespoon melted butter or margarine. Pour the popover mixture into it and bake 30 minutes, or until puffed and browned. Cut into squares. Serve hot.

Serves 12—55 calories in each serving.

*Note:* Batter may be prepared ahead of time for either the popovers or Yorkshire pudding. Chill until ready to bake, then for popovers beat with rotary beater for a few seconds.

## PANCAKES

In preparing pancakes, use the so-called "greaseless" griddles having a smooth polished surface, and greasing will no longer be necessary. (If you don't have one of these griddles, rub unsalted fat over the skillet lightly, using just enough to glaze it and keep the pancakes from sticking. Pour off any excess.) Heat the griddle or skillet until a drop of cold water dances when dropped on it. Pour on the batter, and bake over low heat. Turn only once. Serve the pancakes with one of the syrups in the Dessert section for a filling and delicious dish—just the sweet delicacy a dieter craves.

### PANCAKES ❋

- 1¼ cups sifted flour
- 2½ teaspoons baking powder
- 1 teaspoon sugar
- ¾ teaspoon salt
- 1 egg
- ½ teaspoon liquid Sucaryl
- 1¼ cups skim milk
- 2 tablespoons melted butter or margarine

Sift the flour, baking powder, sugar and salt into a bowl.

Beat the egg and Sucaryl in a bowl. Add the milk and butter. Slowly add to the flour mixture, stirring only until dry ingredients are moistened.

Drop the batter by the tablespoon onto a hot griddle and bake over low heat until the top is covered with broken bubbles. Turn with a pancake turner or spatula and brown other side. Don't turn more than once.

Makes about 24 2½-inch cakes—40 calories in each cake.

#### Blueberry Pancakes

Add ½ cup blueberries sprinkled with 1 teaspoon liquid Sucaryl to the batter.

Makes about 24—45 calories in each pancake.

#### Apple Pancakes

Pare and chop finely 2 apples. Sprinkle with ½ teaspoon cinnamon and 1 teaspoon liquid Sucaryl and add to the batter.

Makes 24—50 calories in each cake.

*Note:* It is not necessary to grease a properly seasoned griddle or skillet. If you find pancakes are sticking, rub griddle with a little unsalted shortening.

## BUTTERMILK PANCAKES ❄

1½ cups sifted flour
1½ teaspoons baking powder
1 teaspoon baking soda
½ teaspoon salt
1 tablespoon sugar
3 egg yolks
1⅔ cups buttermilk or sour milk
2 tablespoons melted butter or margarine
3 egg whites, stiffly beaten

Sift together the flour, baking powder, soda, salt and sugar. Beat the egg yolks; add the buttermilk and butter. Mix well. Stir in the flour mixture only until moistened. Fold in the egg whites.

Drop by the tablespoon onto a hot, lightly greased griddle or skillet. Bake until puffed and top is covered with bubbles. Turn to brown other side. Do not turn more than once.

Makes 24—50 calories in each cake.

## SWEDISH PANCAKES

1 egg yolk
1½ cups skim milk
¼ teaspoon salt
1 tablespoon sugar
½ cup sifted flour
1 egg white
2 tablespoons butter or margarine

Beat the egg yolk, milk, salt and sugar. Add the flour, beating until smooth. Chill 2 hours. Beat the egg white until stiff but not dry and fold it into the batter thoroughly. Melt 2 teaspoons butter in a skillet, griddle or Swedish pancake pan. Drop the batter by the tablespoon and bake until lightly browned on both sides. Add butter as necessary.

Makes about 24—25 calories in each pancake.

## BLINTZES (THIN PANCAKES) ❄

2 eggs
1 cup skim milk
¾ cup sifted flour
½ teaspoon salt
1 tablespoon butter or margarine

Beat the eggs and milk together. Sift the flour and salt into a bowl; gradually add the egg mixture, beating until smooth.

Melt a little of the butter in a 6-inch skillet. Pour about 1 tablespoon of the batter into it, turning the pan quickly to coat the bottom. Pour off any extra batter. Fry until the underside is browned, then turn out onto a plate or napkin. Stack the pancakes browned side up while preparing the remaining ones.

### Cheese Filling (for Blintzes)

1½ cups cottage cheese, drained
1 egg yolk
½ teaspoon salt
2 teaspoons sugar (optional)
½ teaspoon vanilla extract (optional)
1 tablespoon butter or margarine

Beat the cheese, egg yolk, salt, sugar and vanilla together. Place a heaping tablespoon of the mixture on each pancake. Turn two opposite sides in and roll up carefully. Melt the butter in a shallow baking pan. Arrange the blintzes in it.

Bake in a 400° oven 15 minutes, turning them once. Serve hot or cold.

Makes 18—60 calories in each blintz.

*Note:* The blintzes may be prepared early in the day and chilled. Bake just before serving.

## PASTAS

These starch foods are filling and satisfying. However, egg noodles contain half the number of calories macaroni or spaghetti have, so use them whenever possible.

Boil noodles or spaghetti in large quantities of boiling salted water. A safe proportion to follow is ½ pound noodles or spaghetti to 2 quarts of water and 2 teaspoons salt. Follow the time the manufacturer suggests, but deduct two or three minutes for pastas that require further cooking or baking. If you like them the way the Italians do, *al dente*—that is, still chewy—test a few minutes before the specified time is up.

### PARSLEY EGG DROPS

1 egg
3 tablespoons water
3 tablespoons flour
¼ teaspoon salt
1 tablespoon chopped parsley

Beat the egg and water together. Blend in the flour and salt, then the parsley. Drop by the half-teaspoon into boiling beef or chicken soup. Cover and cook over medium heat 10 minutes.

Serves 6—25 calories in each serving.

### CHEESE DROPS

1 egg white
2 tablespoons sifted flour
¼ teaspoon salt
Dash pepper
Dash nutmeg
1 tablespoon grated Parmesan cheese
2 teaspoons chopped chives and green onions

Beat the egg white until stiff. Sift the flour, salt, pepper and nutmeg over it and fold in, then fold in the cheese and chives.

Drop by the teaspoon into boiling soup, stew or water. Cover and cook over low heat 3 minutes.

Serves 6—20 calories in each serving.

## NOCKEDLI (EGG DUMPLINGS)

- 1½ cups sifted flour
- ½ teaspoon salt
- ½ teaspoon baking powder
- 1 egg
- ⅓ cup water
- 2 teaspoons melted butter or margarine

Sift the flour, salt and baking powder together. Beat the egg and water in a bowl. Add the butter and then the flour, beating until smooth.

Drop by the teaspoon into boiling salted water, but don't crowd the pan. Drain when they come to the surface. Keep warm while preparing the balance of the batter. Serve in place of potatoes.

Serves 6—120 calories in each serving.

## PANCAKE NOODLES

- 2 eggs
- 2 tablespoons water
- ½ teaspoon salt
- 2 tablespoons cracker meal
- 2 tablespoons potato starch
- 1 tablespoon shortening

Beat the eggs, water and salt together. Stir in the cracker meal and potato starch.

Melt a little of the shortening in a 7-inch skillet. Pour just enough of the batter into it to coat the bottom. Brown on both sides. Roll up and keep warm while preparing the other pancakes. Add shortening to the pan as necessary. Cut into ⅛-inch strips and serve in soup.

Serves 8—40 calories in each serving.

## HOMEMADE GREEN NOODLES

- 2 cups sifted flour
- ½ teaspoon salt
- 1 egg
- ¼ cup puréed cooked spinach
- 2 drops green food coloring (optional)

Sift the flour and salt onto a board. Make a well in the center and place the egg, spinach and coloring in it. Work in the flour until a dough is formed. Knead until smooth and elastic. Let it rest for 20 minutes, then roll out as thin as possible. Let the dough dry for 20 minutes. Roll up and cut in strips as you like, narrow, medium or wide. Toss the noodles and let them dry. They may be stored in a covered jar.

Cook in boiling salted water 5 minutes, or until tender.

Serves 8—105 calories in each serving.

## HOMEMADE NOODLES

- ¾ cup sifted flour
- ½ teaspoon salt
- 1 egg
- 2 tablespoons lukewarm water

Sift the flour and salt onto a board. Make a well in the center and drop the egg and water in it. Work in the flour until a stiff dough is formed. Add more flour or water if necessary, but the dough should be stiff. Knead until smooth and elastic. Let the dough rest for 15 minutes, then roll it out as thin as possible. Let the rolled dough dry for a few minutes, then fold it over and cut any way you like—fine, medium or broad. Toss the noodles lightly and spread to let them dry. They keep well in a closed jar, after they are dried.

Boil in salted water for 5 minutes.

Serves 6—55 calories in each serving.

## NOODLES ROMANA

- ¾ pound green or egg noodles
- 1 clove garlic, minced
- 1 teaspoon basil
- 3 tablespoons chopped parsley
- 3 tablespoons butter
- ¼ teaspoon freshly ground black pepper
- 3 tablespoons grated Parmesan cheese

Cook the noodles in boiling salted water 2 minutes less than directions on package specify. Drain well.

Combine the noodles in a casserole with the garlic, basil, parsley, butter and pepper. Toss over low heat until the butter melts. Sprinkle with the cheese and serve.

Serves 6—150 calories in each serving.

## NOODLE PUDDING

- ¾ pound medium noodles
- 2 egg yolks
- 1 teaspoon salt
- 2 cups cottage cheese
- ¾ teaspoon liquid Sucaryl (optional)
- 2 egg whites, stiffly beaten

Turn oven on and set at 375°.

Cook the noodles in boiling salted water 2 minutes less than package directs. Drain and rinse with cold water.

Beat the egg yolks and salt; add the cheese and Sucaryl. Stir in the noodles and fold in the egg whites. Turn into a lightly greased 1½-quart casserole. Bake 35 minutes or until browned.

Delicious as a luncheon dish, or with a light fish dinner. You may use the Sucaryl if you like a sweet pudding, omit it if you don't.

Serves 6—150 calories in each serving.

## GNOCCHI

- 4 potatoes (1½ pounds)
- 1 teaspoon salt
- 1 egg yolk, beaten
- ½ cup sifted flour
- 2 tablespoons melted butter
- 3 tablespoons grated Parmesan cheese

Boil and mash the potatoes. Add the salt and egg yolk. Mix well. Add the flour a little at a time, adding just enough to form a dough. Knead until very smooth. Form into sausage-shaped pieces about ¾-inch diameter by 1½ inches long.

Drop a few gnocchi at a time into boiling salted water and cook until they come to the surface. Drain and keep warm while preparing the balance. Pour the melted butter over them and sprinkle with the cheese. Toss lightly and serve.

Serves 6—125 calories in each serving.

*Note:* Gnocchi are delicious served with tomato sauce. Omit the melted butter and cheese.

## BAKED MACARONI AND MEAT

- ½ pound macaroni
- 1 tablespoon butter
- 2 onions, finely chopped
- ¾ pound ground lean beef
- 1 tomato, peeled and chopped
- 2 teaspoons salt
- ½ teaspoon freshly ground black pepper
- ¼ cup grated cheddar cheese
- 1 tablespoon cornstarch
- 1 cup skim milk
- 1 egg
- 2 tablespoons grated Parmesan cheese

Cook the macaroni in boiling salted water 2 minutes less than package specifies. Drain.

Melt the butter in a skillet; sauté the onion 5 minutes. Add the meat and cook over high heat, stirring constantly until it turns brown. Add the tomato, 1½ teaspoons salt and the pepper. Cook 3 minutes. Stir in the cheddar cheese.

Mix the cornstarch and milk until smooth. Cook over low heat, stirring constantly to the boiling point. Beat the egg and remaining salt in a bowl. Gradually add the sauce, stirring constantly to prevent curdling. Add the Parmesan cheese.

Place half the macaroni on the bottom of a 2-quart casserole. Spread the meat mixture over it and cover with the remaining macaroni. Pour the sauce over all.

Bake in a 375° oven 30 minutes or until browned. Serve from the casserole.

Serves 6—320 calories in each serving.

## BAKED MACARONI AND CHEESE

1½ cups macaroni
1 egg
¾ cup skim milk
½ teaspoon salt
Dash cayenne pepper
½ cup grated American cheese

Turn oven on and set at 400°.

Cook the macaroni in boiling salted water 2 minutes less than package directs. Drain and rinse with cold water.

Beat the egg, milk, salt and cayenne pepper together. Blend in the cheese and then toss the macaroni in it. Turn into a lightly greased 1½ quart casserole. Bake 20 minutes, or until browned.

Serves 6—140 calories in each serving.

## NOODLES WITH TUNA SAUCE

1 tablespoon olive oil
2 cloves garlic
½ pound mushrooms, sliced
1 cup canned tomato sauce
1 cup water
1 teaspoon salt
¼ teaspoon freshly ground black pepper
¼ teaspoon basil
1 can (7¾ ounces) tuna fish
3 tablespoons chopped parsley

Heat the oil in a saucepan; sauté the garlic and mushrooms 5 minutes. Add the tomato sauce, water, salt, pepper and basil. Cover and cook over low heat 45 minutes. Drain the tuna, wash under cold running water and drain again. Flake it and add to the sauce with the parsley. Cook 10 minutes. Taste for seasoning and serve over ½ cup broad noodles for each.

Serves 6—130 calories in each serving.

## NOODLE RING

½ pound medium-fine noodles
2 egg yolks
½ cup skim milk
2 teaspoons melted butter
1 teaspoon salt
¼ teaspoon freshly ground black pepper
½ teaspoon paprika
2 egg whites, stiffly beaten

Cook the noodles in boiling salted water 2 minutes less than package directs. Drain and rinse with cold water. Turn oven on and set at 375°.

Beat together the egg yolks, milk, butter, salt, pepper and paprika. Stir in the noodles and fold in the egg whites. Turn into a lightly greased 8-inch ring mold. Set in a shallow pan of water.

Bake 40 minutes, or until set and lightly browned. Carefully turn out.

Serves 6—85 calories in each serving.

## GREEN RICE

- 1 tablespoon butter or margarine
- 1 cup chopped raw spinach
- 4 scallions (green onions), chopped
- ½ cup chopped parsley
- 2 carrots, grated
- 1 cup raw rice
- 3 cups chicken consommé, fresh or canned
- 1½ teaspoons salt
- ¼ teaspoon pepper

Melt the butter in a casserole; sauté the spinach, scallions, parsley and carrots for 10 minutes, stirring frequently. Add the rice and stir until it is well coated with the vegetable mixture. Add the consommé, salt and pepper. Cover and cook over low heat 30 minutes or until rice is tender.

Serves 6—145 calories in each serving.

## WILD RICE

- 1 cup wild rice
- 3 cups water
- 2 teaspoons salt
- 2 tablespoons butter or margarine
- 1 onion, chopped fine
- 3 tablespoons chopped green pepper
- ½ pound mushrooms, sliced
- 2 teaspoons Worcestershire sauce
- ¼ teaspoon freshly ground black pepper

Wash the rice in several changes of water. Combine in a saucepan with the water and salt. Cover and bring to a boil. Remove the cover and cook over medium heat 30 minutes, or until rice is tender. Drain if any water remains.

Melt the butter in a skillet; sauté the onion and green pepper 5 minutes. Add the mushrooms and sauté 5 minutes, stirring frequently. Combine with the rice, Worcestershire sauce and pepper. Toss lightly and taste for seasoning.

Serves 6—140 calories in each serving.

## CURRIED RICE

- 1 cup rice
- 1 tablespoon butter or margarine
- 3 tablespoons chopped onion
- 1 tablespoon curry powder
- 2 cups beef broth, fresh or canned
- 2 tomatoes, peeled and chopped
- 1½ teaspoons salt
- ¼ teaspoon freshly ground black pepper
- 1 tablespoon heavy cream

Wash the rice under running water until the water runs clear. Drain and dry thoroughly.

Melt the butter in a saucepan. Stir in the onion and curry powder; cook over low heat 2 minutes, stirring almost constantly. Add the rice and cook, stirring constantly for 2 minutes. Add the broth, tomatoes, salt, pepper and cream. Cover and cook over low heat 35 minutes or until the rice is tender. Watch carefully to avoid burning and add a little more broth if necessary.

Serves 6—150 calories in each serving.

## SPANISH RICE

- 1 tablespoon olive or salad oil
- 2 onions, sliced thin
- 1 cup rice
- 1 cup boiling water
- 1 can (#2½) tomatoes
- ½ cup minced green pepper
- 1½ teaspoons salt
- 1 bay leaf
- 2 tablespoons chopped parsley
- ⅛ teaspoon dried ground red peppers
- ¼ teaspoon saffron (optional)

Turn oven on and set at 375°.

Heat the olive oil in a casserole; sauté the onions 10 minutes, stirring frequently. Add the rice and stir until it turns yellow. Add the water, tomatoes, green pepper, salt, bay leaf, parsley, red peppers and saffron. Mix gently. Cover. Bake 50 minutes or until rice is tender. Taste for seasoning and serve from the casserole.

Serves 6—150 calories in each serving.

## RISOTTO

- 1 tablespoon butter or margarine
- 1 onion, chopped fine
- 1 cup rice
- 3 cups chicken consommé, fresh or canned
- 2 tablespoons sherry
- 1½ teaspoons salt
- ¼ teaspoon freshly ground black pepper
- 3 tablespoons grated Parmesan cheese

Melt the butter in a casserole; sauté the onion for 5 minutes, stirring frequently. Add the rice and cook over low heat stirring constantly until it turns yellow. Add the consommé, sherry, salt and pepper. Cover and cook over low heat 30 minutes, or until rice is tender and consommé absorbed. Sprinkle with the cheese and serve from the casserole.

Serves 6—150 calories in each serving.

## TOMATO SAUCE (FOR PASTAS) ✻

- 2 tablespoons olive oil
- 3 onions, chopped
- 3 cloves garlic, minced
- 3 tablespoons chopped parsley
- 2 cans (#2½) Italian-style tomatoes
- 3 tablespoons white wine
- 2 teaspoons salt
- ½ teaspoon freshly ground black pepper
- ½ teaspoon oregano
- 1 bay leaf
- ¼ pound mushrooms, chopped

Heat the oil in a saucepan; sauté the onions and garlic for 10 minutes, stirring frequently. Add the parsley, tomatoes, wine, salt, pepper, oregano and bay leaf. Cover and cook over low heat 2 hours. Add the mushrooms and cook 1 hour longer. Discard the bay leaf and taste for seasoning. For a smooth sauce, force through a sieve or purée in an electric blender.

Makes about 6 cups—40 calories in ½ cup.

*Note:* The sauce freezes well, so make larger quantities and keep on hand.

## BUCKWHEAT GROATS (KASHA)

1 cup buckwheat groats
1 egg
Boiling water
1½ teaspoons salt

Combine the groats and egg in a saucepan. Stir constantly over low heat until each grain is separate. Add enough water to cover the groats; add the salt. Cover and cook over low heat 12 minutes. Drain if any water remains. Serve with meat or poultry dishes in place of potatoes.

Serves 6—50 calories in each serving.

## WHITE CLAM SAUCE (FOR PASTAS) ❋

1 tablespoon olive oil
1 tablespoon butter or margarine
1 clove garlic, minced
4 tablespoons finely chopped onion
1 cup clam juice, fresh or canned
Dash dried ground red peppers
1 cup minced clams, fresh or canned
¼ cup finely chopped parsley

Heat the olive oil and butter in a saucepan; sauté the garlic and onion 5 minutes. Add the clam juice and peppers; cook over low heat 5 minutes. Stir in the clams and parsley. Heat and serve over linguini or fine noodles.

Serves 6—50 calories in each serving.

## RED CLAM SAUCE (FOR PASTAS) ❋

2 tablespoons olive oil
2 cloves garlic, minced
1 can (#2) tomatoes
1 can tomato paste
1 teaspoon salt
¼ teaspoon black pepper
½ teaspoon oregano
1½ cups undrained chopped clams, fresh or canned
2 tablespoons chopped parsley

Heat the oil in a saucepan; sauté the garlic 2 minutes. Add the tomatoes, tomato paste, salt, pepper and oregano. Cook over low heat 30 minutes. Add the clams and parsley; cook 3 minutes. Serve on noodles or spaghetti.

Serves 6—65 calories.

## MARINARA SAUCE (FOR PASTAS) ❋

2 tablespoons olive oil
2 onions, chopped
1 clove garlic, minced
1 can (#2) tomatoes
1 teaspoon salt
¼ teaspoon pepper
½ teaspoon basil
¼ teaspoon oregano
¼ teaspoon sugar
2 fillets of anchovy

Heat the oil in a saucepan; sauté the onions and garlic 5 minutes. Add the tomatoes, salt, pepper, basil, oregano and sugar. Cook over low heat 1 hour. Stir in the anchovies and cook 10 minutes longer. Taste for seasoning. Serve on spaghetti.

Serves 6—50 calories in each serving.

## ANCHOVY SAUCE (FOR PASTAS)

2 tablespoons olive oil
1 clove garlic, minced
12 anchovy fillets, chopped
1 cup canned tomato sauce
1 cup water
¼ teaspoon freshly ground black pepper
3 tablespoons chopped parsley

Heat the oil in a saucepan; sauté the garlic 1 minute. Add the anchovies, tomato sauce, water and pepper. Cook over low heat 30 minutes. Taste for seasoning. Add the parsley and serve on noodles or spaghetti.

Serves 6—65 calories in each serving.

# SALAD DRESSINGS & SAUCES

The symbol ✻ indicates dishes that can be frozen.

Here are two categories where literally hundreds of calories can be saved, almost without being noticed, by carefully following the recipes in this section. Oils and fats are particularly high in calories and because of this, most commercial salad dressings have about 100 calories to the tablespoon —much too high for weight watchers. You'll be able to reduce the calories in most dressings by *two thirds* by preparing your own, and at the same time you'll be serving appetizing, well-flavored salads.

Sauces, too, are usually very high in calories as ordinarily prepared, but not if you use these calorie-reduced recipes. A further reduction in calories may be made by cutting down on the amount of sauce served with each portion. Don't drown a dish in a flood of sauce; measure carefully and serve the amount specified in each recipe. Large quantities of sauce do not enhance it, so serve just enough to flavor it. A sauce can't change a poor dish into a masterpiece, but it can make a good dish even better.

In preparing sauces, remember that smoothness is important in the finished product. When a recipe specifies "stir constantly," do just that to avoid undesirable lumps. If lumps do form, force the mixture through a strainer. To eliminate additional calories, skim the fat before serving.

## BOILED DRESSING

- ⅓ cup nonfat dry milk
- ⅓ cup water
- 2 eggs
- ½ teaspoon salt
- ½ teaspoon paprika
- ½ teaspoon dry mustard
- Dash cayenne pepper
- 2 tablespoons cider vinegar

Mix the dry milk and water. Lightly beat the eggs in the top of a double boiler. Blend in the milk, salt, paprika, mustard, cayenne pepper and vinegar. Place over hot water and cook, stirring constantly until thickened. Chill and serve with salads.

Makes about 1 cup—20 calories in 1 tablespoon.

### Russian Dressing

Add 3 tablespoons of chili sauce to the boiled dressing.

Makes about 1¼ cups—25 calories in 1 tablespoon.

### Tartar Sauce

Add 3 tablespoons minced pickle and 1 tablespoon chopped capers.

Makes about 1¼ cups—25 calories in 1 tablespoon.

## COTTAGE-CHEESE DRESSING

- 1 cup cottage cheese
- 2 tablespoons milk
- ½ cup canned tomato sauce
- 1 tablespoon grated onion
- ½ teaspoon chili powder
- 1 teaspoon lemon juice

Beat all the ingredients with a rotary beater or in an electric blender. Good with vegetables or green salad.

Makes about 1¾ cups—20 calories in 1 tablespoon.

## ROQUEFORT-CHEESE DRESSING

- 1 2-inch cube Roquefort cheese
- 1 cup canned tomato sauce
- 2 tablespoons chili sauce
- 2 teaspoons lemon juice
- 1 teaspoon grated onion
- ½ teaspoon paprika

Mash the Roquefort cheese and gradually beat in the tomato sauce, chili sauce, lemon juice, onion and paprika. Mix well. Chill and serve with green salad.

Makes about 1¼ cups—20 calories in 1 tablespoon.

## EGG DRESSING

- 1 hard-cooked egg yolk
- 1 egg yolk
- ½ teaspoon salt
- ½ cup yogurt
- 1 teaspoon lemon juice
- Dash cayenne pepper

Mash the hard-cooked yolk to a paste; gradually add the raw yolk, mixing steadily. Beat in the salt, yogurt, lemon juice and cayenne pepper. Chill. Good with any salad or cold sea food.

Makes about ¾ cup—15 calories in 1 tablespoon.

## COOKED FLUFFY DRESSING

- 2 tablespoons cornstarch
- ½ teaspoon salt
- ¼ teaspoon dry mustard
- ½ teaspoon paprika
- 1 cup skim milk
- 2 tablespoons lemon juice
- 1 egg white, stiffly beaten

Sift the cornstarch, salt, mustard and paprika into a saucepan. Gradually add the milk; cook over low heat, stirring constantly until thick. Remove from heat and beat in the lemon juice. Cool, then fold in the beaten egg white. Chill, but use within 2-3 hours, as the egg white will collapse. Delicious with any salad.

Makes about 1½ cups—about 10 calories in 1 tablespoon.

## COOKED SALAD DRESSING

- 1¼ cups skim milk
- 1½ tablespoons cornstarch
- 1½ teaspoons salt
- ½ teaspoon dry mustard
- Dash cayenne pepper
- 2 egg yolks, beaten
- ½ teaspoon liquid Sucaryl
- ⅓ cup cider vinegar
- 1 tablespoon melted butter or margarine

Scald the milk. Combine the cornstarch, salt, mustard and cayenne pepper in the top of a double boiler; stir in the egg yolks and Sucaryl. Mix well. Gradually add the milk, stirring constantly. Place over hot water and cook, stirring steadily until thick, about 7 minutes. Remove from the heat and stir in the butter and the vinegar. Chill.

Makes about 1½ cups—15 calories in 1 tablespoon.

## LEMON-JUICE DRESSING

- ½ cup lemon juice
- 2 tablespoons olive or salad oil
- ½ cup water
- ½ teaspoon salt
- ¼ teaspoon pepper
- ½ teaspoon celery salt
- ¼ teaspoon dry mustard

Beat the lemon juice into the oil, then gradually add the water. Add the salt, pepper, celery salt and mustard. Chill; beat or shake vigorously before serving. Serve on fruit or vegetable salads.

Makes about 1⅛ cups—15 calories in 1 tablespoon.

## COOKED THOUSAND-ISLAND DRESSING

1 egg
2 tablespoons vinegar
¼ cup milk
½ teaspoon salt
¼ teaspoon paprika
¼ teaspoon dry mustard
½ teaspoon chili powder
2 tablespoons tomato paste
2 tablespoons chopped stuffed olives
2 tablespoons chopped dill pickle

Beat the egg and vinegar in the top of a double boiler: gradually add the milk. Stir in the salt, paprika, mustard, chili powder and tomato paste. Place over hot water and cook, stirring constantly until thick, about 5 minutes. Pour into a bowl or jar and cool. Stir in the olives and pickles. Chill. Excellent with any salad except fruit.

Makes about ¾ cup—15 calories in 1 tablespoon.

## FRENCH DRESSING

1 tablespoon cornstarch
1 cup water
¼ cup wine vinegar
2 tablespoons olive or salad oil
1 clove garlic, minced
¾ teaspoon salt
¼ teaspoon freshly ground black pepper
¾ teaspoon paprika

Mix the cornstarch with a little of the water until smooth, then gradually add the remaining water. Cook over low heat, stirring constantly to the boiling point. Cook 5 minutes. Cool. Beat in the vinegar, oil, garlic, salt, pepper and paprika. Keep in the refrigerator until needed and shake before using.

Makes about 1¼ cups—20 calories in 1 tablespoon.

## FRUIT-JUICE DRESSING

1 tablespoon cornstarch
½ teaspoon salt
2 tablespoons lemon juice
1 cup orange juice
1 teaspoon liquid Sucaryl
2 egg yolks

Mix the cornstarch, salt and lemon juice in the top of a double boiler. Gradually add the orange juice and Sucaryl. Place over hot water and cook, stirring constantly to the boiling point. Cook 5 minutes.

Beat the egg yolks in a bowl. Gradually add the hot mixture, stirring constantly to prevent curdling. Return to the double boiler and cook, stirring constantly, until thickened. Chill and serve with fruit salads.

Makes about 1½ cups—10 calories in 1 tablespoon.

## TOMATO-FRENCH DRESSING

- ½ cup condensed tomato soup
- ¼ cup water
- 2 tablespoons vinegar
- 1 tablespoon grated onion
- 2 tablespoons finely chopped green pepper
- 1 teaspoon Worcestershire sauce
- ½ teaspoon salt
- ½ teaspoon dry mustard
- ⅛ teaspoon garlic powder
- ¼ teaspoon liquid Sucaryl

Beat all the ingredients together until smooth or use the electric blender for a few seconds. Very piquant with green salads or cold meats.

Makes about 1 cup—10 calories in 1 tablespoon.

## HERB DRESSING

- 2 tablespoons olive or salad oil
- 4 tablespoons wine vinegar
- 4 tablespoons tomato juice
- 1 clove garlic, minced
- ½ teaspoon salt
- ⅛ teaspoon freshly ground black pepper
- ½ teaspoon paprika
- 1 teaspoon mixed herbs (parsley, chervil, thyme, basil)

Beat all the ingredients together and chill. Beat again before serving with salads.

Makes about ⅔ cup—25 calories in 1 tablespoon.

### Garlic Dressing

Omit the herbs and use 2 cloves of garlic.

## MAYONNAISE

- 2 eggs
- ¾ teaspoon salt
- ½ teaspoon paprika
- ¼ teaspoon dry mustard
- 3 tablespoons lemon juice
- ½ cup milk
- 1 tablespoon salad oil

Beat the eggs, salt, paprika and mustard in the top of a double boiler. Gradually add the lemon juice and milk. Place over hot water and cook, stirring constantly until thick, about 3 minutes. Remove from the heat and stir in the oil. Pour into a jar, cover and cool. Keep in the refrigerator.

Makes about 1 cup—20 calories in 1 tablespoon.

## VINAIGRETTE SAUCE

- 2 tablespoons olive or salad oil
- ½ cup wine vinegar
- 2 tablespoons cold water
- 2 teaspoons grated onion
- 1 teaspoon chopped chives
- 1 teaspoon chopped capers
- ½ teaspoon salt
- ¼ teaspoon freshly ground black pepper
- ½ teaspoon paprika
- 2 tablespoons chopped pickles
- 2 teaspoons chopped parsley

Combine all the ingredients and stir or shake vigorously before serving. Delicious with artichokes, salads or cold meats.

Makes about ¾ cup—25 calories in 1 tablespoon.

## WINE DRESSING

- ½ cup marsala or sweet sherry
- ½ cup lemon juice
- 1 tablespoon water
- ⅛ teaspoon salt

Mix all the ingredients together. Chill and serve with fruit salads.

Makes about 1 cup—20 calories in 1 tablespoon.

## YOGURT DRESSING

- 1 egg yolk
- ¼ teaspoon salt
- ¼ teaspoon dry mustard
- ¼ teaspoon paprika
- Dash cayenne pepper
- ¾ cup yogurt
- 1 tablespoon lemon juice

Beat the egg yolk, salt, mustard, paprika and cayenne; add the yogurt and lemon juice. Chill and serve with salads.

Makes about 1 cup—15 calories in 1 tablespoon.

## BARBECUE SAUCE

- 1 cup water
- 1 cup vinegar
- 2 tablespoons Worcestershire sauce
- ¼ teaspoon cayenne pepper
- ½ teaspoon dry mustard
- 1 teaspoon tabasco sauce
- ½ teaspoon liquid Sucaryl
- 1 teaspoon paprika
- 2 cloves garlic, minced
- 2 onions, chopped fine
- ½ cup chili sauce

Combine all the ingredients in a saucepan. Bring the mixture to a boil. Marinate spareribs or chicken in this sauce for 2 hours at room temperature and then broil. Sauce may also be served with broiled meats.

Makes about 2½ cups—5 calories in each tablespoon.

## BROWN SAUCE ❋

1 tablespoon butter or margarine
1 tablespoon flour
1½ cups beef broth, fresh or canned

Melt the butter in a saucepan; stir in the flour. Cook over low heat, stirring frequently until it is very brown (but not burnt). Gradually add the broth, stirring constantly to the boiling point. Cook over very low heat 30 minutes, stirring occasionally. Skim the fat. Brown sauce is used as a base for many sauces and gravies.

Makes about 1¼ cups—10 calories in 1 tablespoon.

## SAUCE DIABLE

⅓ cup dry white wine
1 onion, chopped
6 peppercorns, crushed
1 cup brown sauce (see recipe)
1 teaspoon Worcestershire sauce
1 teaspoon chopped parsley

Cook the wine, onion and peppercorns over low heat 15 minutes. Force through a sieve and add to the brown sauce with the Worcestershire sauce and parsley. Serve with broiled foods; especially good with chicken.

Makes about 1 cup—15 calories in 1 tablespoon.

## HUNTER'S SAUCE ❋

1 tablespoon butter
¼ pound mushrooms, thinly sliced
½ teaspoon salt
¼ teaspoon freshly ground black pepper
3 tablespoons chopped onion
½ cup dry white wine
2 tablespoons canned tomato sauce
1 cup brown sauce (see recipe)
1 teaspoon chopped parsley

Melt the butter in a saucepan; add the mushrooms, salt and pepper. Cook over low heat 10 minutes, stirring frequently. Add the onion, wine and tomato sauce. Cook 15 minutes. Stir in the brown sauce and parsley. Heat and serve with meat or poultry.

Makes about 1¼ cups—20 calories in 1 tablespoon.

## BEARNAISE SAUCE

2 egg yolks
½ teaspoon salt
⅓ cup dry white wine
2 teaspoons tarragon vinegar
1 tablespoon butter
½ teaspoon chervil
1 teaspoon chopped parsley

Beat the egg yolks and salt in the top of a double boiler. Slowly beat in the wine, vinegar and butter. Place over hot water and cook, stirring constantly until thickened. Stir in the chervil and parsley. The classic sauce for steaks and fish.

Makes about ½ cup—25 calories in 1 tablespoon.

## CUCUMBER SAUCE

2 cucumbers
2 tablespoons lemon juice
½ cup cottage cheese
1 teaspoon grated onion
1 teaspoon salt
¼ teaspoon freshly ground black pepper

Pare the cucumber and chop very fine. Add the lemon juice, cottage cheese, onion, salt and pepper. Continue chopping until well blended and smooth. If you prefer, run the mixture in the blender. Serve cold with fish.

Makes about 1 cup—10 calories in 1 tablespoon.

## EGG SAUCE

2 egg yolks
2 teaspoons tarragon vinegar
1 tablespoon butter
¼ teaspoon salt
⅛ teaspoon white pepper
Dash nutmeg
1 hard-cooked egg, chopped
1 teaspoon chopped dill (optional)
2 egg whites, stiffly beaten

Lightly beat the eggs and vinegar in the top of a double boiler. Add the butter and place over hot water. Cook, stirring constantly, until thickened to the consistency of heavy cream. Remove from the heat and stir in the salt, pepper, nutmeg and chopped egg. Fold in the egg whites. Serve at once with fish dishes.

Makes about 1 cup—20 calories in 1 cup.

## HOLLANDAISE SAUCE ❊

2 egg yolks
½ teaspoon salt
⅓ cup water
1 tablespoon lemon juice
1 tablespoon butter

Beat the egg and salt in the top of a double boiler. Slowly beat in the water, lemon juice, and then the butter. Place over hot water and cook, stirring constantly for 5 minutes or until thickened. Remove from heat. Delicious with asparagus, broccoli or almost any vegetable. If you like a tart sauce, add a little more lemon juice.

Makes about ½ cup—25 calories in 1 tablespoon.

## MOCK HOLLANDAISE

1 tablespoon cornstarch
¼ teaspoon salt
1 cup canned consommé
1 tablespoon lemon juice
1 tablespoon butter

Mix the cornstarch and salt with a little of the consommé until smooth. Gradually add the remaining consommé, the lemon juice and butter. Cook over low heat, stirring constantly until thickened. Taste for seasoning. Serve with vegetables or fish.

Makes about 1 cup—10 calories in 1 tablespoon.

## MORNAY SAUCE ❋

1 egg yolk
1 cup hot thin white sauce (see recipe)
3 tablespoons grated Parmesan or Swiss cheese

Beat the egg yolk in a saucepan. Gradually add the sauce, stirring constantly over low heat until the boiling point. Remove from the heat at once and stir in the cheese. Serve with fish, vegetables, eggs, poultry or noodles.

Makes about 1¼ cups—30 calories in 1 tablespoon.

## RAISIN SAUCE ❋

¼ cup seedless raisins
1 teaspoon brown sugar
1 teaspoon vinegar
1 cup brown sauce (see recipe)

Cover the raisins with boiling water and let soak 10 minutes. Drain. Place the brown sugar in a saucepan and cook over low heat until it sizzles. Add the vinegar and brown sauce. Bring to a boil, reduce the heat and bring to a boil again. Add the raisins and heat. Serve with ham or tongue.

Makes about 1¼ cups—15 calories in 1 tablespoon.

## MUSTARD SAUCE

2 teaspoons cornstarch
½ teaspoon salt
1½ tablespoons dry mustard
⅔ cup nonfat dry milk
1 cup water
10 Sucaryl tablets
2 egg yolks
¼ cup cider vinegar

Mix the cornstarch, salt, mustard and dry milk in the top of a double boiler. Very gradually add the water, stirring until smooth. Add the Sucaryl. Cook over low heat, stirring constantly until the boiling point. Place over hot water; cover and cook 10 minutes, stirring occasionally.

Beat the egg yolks in a bowl; gradually add some of the hot mixture, beating steadily to prevent curdling. Return to the double boiler and cook, stirring steadily until thickened. Stir in the vinegar. Serve hot or cold with meat or vegetables.

Makes about 1¼ cups—25 calories in 1 tablespoon.

## WHITE SAUCE

- 1 tablespoon flour
- ½ cup nonfat dry milk
- ½ teaspoon salt
- ⅛ teaspoon white pepper
- 1 cup water
- 1 tablespoon butter

Mix the flour, dry milk, salt and pepper in a saucepan. Add the water and beat with a rotary beater until smooth. Cook over low heat, stirring steadily until thickened. Stir in the butter. These proportions make a thin white sauce.

For medium white sauce use 2 tablespoons flour, for thick, 3 tablespoons.

Makes 1 cup—20 calories in 1 tablespoon thin sauce
25 calories in 1 tablespoon thick sauce

### Cheese Sauce

Stir ½ cup grated cheddar or American cheese into the medium white sauce and stir until melted.

Makes 1¼ cups—40 calories in 1 tablespoon.

### Curry Sauce

Add 1 tablespoon curry powder to 1 cup white sauce.

Makes 1 cup—20 calories in 1 tablespoon thin sauce
25 calories in 1 tablespoon thick sauce

## CHINESE SWEET-AND-SOUR SAUCE ❋

- 2 tablespoons cornstarch
- 1 tablespoon sugar
- ¼ teaspoon salt
- ½ teaspoon ginger
- 2 tablespoons vinegar
- 1 teaspoon soy sauce
- 1 cup unsweetened pineapple juice
- ½ teaspoon liquid Sucaryl

Mix the cornstarch, sugar, salt and ginger in a saucepan. Stir in the vinegar and soy sauce, then the pineapple juice and Sucaryl. Cook over low heat, stirring constantly, until the boiling point; cook 5 minutes. Good with pork, ham or tongue.

Makes 1 cup—15 calories in 1 tablespoon.

## HOT RAVIGOTE SAUCE

3 tablespoons dry white wine
2 tablespoons cider vinegar
4 tablespoons chopped onion
1 cup medium white sauce (see recipe)
⅛ teaspoon tarragon
⅛ teaspoon chervil
½ teaspoon chopped chives

Cook the wine, vinegar and onion until it is reduced to half its original quantity. Add the white sauce, tarragon, chervil and chives. Heat and serve with boiled chicken or fish.

Makes about 1⅛ cups—25 calories in 1 tablespoon.

Although low in calories, pickles and relishes are intended, in point of fact, to whet the appetite. Of course, anything that stirs and stimulates you to eating more than you require is not desirable. But served judiciously, they enhance a meal and in many cases may be served in place of a salad for variety and contrast as well as for unexpected guests.

Use fresh, firm vegetables and fruits. Don't overcook, because it is the crisp and crunchy quality of a pickle or relish that delights the palate. Pack in sterile jars, label carefully as to type and date of packing. Seal and store in a cool, dark place. Always chill before serving.

## PICKLED ARTICHOKES

- 2 teaspoons pickling spice
- 5 cloves
- ¼ teaspoon thyme
- ¼ teaspoon mace
- 1-inch piece cinnamon stick or 2 teaspoons, ground
- 1 quart cider vinegar
- 2 tablespoons sugar
- 15 Sucaryl tablets
- 2 packages frozen artichoke hearts

Tie the pickling spice, cloves, thyme, mace and cinnamon in a piece of cheesecloth. Let soak in the vinegar 1 hour; add the sugar and Sucaryl and bring to a boil. Cook over low heat 20 minutes. Drop a few artichokes at a time into the liquid and cook 2 minutes. Carefully remove to a sterilized 1-quart jar or 2 pint jars. Pour the liquid over the artichokes and seal. Let pickle 5 days before serving.

Makes about 40—5 calories in each.

## PICKLED BEETS

- 8 beets or 2 cans (#2) sliced beets
- 1 onion, sliced thin
- 1½ cups cider vinegar
- 1½ teaspoons salt
- ¼ teaspoon freshly ground black pepper
- 2 teaspoons sugar
- ¾ teaspoon liquid Sucaryl
- 1 teaspoon caraway seeds

If fresh beets are used, scrub them well and remove the root ends. Cook in water to cover 25 minutes, or until tender but firm. Drain and cool. Peel and slice (if canned beets are used, drain).

Place the beets in a bowl or jar and add the onion, vinegar, salt, pepper, sugar, Sucaryl and caraway seeds. Mix well. Cover and chill for at least 12 hours before serving.

Makes about 2 pints—20 calories in ¼ cup.

## BREAD-AND-BUTTER PICKLES

- 18 cucumbers
- 3 onions, thinly sliced
- 1 green pepper, chopped
- 3 tablespoons coarse salt
- 2 cups cider vinegar
- 2 tablespoons brown sugar
- 60 Sucaryl tablets
- 2 teaspoons mustard seed
- ¾ teaspoon celery seed
- ⅛ teaspoon ground cloves

Buy even-sized cucumbers. Scrub and slice (with the skin on) into thin, even slices. Combine in a bowl with the onion, green pepper and salt. Cover and chill for 3 hours. Drain, rinse with cold water and drain again.

Bring to a boil the vinegar, sugar, Sucaryl, mustard, celery seed and cloves. Add the vegetables and bring to the boiling point. Remove from the heat immediately. Pack into sterilized jars and seal at once. Let stand 3 days before serving.

Makes about 1½ quarts—10 calories in 7 slices.

## CHOW-CHOW

1 cup sliced unpeeled cucumbers
1 cup chopped cucumbers
1 cup small white onions
1 cup chopped onions
3 green tomatoes, quartered
1 cup green beans, French style
1 small head cauliflower, broken into flowerets
¾ cup salt
3 cups cider vinegar
1 tablespoon cornstarch
2 tablespoons sugar
1½ tablespoons dry mustard
½ teaspoon turmeric
¼ cup cold water
20 Sucaryl tablets

Combine all the vegetables in a deep bowl. Cover with water mixed with the ¾ cup salt and let soak overnight. Drain well, rinse with cold water and drain again.

Bring the vinegar and vegetables to a boil in a deep saucepan. Mix to a smooth paste the cornstarch, sugar, mustard, turmeric and water. Add the vegetables with the Sucaryl, stirring constantly for 5 minutes over low heat.

Pour into sterilized jars and seal. Store in a cool dark place for 2 weeks before serving.

Makes 3 pints—5 calories in 1 tablespoon.

## PICKLED PEPPERS

12 green peppers
1½ cups cider vinegar
2 cups water
2 bay leaves
2 teaspoons salt
2 teaspoons sugar
Dash cayenne pepper
2 cloves garlic, minced

Wash the peppers; cut in half and remove the fibers. Broil as close to the heat as possible, or hold over a flame until the skins brown. Remove the skins and slice the peppers into a jar.

Combine the vinegar, water, bay leaves, salt, sugar and cayenne pepper in a saucepan. Bring to a boil and cook 2 minutes. Cool 5 minutes and pour over the peppers. Cover tightly and chill for at least 4 hours before serving. Keeps about 1 week.

Makes about 1½ pints—15 calories in ¼ cup.

## BEET RELISH

2 cups chopped beets
2 cups shredded cabbage
1 cup chopped onion
1 cup chopped celery
2 cups vinegar
2 tablespoons sugar
18 Sucaryl tablets
2 tablespoons salt
2 tablespoons mustard seed
1 tablespoon celery seed

Combine all the ingredients in a saucepan and cook over low heat 25 minutes, or until the vegetables are tender. Pack into sterile jars and seal. Store in a cool dark place for 24 hours before using.

Makes about 3 quarts—20 calories in ½ cup.

## PICKLED STUFFED PEPPERS

18 green peppers
6 cups finely shredded cabbage
3 cups chopped sweet red peppers
2 teaspoons salt
3 tablespoons mustard seed
2 tablespoons celery seed
½ teaspoon dried ground red peppers
2 tablespoons sugar
2 tablespoons liquid Sucaryl
18 cloves
9 cloves garlic, cut in half
1 quart tarragon vinegar

Buy even-sized firm peppers. Cut a 1-inch piece from the top of each and remove the seeds and fibers. Soak overnight in cold water to cover mixed with 1 cup salt. Rinse and drain thoroughly.

Mix the cabbage, pepper, 2 teaspoons salt, mustard seed, celery seed, red peppers, sugar and Sucaryl. Stuff the peppers and stick a clove and a piece of garlic in each. Arrange the peppers in an upright position in glass jars or stone crocks. Bring the vinegar to a boil and pour over them—you may need more or less vinegar but be sure the peppers are covered with it. Seal and store in a cool place for 3 weeks before serving. Taste cabbage to see if it's pickled at the end of that time. Chill and serve in place of salad or as an accompaniment to meat.

Makes 18—35 calories in each.

## CABBAGE RELISH

4 green peppers
2 pounds cabbage
2 onions
1 tablespoon brown sugar
½ teaspoon liquid Sucaryl
1½ tablespoons salt
1½ tablespoons mustard seed
3 cups cider vinegar
8 allspice
8 whole cloves
1 stick cinnamon
¼ teaspoon mace

Cut the peppers in half and remove the seeds and fibers. Chop or grind the peppers, cabbage and onions. Add the sugar, Sucaryl and salt. Combine the vinegar, allspice, cloves, cinnamon and mace; bring to a boil. Cool 10 minutes, then strain over the vegetables. Mix well. Pack into sterile jars. Seal and store in a cool dark place 2 days before using.

Makes about 2½ quarts—15 calories in ½-cup.

## SPICED CRANBERRIES

2 pounds cranberries, ground
3 tablespoons brown sugar
12 Sucaryl tablets
¾ cup cider vinegar
¾ cup water
½ teaspoon ground allspice
¾ teaspoon cinnamon
1 teaspoon ginger

Combine everything in a saucepan; bring to a boil and cook 45 minutes, or until thick. Pack into sterile jars and seal.

Makes about 2 pints—15 calories in 1 tablespoon.

## CHUTNEY

½ cup fresh ginger
2 onions
½ cup seedless raisins
4 pounds apples or peaches
2 tablespoons chili powder
1 tablespoon mustard seed
1 tablespoon salt
1 quart cider vinegar
¼ cup brown sugar
50 Sucaryl tablets

Grind together the ginger, onions and raisins. Peel the fruit and cut in small pieces. Combine the ginger mixture, fruit, chili powder, mustard seed, salt, vinegar, sugar and Sucaryl. Cook over medium heat 1 hour or until thick and brown.

Pour into jars and seal at once. Set aside for at least 1 week before using.

Makes about 3 pints—25 calories in 1 tablespoon.

## CORN RELISH

2 pounds cabbage
4 onions, peeled
3 green peppers, sliced
3 cups corn kernels, fresh or canned
1 quart cider vinegar
1½ tablespoons salt
1 teaspoon celery seed
1 teaspoon mustard seed
2 teaspoons dried ground chili peppers
2 tablespoons brown sugar
40 Sucaryl tablets

Grind the cabbage, onions and green peppers. Combine in a saucepan with the corn, vinegar, salt, celery and mustard seeds, chili pepper, sugar and Sucaryl. Cook over medium heat 20 minutes.

Pack into jars and seal. Let stand 3 days before serving.

Makes about 1½ pints—15 calories in 1 tablespoon.

## CRANBERRY ORANGE RELISH

1 pound cranberries
1 orange
3 tablespoons sugar
1½ tablespoons liquid Sucaryl

Wash and pick over the cranberries. Wash and dry the orange. Cut into eighths and remove the seeds and fibers. Using the medium blade, grind the fruit in the food chopper. Blend in the sugar and Sucaryl. Taste, and add more Sucaryl if needed. Turn into jars and chill.

Makes about 4 cups—10 calories in 1 tablespoon.

## TOMATO RELISH

3 pounds ripe tomatoes, peeled
2 onions
1 cup sliced celery
¼ cup diced green pepper
1 tablespoon sugar
3 teaspoons liquid Sucaryl
2 teaspoons salt
1 tablespoon mustard seed
½ cup white vinegar

Chop together the tomatoes, onions, celery and green pepper. Drain. Add the sugar, Sucaryl, salt, mustard seed and vinegar. Mix well. Turn into sterile jars and cover tightly. Set aside in a cool dark place for 24 hours before serving.

Makes about 1 quart—5 calories in 1 tablespoon.

## EGGPLANT RELISH

- 1 large eggplant
- 1 onion
- 2 tomatoes
- 3 tablespoons cider vinegar
- 1 slice white bread, trimmed
- 1 tablespoon salad oil
- 2 teaspoons salt
- ½ teaspoon freshly ground black pepper
- 1 teaspoon sugar

Wash the eggplant and wrap in aluminum foil. Place on a baking pan and bake in a 350° oven 1 hour. Cool and peel the eggplant.

Chop the onion very fine, then chop the eggplant and tomatoes with it. Pour the vinegar over the bread and add to the eggplant mixture with the oil, salt, pepper and sugar. Continue chopping until well blended.

Makes about 1 quart—50 calories in ½ cup.

## INDIA RELISH

- 2 pounds green tomatoes, peeled and chopped
- 2 tablespoons salt
- 4 cups chopped cabbage
- 3 cups cider vinegar
- 1 cup chopped onion
- 1 cup chopped green peppers
- 3 tablespoons sugar
- 40 Sucaryl tablets
- 2 teaspoons celery seed
- 2 teaspoons mustard seed
- 1 teaspoon cloves
- ½ teaspoon peppercorns
- 2 teaspoons cinnamon

Combine the tomatoes and salt in a bowl; cover with a cloth and let stand overnight. Drain well.

Cook the tomatoes, cabbage and vinegar 20 minutes. Add the onions, green pepper, sugar, Sucaryl, celery and mustard seed, cloves, peppercorns and cinnamon. Cook over low heat 20 minutes. Taste for seasoning. Pack into sterilized jars and seal at once.

Makes about 3 pints—5 calories in 1 tablespoon.

## PEPPER RELISH

- 6 green peppers
- 6 red peppers
- 6 onions
- 1 cup vinegar
- 2 tablespoons brown sugar
- 18 Sucaryl tablets
- 1 tablespoon salt
- 1 tablespoon celery seed

You may use one color peppers if you can't get both red and green.

Chop the peppers and onions together. Cover with boiling water and cook over low heat 10 minutes. Drain; add the vinegar, brown sugar, Sucaryl, salt and celery seed. Bring to a boil and cook 10 minutes. Pack into sterile jars and seal at once. Store in a cool dark place for 24 hours before using.

Makes about 1 pint—15 calories in 1 tablespoon.

## RHUBARB RELISH

- 2 pounds rhubarb
- ¾ cup cider vinegar
- 3 onions, thinly sliced
- 1 tablespoon sugar
- 12 Sucaryl tablets
- 1 teaspoon salt
- 2 teaspoons curry powder

Wash the rhubarb and cut in 1-inch pieces. Cook the onions and vinegar 5 minutes. Add the rhubarb, sugar, Sucaryl, salt and curry powder. Cook over low heat about 7 minutes, or until rhubarb is soft.

Pour into jars and seal. Let stand 3 days before serving. Good with bland meat or poultry dishes.

Makes about 1½ pints—5 calories in 1 tablespoon.

## SUMMER FRUIT RELISH

- 6 large peaches, peeled and pitted
- 1 pound cherries, pitted
- 2 onions
- 3 tomatoes, peeled
- 1 green pepper, sliced
- 2 tablespoons sugar
- 30 Sucaryl tablets
- 1½ cups cider vinegar
- 2 teaspoons salt
- ¼ teaspoon ginger
- ¼ teaspoon cinnamon

Grind the peaches, cherries, onions, tomatoes and green pepper in a food chopper, using the medium blade. Add the sugar, Sucaryl, vinegar and salt. Cook over low heat 1½ hours or until mixture is very thick. Stir in the ginger and cinnamon. Pack into sterile jars and seal.

Makes about 3 pints—10 calories in 1 tablespoon.

## JELLY

You may use any fruit or combination of fruits for making jelly. Cook 2 quarts of soft fruit in ½ cup of water, mash when soft. Press the fruit through a jelly bag (cheesecloth or flannel). For each cup of juice add 2 tablespoons sugar and 30 Sucaryl tablets. Boil for 5 minutes. For each cup of juice add 1 teaspoon gelatin dissolved in 1 tablespoon water. Stir until dissolved. Pour into sterile glasses and seal with paraffin.

Makes about 1½ pints—5 calories in 1 tablespoon.

## BERRY JAM

- 2 teaspoons gelatin
- 1 tablespoon cold water
- 4 cups strawberries, raspberries or blackberries
- 3 tablespoons sugar
- 65 Sucaryl tablets
- 1 tablespoon lemon juice
- 3 tablespoons liquid pectin

Soften the gelatin in the water. Mash the berries and combine in a saucepan with the sugar, Sucaryl and lemon juice. Bring to a boil and cook 1 minute, stirring constantly. Remove from the heat and stir in the pectin and gelatin. Stir rapidly for 2-3 minutes.

Pour into sterile jars and seal with paraffin wax if you plan to store it for any length of time.

Makes about 1 pint—5 calories in 1 tablespoon.

Don't think you must have a huge space to be able to take advantage of outdoor cookery. A small terrace, a tiny back yard or perhaps the fireplace of a small apartment will accommodate a grill, and with proper organization you'll have a delightful barbecue.

Of course the first thing that comes to mind for the charcoal fire is steak. It *is* wonderful prepared on an open fire, but there are other more exciting dishes that lend themselves to outdoor cookery. When you *do* grill steak, buy a choice thick cut to really enjoy it. Let the flames die down so that you just have hot embers glowing. This prevents too much charring (caused by the fat dripping onto the coals). Turn the meat frequently until it is done the way you like it (make a cut next to the bone to test it). Season the meat with salt and pepper after you remove it from the fire.

Allow 3 slices ¼-inch thick of a 2-inch porterhouse steak. 350 calories in each serving.

## ROAST CLAMS

Buy cherrystone clams and allow 6 for each person. Scrub thoroughly and wrap in aluminum foil. Place on the coals until shells open, about 5 minutes. Serve with 1 tablespoon lemon juice and 2 teaspoons butter heated together.

—130 calories in a serving.

## GRILLED CHICKEN

- 3 1¼-pound broilers, split
- 2 tablespoons melted butter, margarine or oil
- 1½ teaspoons salt
- ½ teaspoon freshly ground black pepper
- ¼ teaspoon dry mustard
- 2 teaspoons paprika
- 1 teaspoon Worcestershire sauce
- ½ cup lemon juice
- ½ cup boiling water

Wash and dry the chickens. Fasten the wings and legs to the bodies with skewers to keep them flat during broiling.

Mix the butter, salt, pepper, mustard, paprika, Worcestershire sauce, lemon juice and water in a bowl. Dip the chickens in the mixture on both sides. Broil directly on a grill, or for easier turning, place in a double-hinged wire broiler. Turn chickens every 5 minutes and baste frequently until done, about 25 minutes.

Serves 6—175 calories in each serving.

## LAMB EN BROCHETTE

- ⅓ cup soy sauce
- 3 tablespoons lemon juice
- 1 tablespoon olive or salad oil
- ¼ teaspoon freshly ground black pepper
- 3 tablespoons grated onion
- 2 pounds lamb, cut in 1-inch cubes

Mix together the soy sauce, lemon juice, oil, pepper and onion. Marinate the lamb in it for 3 hours or overnight, basting frequently.

Thread on 6 skewers and grill until cooked the way you like it, turning the skewers frequently.

Serves 6—425 calories in each serving.

## HAWAIIAN STEAK

- ¾ cup soy sauce
- ¼ cup water
- 2 cloves garlic, minced
- ½ teaspoon liquid Sucaryl
- 6 minute steaks (2 pounds)

Mix the soy sauce, water, garlic and Sucaryl in a bowl. Marinate the steaks 2 hours, basting and turning them frequently.

Grill over a hot fire to the degree of rareness you like.

Serves 6—400 calories in each serving.

## SHASHLIK

- 1½-pound boned leg or shoulder of lamb
- ½ cup wine vinegar
- ½ cup dry red wine
- ½ teaspoon oregano
- 1 onion, chopped
- ½ teaspoon garlic powder
- 1 tablespoon olive oil

Trim the fat and cut the meat into ¾-inch cubes. Place in a bowl.

Bring to a boil the vinegar, wine and oregano. Pour over the meat and add the onion and garlic powder. Let marinate at room temperature 3 hours or overnight in the refrigerator. Drain and dry the meat.

Thread the cubes on 6 individual skewers. If you like, you can alternate the lamb with mushroom caps and small white onions.

Oil a broiling pan and place the skewers on it. Broil in a hot broiler, 3 inches under the heat (or over an open fire). Turn the skewers to brown the meat on all sides. Sprinkle with salt and serve.

Serves 6—300 calories in each serving.

## MEAT BALLS EN BROCHETTE

- 1¼ pounds lean ground beef
- 1 teaspoon salt
- ¼ teaspoon pepper
- 1 teaspoon curry powder
- ⅛ teaspoon garlic powder
- ¼ cup grated onion
- 1 egg
- 3 tablespoons cold water
- 2 tablespoons bread crumbs
- 3 onions, cut in quarters
- 3 tomatoes, cut in quarters

Mix together the beef, salt, pepper, curry powder, garlic powder, onion, egg and bread crumbs. Shape into 24 balls.

Thread the meat balls, onions and tomatoes on 6 skewers. Grill until browned, turning the skewers frequently. Serve with barbecue sauce.

Serves 6—305 calories in each serving.

## SKEWERS OF STEAK

- ½ cup dry red wine
- 1 teaspoon salt
- ¼ teaspoon freshly ground black pepper
- 1 teaspoon Worcestershire sauce
- 2 tablespoons chili sauce
- 1 tablespoon vinegar
- ½ teaspoon marjoram
- ¼ teaspoon liquid Sucaryl
- 1½ pounds sirloin steak
- 18 mushroom caps

Mix the wine, salt, pepper, Worcestershire sauce, chili sauce, vinegar, marjoram and Sucaryl. Cut the steak into 1½-inch squares and marinate in the sauce 2 hours. Baste frequently.

Arrange the steak and mushrooms alternately on skewers. Grill until browned on all sides, turning the skewers frequently and basting with the sauce.

Serves 6—320 calories in each serving.

## FOIL ROASTED CORN

3 tablespoons butter
2 tablespoons milk
4 teaspoons chopped parsley
6 young corn

Cream the butter and milk until smooth. Blend in the parsley. Husk the corn and rub some of the butter mixture into each. Wrap in aluminum foil, covering the ear completely. Place on the grill for 15 minutes, turning frequently. Serve in the foil with salt, pepper and paprika.

Serves 6—135 calories in each serving.

## CORN IN HUSKS

6 young corn
3 tablespoons butter

Loosen the husks so that you can pull out the silk. Press the husks back against the corn and soak in cold water for 30 minutes. Place on the grill for 15 minutes, turning them frequently. Remove husks and serve with the butter, salt and pepper.

Serves 6—135 calories in each serving.

## GRILLED FRUIT

**Bananas** —Allow 1 banana for serving. Leave it in the skin and grill 8-10 minutes, turning frequently. 100 calories in each banana.

**Pineapple** —Peel a pineapple and cut in 6 lengthwise. Sprinkle each piece with 1 teaspoon honey and let stand 30 minutes. Grill until delicately browned on all sides. 85 calories in each piece.

**Grapefruit** —Cut the grapefruit in half and grill, cut side down until delicately browned. Turn over, segment, and sprinkle each half with 1 teaspoon brown sugar and 1 teaspoon sherry. Grill skin side down until sugar melts. 100 calories in each half.

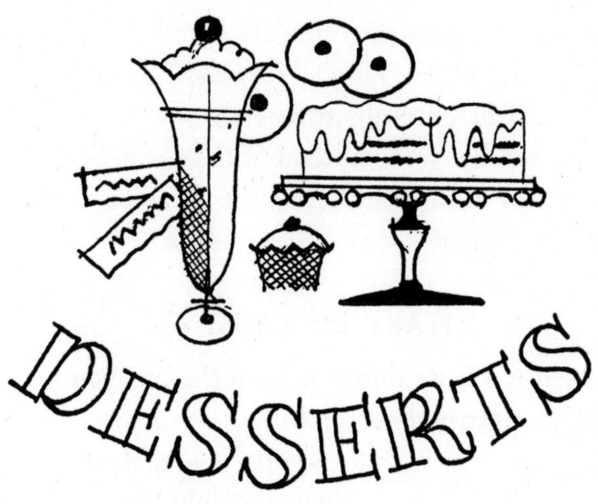


The symbol ⁂ indicates dishes that can be frozen.

Above all else, desserts are missed most by people on diets, and it is the lack of them that causes the downfall of many would-be dieters. Don't deny yourself the pleasure of a dessert that does so much to round off a meal, and permits you to leave the table with a pleasant taste in your mouth. Use the recipes in this section, observe the size of the portions, and you'll never have to do without sweets. The dessert section which follows is particularly complete, and your favorites should be included. Many of them can be prepared for the freezer, so even if the recipe says "serves 16," as for a large cake, and you have a small family, don't let it trouble you. Prepare the full recipe and freeze what you don't need for future use.

You'll find an electric mixer of the utmost importance for beating nonfat dry milk into a delectable, frothy whipped consistency. It can be done by hand with a rotary beater or wire whisk, but it takes considerable time and patience.

The puddings and frozen desserts supply the milk so necessary to the daily diet in a delicious form. Cakes and pies have been sugar- and fat-reduced without impairing the flavor. Follow the recipes carefully and be sure to use standard measuring utensils; avoid deviations, for in desserts this may bring about failure. Don't "improve" recipes or vary them, for the instructions must be carefully followed.

Always plan the dessert to complement the meal. Serve a light, buoyant dessert after a heavy meal and serve the heavier cakes and pies as a follow-up to a light dinner.

## FLAKY PIE CRUST ❋

The method used is a little different from the one you are probably accustomed to. Follow the instructions carefully.

- 1½ cups sifted flour
- 1 teaspoon salt
- 6 tablespoons cold shortening
- 4 tablespoons ice water (approximately)

Sift the flour and salt into a bowl. Break the shortening into several pieces and cut in with a pastry blender or 2 knives (or use the fingertips lightly) until the size of peas. Remove 4 tablespoons and set aside.

Sprinkle a teaspoon of the water over the mixture in the bowl and toss lightly with a fork. Repeat in dry parts until all the mixture is dampened; press into a ball. Roll out on a lightly floured surface and sprinkle with the 4 tablespoons flour mixture. Roll up like a jelly roll and cut in half. Press one half over the other and shape into a round mound. Chill one hour. Cut in 2 equal pieces and roll out as thin as possible. Fit into an 8-inch pie plate. Fill as desired. Cover with remaining rolled-out dough, sealing the edges. Cut 2 or 3 slits in the top. Bake as directed in recipe.

For a one-crust shell, halve the recipe. Fit into the pie plate. Place another pie plate of the same size over it and bake in a 450° oven 15 minutes, or until browned.

Serves 8—2-crust, pastry only, 150 calories in each serving.
1-crust, pastry only, 75 calories in each serving.

## GINGERSNAP CRUST

12 gingersnaps
2 tablespoons melted butter or margarine

Crush the gingersnaps into very fine crumbs. Mix with the butter and press against the sides and bottom of an 8-inch pie plate.

If the filling you intend to use does not require baking, prebake the shell in a 375° oven 5 minutes. Cool before filling.

For a filling to be baked, chill the shell for 10 minutes before filling. Then bake as recipe directs.

Serves 8—60 calories in each serving.

## GRAHAM CRACKER CRUST

7 graham crackers
¼ cup nonfat dry milk
1½ tablespoons sugar
1½ tablespoons softened butter or margarine

Turn oven on and set at 375°.

Roll the crackers into fine crumbs. They should make ½ cup. Mix with the dry milk, sugar and butter. Press against an 8-inch pie plate with the fingers. Bake 7 minutes. Cool before filling.

Serves 8—65 calories in each serving.

## MERINGUE PASTRY CRUST

2 egg whites
¼ teaspoon salt
¼ teaspoon cream of tartar
⅓ cup sugar
½ teaspoon liquid Sucaryl
½ teaspoon vanilla extract
1 teaspoon vinegar

Turn oven on and set at 275°.

Beat the egg whites until frothy. Add the salt and cream of tartar. Beat until stiff but not dry; then beat in a tablespoon of the sugar at a time, then the Sucaryl, vanilla and vinegar. Continue beating until stiff peaks are formed. Spread on the bottom and sides of an 8-inch pie plate. Bake 35 minutes or until delicately browned and firm. Cool and fill as desired.

Serves 8—40 calories in each serving, crust only.

## APPLE PIE ❋

- 2-crust flaky pie crust (see recipe)
- 5 large tart apples
- 1 tablespoon liquid Sucaryl
- 1 tablespoon brown sugar
- ⅛ teaspoon salt
- ½ teaspoon cinnamon
- ½ teaspoon grated lemon rind
- 2 teaspoons lemon juice
- 1 tablespoon milk

Turn oven on and set at 425°. Line an 8-inch pie plate with half the pastry.

Pare the apples and slice them. Mix with the Sucaryl, sugar, salt, cinnamon, lemon rind and juice. Turn into the pie plate and cover with the remaining pastry. Seal the edges and brush with the milk. Make a few slits on top. Bake 45 minutes or until browned. Serve warm or cold.

Serves 8—250 calories in each serving.

### Deep-dish Apple Pie

Use one crust only. Fill a deep 8-inch dish with the apple mixture, using 6 apples. Cover with the pastry and bake as directed.

Serves 8—180 calories in each serving.

## CHERRY PIE ❋

- 3 cups pitted sour red cherries, fresh, frozen or canned
- 2 tablespoons sugar
- 1 tablespoon liquid Sucaryl
- 1½ tablespoons cornstarch
- 2-crust flaky pie crust (see recipe)

Turn oven on and set at 375°. Line an 8-inch pie plate with half the pastry.

Mix the cherries, sugar, Sucaryl and cornstarch. Turn into the pie plate. Cover with the remaining pastry; make a few slits on the top. Bake 45 minutes, or until browned and fruit is tender. Serve warm or cold.

Serves 8—210 calories in each serving.

## BERRY PIE ❋

- 2-crust flaky pie crust (see recipe)
- 3 cups blueberries, raspberries or blackberries
- 2 tablespoons sugar
- 1 tablespoon liquid Sucaryl
- 2 teaspoons lemon juice
- 1 tablespoon cornstarch
- 1 tablespoon milk

Turn oven on and set at 425°. Line an 8-inch pie plate with half the pastry.

Mix the berries with the sugar, Sucaryl, lemon juice and cornstarch. Turn into the pie plate and cover with remaining pastry, sealing the edges well. Brush with the milk and cut a few slits in the top. Bake 45 minutes, or until browned. Serve warm or cold.

Serves 8—200 calories in each serving.

*Note:* If frozen berries are used, omit the sugar, but not the Sucaryl.

## PEACH PIE ✻

- 2-crust flaky pie crust (see recipe)
- 3 cups sliced peaches
- 2 tablespoons sugar
- 2 teaspoons liquid Sucaryl
- ¼ teaspoon salt
- ¼ teaspoon almond extract
- 1 tablespoon cornstarch
- 1 egg yolk
- 2 tablespoons light cream

Turn oven on and set at 425°. Line an 8-inch pie plate with half the pastry.

Mix the peaches with the sugar, Sucaryl, salt, almond extract and cornstarch. Turn into the pie plate. Beat the egg yolk and cream together and pour over the peaches. Cover with the remaining pastry, sealing the edges well. Make a few slits on the top. Bake 45 minutes, or until browned. Cool.

Serves 8—210 calories in each serving.

## BANANA CREAM PIE

- 1 teaspoon butter
- ⅓ cup gingersnap crumbs
- 1 tablespoon gelatin
- ¾ cup water
- 2 eggs
- 1½ cups skim milk
- 1 tablespoon sugar
- 2 teaspoons liquid Sucaryl
- ¼ teaspoon salt
- ½ teaspoon almond extract
- 2 bananas, sliced
- 2 teaspoons grated chocolate

Grease an 8-inch pie plate with the butter; press the crumbs against the bottom and sides. Chill.

Soften the gelatin in the water. Beat the eggs in the top of a double boiler; add the milk, sugar, Sucaryl and salt. Place over hot water and cook, stirring constantly until the mixture coats the spoon. Stir in the gelatin until dissolved. Remove from the hot water and cool. Carefully fold in the almond extract and bananas. Turn into the pie shell. Chill. Sprinkle with the chocolate.

Serves 6—110 calories in each serving.

## CHOCOLATE CHIFFON PIE

- 1 teaspoon butter or margarine
- ½ cup shredded coconut
- 1 tablespoon gelatin
- ½ cup skim milk
- 1 square (ounce) unsweetened chocolate
- 1 tablespoon sugar
- 1½ tablespoons liquid Sucaryl
- ¼ teaspoon salt
- 2 egg yolks
- 1 teaspoon vanilla extract
- 2 egg whites, stiffly beaten
- ¼ cup heavy cream, whipped

Grease an 8-inch pie plate with the butter. Press the coconut against the bottom and sides. Chill.

Soften the gelatin in the milk; place over hot water and stir until dissolved. Break the chocolate into small pieces and add to the milk with the sugar, Sucaryl and salt. Mix until smooth.

Beat the egg yolks and vanilla in a bowl; gradually add the chocolate mixture, stirring constantly to prevent curdling. Cool 15 minutes. Fold in the egg whites and cream and turn into the shell. Chill.

Serves 6—125 calories in each serving.

## LEMON MERINGUE PIE

- 4 egg yolks
- ½ cup sugar
- 1 tablespoon liquid Sucaryl
- ¼ teaspoon salt
- 2 tablespoons cornstarch
- ⅓ cup lemon juice
- 1 teaspoon grated lemon rind
- 1⅓ cups skim milk
- 4 egg whites
- ¼ teaspoon cream of tartar
- Dash salt
- 1 baked 9-inch pie shell

Turn oven on and set at 425°.

Beat the egg yolks in the top of a double boiler until foamy. Add half the sugar, the Sucaryl, salt and cornstarch. Mix until smooth. Stir in the lemon juice, rind and milk. Place over hot water and cook, stirring constantly until thick.

Beat the egg whites until stiff. Transfer ¼ of the quantity to another bowl and pour 2 tablespoons of the lemon mixture over it. Mix until smooth. Add a little more hot mixture, mix until smooth, then return to balance of hot mixture, stirring constantly. Cook until very thick. Cool in a bowl of ice water, then pour into the pie shell.

Add the cream of tartar, salt and remaining sugar to the remaining beaten egg whites and beat until very stiff. Pile on top of the lemon mixture. Bake 5 minutes, or until delicately browned. Cool on a cake rack.

Serves 8—185 calories in each serving.

## LIME PIE

- 1 tablespoon gelatin
- ½ cup cold water
- 3 egg yolks
- ½ cup lime or lemon juice
- 2 tablespoons sugar
- ¾ teaspoon liquid Sucaryl
- ¼ teaspoon salt
- 1 teaspoon grated lime or lemon rind
- 3 drops green food coloring
- ¼ cup nonfat dry milk
- 3 egg whites
- 8-inch baked gingersnap crust

Soften the gelatin in ¼ cup water. Beat the egg yolks, lime juice, 1 tablespoon sugar, Sucaryl and salt in the top of a double boiler. Place over hot water and cook, stirring constantly until thick. Stir in the gelatin until dissolved. Add the rind and food coloring. Chill for 20 minutes.

Beat the remaining ¼ cup water with the dry milk until the consistency of whipped cream. Beat the egg whites until stiff but not dry, and fold in the remaining sugar. Combine with the whipped milk and fold in the lime mixture. Turn into the pie shell. Chill until set. If you like, reserve a few tablespoons whipped milk to decorate the top, or grate a little rind over it.

Serves 8—110 calories in each serving.

## COCONUT CREAM PIE

2 teaspoons butter or margarine
¾ cup toasted coconut
4 eggs
2 tablespoons sugar
1¾ teaspoons liquid Sucaryl
¼ teaspoon salt
1 teaspoon vanilla
2½ cups skim milk, scalded
Nutmeg

Turn oven on and set at 375°. Butter an 8-inch pie plate and press the coconut against the bottom and sides.

Beat the eggs, sugar, Sucaryl, salt and vanilla in a bowl. Gradually add the milk, stirring constantly to prevent curdling. Pour into the prepared pie plate.

Bake 35 minutes, or until a knife inserted in the center comes out clean. Sprinkle with nutmeg.

Serves 8—90 calories in each serving.

## CUSTARD PIE

1¾ cups skim milk
4 tablespoons nonfat dry milk
2 eggs
¼ cup sugar
1 tablespoon liquid Sucaryl
¼ teaspoon salt
½ teaspoon vanilla extract
8-inch pie plate, lined with unbaked flaky pastry
½ teaspoon nutmeg

Turn oven on and set at 425°.

Mix the skim milk and dry milk and scald.

Beat the eggs, gradually adding the sugar, Sucaryl, salt and vanilla. Gradually add the scalded milk, beating steadily to prevent curdling. Pour ¾ of the mixture into the prepared pie plate. Sprinkle with the nutmeg and add the remaining custard.

Bake 10 minutes, then reduce heat to 325° and bake 30 minutes longer, or until a knife inserted in the center comes out clean. Cool on a cake rack.

Serves 8—160 calories in each serving.

## NESSELRODE PIE

2 teaspoons gelatin
1 tablespoon cold water
3 egg yolks
1½ cups skim milk
¼ teaspoon salt
3 tablespoons sugar
1 tablespoon liquid Sucaryl
3 egg whites
2 tablespoons rum
¼ cup chopped maraschino cherries
Baked 9-inch pie shell
2 tablespoons shaved sweet chocolate

Soften the gelatin in the water. Beat the egg yolks in the top of a double boiler. Add the milk, salt, 1 tablespoon sugar and the Sucaryl. Place over hot water and cook, stirring constantly until thick. Remove from the heat and stir in the gelatin until dissolved. Chill until mixture begins to thicken.

Beat the egg whites until peaks form, then beat in the remaining 2 tablespoons sugar. Fold into the gelatin mixture with the rum and cherries. Turn into the pie shell and sprinkle with the chocolate. Chill.

Serves 8—175 calories in each serving.

## PUMPKIN PIE

- 2 eggs
- 1 cup cooked or canned pumpkin
- ½ cup brown sugar
- 1 tablespoon liquid Sucaryl
- ½ teaspoon salt
- ½ teaspoon nutmeg
- ¾ teaspoon ginger
- ¾ teaspoon cinnamon
- 1 tablespoon hot water
- 2 tablespoons orange juice
- ¾ cup skim milk
- 8-inch pie plate lined with flaky pastry

Turn oven on and set at 425°.

Beat the eggs until foamy. Add the pumpkin, brown sugar, Sucaryl and salt. Beat until thick. Mix the nutmeg, ginger and cinnamon in the hot water; add with orange juice and milk. Mix well. Pour into the prepared pie plate.

Bake 20 minutes; reduce the heat to 300°, bake 30 minutes longer or until a knife inserted in the center comes out clean. Cool on a cake rack.

Serves 8—165 calories in each serving.

*Note:* If you like a spicy pie add ¼ teaspoon ground cloves to the hot water.

## STRAWBERRY FLUFF PIE

- ¼ cup sugar
- 2 tablespoons water
- 2 egg whites
- 1 tablespoon gelatin
- ¼ cup skim milk
- ⅛ teaspoon salt
- 1 tablespoon lemon juice
- 1 teaspoon almond extract
- ½ cup nonfat dry milk
- ½ cup ice water
- 8-inch baked gingersnap crust
- ½ teaspoon liquid Sucaryl
- 1 cup strawberries

Boil the sugar and water about 3 minutes, or until a soft ball forms when a drop is placed in cold water. Beat the egg whites until stiff but not dry; gradually beat in the sugar syrup.

Soften the gelatin in the milk; place over hot water and stir until dissolved. Add to the egg whites and beat 1 minute. Stir in the salt, lemon juice and almond extract. Cool.

Beat the dry milk and ice water until the consistency of whipped cream; fold into the egg-white mixture. Turn into the pie shell. Sprinkle the Sucaryl over the berries and arrange on top of the pie. Chill.

Serves 8—110 calories in each serving.

## BLANCMANGE

- 2 tablespoons gelatin
- 3 cups skim milk
- 1 tablespoon sugar
- 1 teaspoon liquid Sucaryl
- 2 teaspoons almond extract
- ¼ teaspoon salt

Soften the gelatin in a half cup milk. Heat the remaining milk and add the gelatin, stirring until dissolved. Add the sugar, Sucaryl, almond extract and salt. Mix well and cook until syrupy. Beat with a rotary beater or electric mixer until frothy and almost double in quantity. Pour into a mold or 8 individual dishes.

Serves 8—45 calories in each serving.

## ORANGE CUSTARD

- 3 tablespoons cornstarch
- 1 tablespoon sugar
- 3 cups skim milk
- 4 egg yolks, lightly beaten
- 2 teaspoon liquid Sucaryl
- 1 teaspoon orange extract
- 2 oranges, peeled and segmented

Mix the cornstarch and sugar in the top of a double boiler. Gradually stir in the milk, mixing until smooth. Add the egg yolks and Sucaryl; place over hot water and cook, stirring constantly until thick. Remove from heat; add the orange extract and orange sections. Turn into a bowl or individual serving dishes. Chill.

Serves 6—125 calories in each serving.

## RENNET DESSERT

- 2 cups skim milk
- 2 tablespoons dry skim milk
- 1 tablespoon sugar
- ¼ teaspoon liquid Sucaryl
- 2 rennet tablets
- 2 teaspoons cold water
- 1½ teaspoons vanilla extract

Beat the milk, dry milk, sugar and Sucaryl together in a saucepan. Cook over very low heat until milk is warm—do not overheat.

Dissolve the rennet in the water and add to the milk with the vanilla. Mix well and pour into 8 dishes. Don't move the dishes until the rennet sets, about 15 minutes. Chill.

Serves 8—75 calories in each serving.

### Coffee Rennet

Substitute 2 tablespoons coffee essence for the water.

## CREAM PUFFS ❋

- ½ cup water
- 3 tablespoons butter or margarine
- ¼ teaspoon salt
- ½ cup sifted flour
- 2 eggs

Turn oven on and set at 375°.

Bring the water and butter to a boil. When butter melts, add the salt and flour all at once. Beat over low heat until the mixture leaves the side of the pan. Remove from the heat and beat for 1 minute. Add one egg at a time, beating after each addition until shiny.

Drop the mixture by the spoon into 8 mounds on a lightly greased baking sheet. Leave about 2 inches between each. Bake 45 minutes, or until browned. Slit sides and return to the oven for 5 minutes. Cool on a cake rack and fill as you like.

Serves 8—110 calories in each serving.

*Note:* To make eclairs, after mounds are formed use a spatula and shape into 4-inch x 1-inch rectangles.

## BAKED CUSTARD

- 3 tablespoons nonfat dry milk
- 3 cups skim milk
- 4 eggs
- 1 tablespoon sugar
- 2 teaspoons liquid Sucaryl
- 1½ teaspoons vanilla extract
- Nutmeg

Turn oven on and set at 325°.

Mix the dry milk with the liquid milk and scald. Beat the eggs, sugar and Sucaryl in a bowl. Add the milk, stirring steadily. Strain into 6 custard cups. Place in a shallow pan of hot water. Sprinkle with nutmeg.

Bake 50 minutes, or until a knife inserted in the center of the custard comes out clean. Chill.

Serves 6—105 calories in each serving.

## AMBROSIA

- ¼ cup milk
- 2 tablespoons nonfat dry milk
- ⅓ cup shredded coconut
- 1 tablespoon sugar
- 3 oranges

Beat the milk and dry milk together. Stir in the coconut and sugar and let soak 10 minutes. Peel and segment the oranges. Add to the coconut milk and chill. Taste, and if not sweet enough add a little liquid Sucaryl.

Serves 6—75 calories in each serving.

## PRUNE PUDDING

- 3 tablespoons cornstarch
- 2 tablespoons sugar
- 1 cup water
- ½ teaspoon liquid Sucaryl
- 1½ cups (3 jars baby food) strained prunes
- 1 teaspoon grated lemon rind
- 1 tablespoon lemon juice
- ¼ teaspoon cinnamon
- ⅛ teaspoon ground allspice

Mix the cornstarch and sugar in a saucepan; gradually add the water, stirring until smooth. Add the Sucaryl, prunes, lemon rind, lemon juice, cinnamon and allspice. Cook over low heat, stirring constantly until thickened. Cool slightly and pour into 6 individual glasses. Chill.

Serves 6—125 calories in each serving.

## SNOW PUDDING

- 2 tablespoons gelatin
- ¼ cup cold water
- 2¾ cups boiling water
- 2 tablespoons sugar
- 2 tablespoons liquid Sucaryl
- ¾ cup lemon juice
- 1 teaspoon grated lemon rind
- Dash salt
- 2 egg whites, stiffly beaten

Soften the gelatin in the water; add the boiling water and stir until dissolved. Stir in the sugar, Sucaryl, lemon juice, rind and salt. Chill until mixture begins to set, then beat with a rotary beater until frothy. Fold in the egg whites. Chill in a mold or 6 individual dishes.

Serves 6—35 calories in each serving.

## OEUFS À LA NEIGE (FLOATING ISLAND)

- 1⅔ cups milk
- 3 teaspoons liquid Sucaryl
- 1 teaspoon vanilla extract
- 5 egg whites
- Dash salt
- 3 tablespoons sugar
- 5 egg yolks

In a large, deep skillet, bring the milk to a boil; stir in 1 teaspoon Sucaryl and the vanilla.

Beat the egg whites and salt until stiff; gradually add the sugar and remaining Sucaryl. Beat until very stiff. Shape the meringue into 12 egg-shaped balls with 2 spoons and drop them into the milk. Cook over very low heat 2 minutes, turn the meringues and let cook 2 minutes longer. Do not let the milk boil. Carefully remove the meringues with a slotted spoon. Strain the milk.

Beat the egg yolks in the top of a double boiler and gradually add the hot milk, stirring constantly to prevent curdling. Place over hot water and cook, stirring constantly until mixture coats the spoon. Chill.

Divide the custard among 6 dessert dishes and float 2 meringues in each.

Serves 6—135 calories in each serving.

## POT DE CRÈME CHOCOLAT

- 4 tablespoons cornstarch
- 4 tablespoons unsweetened cocoa
- 2 tablespoons sugar
- ⅛ teaspoon salt
- 3 cups skim milk
- 2 teaspoons liquid Sucaryl
- 2 teaspoons vanilla extract

Sift the cornstarch, cocoa, sugar and salt into a saucepan. Gradually add the milk, stirring until smooth. Cook over low heat, stirring constantly until thick. Add the Sucaryl and vanilla. Pour into 6 *pots* or custard cups. Chill.

Serves 6—90 calories in each serving.

## LEMON PUDDING

4 tablespoons cornstarch
¼ teaspoon salt
3 egg yolks
⅓ cup lemon juice
1½ cups skim milk
3 tablespoons nonfat dry milk
1 tablespoon melted butter
3 egg whites
1 tablespoon sugar
2 teaspoons liquid Sucaryl

Turn oven on and set at 350°.

Sift the cornstarch and salt into a bowl. Add the egg yolks and lemon juice, beating until smooth. Gradually add the milk and dry milk. Beat again.

Beat the egg whites until stiff but not dry. Beat in the sugar and Sucaryl. Fold the lemon mixture into the egg whites. Turn into a 1½-quart casserole or baking dish. Place in a shallow pan of hot water.

Bake 55 minutes, or until set and browned. Remove from oven and let cool in the pan of water.

Serves 6—110 calories in each serving.

## MERINGUE RICE PUDDING

½ cup rice
2 cups water
¾ teaspoon salt
3 egg yolks
2 teaspoons liquid Sucaryl
½ teaspoon vanilla extract
3 cups skim milk, scalded
3 egg whites
2 tablespoons sugar
¼ teaspoon almond extract

Wash the rice well and combine in a saucepan with the water and salt. Bring to a boil and cook over low heat 25 minutes. Drain.

Turn oven on and set at 325°.

Beat together the egg yolks, Sucaryl and vanilla in a saucepan. Gradually add the scalded milk, beating steadily. Cook over low heat, stirring constantly until the mixture coats the spoon. Add the rice; mix well and turn into a 2-quart baking dish.

Beat the egg whites until stiff but not dry. Fold in the sugar and almond extract. Pile on the rice mixture. Bake 15 minutes. Serve hot or cold.

Serves 6—155 calories in each serving.

### Mocha Meringue Rice Pudding

Use 2 cups double-strength coffee and 1 cup scalded skim milk in place of the 3 cups skim milk.

Serves 6—135 calories in each serving.

## MERINGUE SURPRISE

- 3 egg whites
- ¼ teaspoon cream of tartar
- Dash salt
- 2 tablespoons sugar
- ½ teaspoon liquid Sucaryl
- 1 teaspoon almond extract
- ¼ cup shredded coconut, chopped
- 6 canned peach halves, drained

Turn oven on and set at 325°.

Beat the egg whites until frothy. Add the cream of tartar, salt and sugar, continuing to beat until stiff but not dry. Beat in Sucaryl and almond extract, then fold in the coconut.

Lightly grease a cooky sheet and line with waxed paper. Grease the paper. Drop 6 mounds of the meringue on it, about 2 inches apart, using half the meringue. Carefully place a half peach on it and cover with the remaining meringue. Bake 30 minutes or until delicately browned. Remove from paper and cool.

Serves 6—80 calories in each serving.

## PINEAPPLE-TAPIOCA PUDDING

- 1 egg yolk
- 2 cups skim milk
- 2 tablespoons sugar
- ⅛ teaspoon salt
- 2 tablespoons quick-cooking tapioca
- 2 egg whites
- ½ teaspoon vanilla extract
- ½ cup canned pineapple tidbits, drained

Lightly beat the egg yolk in a saucepan; gradually add the milk, mixing well. Stir in 1 tablespoon sugar, the salt and tapioca. Cook over low heat, stirring constantly until mixture comes to a boil. Remove from heat (it will thicken as it cools).

Beat the egg whites until peaks form, then beat in the sugar. Pour the hot tapioca over the egg whites, stirring constantly. Stir in the vanilla. Cool. Fold in the pineapple. Chill in a mold or 6 individual glasses.

Serves 6—95 calories in each serving.

## LEMON SHERRY PUDDING

- 2 tablespoons sifted flour
- 2 tablespoons sugar
- ½ teaspoon salt
- ½ teaspoon cinnamon
- 2 eggs
- 1 egg yolk
- 1 tablespoon liquid Sucaryl
- 3 tablespoons sherry
- 2 tablespoons lemon juice
- 1 cup skim milk
- 2 egg whites, stiffly beaten

Turn oven on and set at 350°.

Sift the flour, sugar, salt and cinnamon into a bowl. Beat the eggs, egg yolk, Sucaryl, sherry and lemon juice together. Gradually add to the dry ingredients, beating well. Stir in the milk and then fold in the egg whites. Turn into a 1½-quart casserole or baking dish. Place in a shallow pan of hot water. Bake 30 minutes. Serve cold.

Serves 6—90 calories in each serving.

## CHOCOLATE CUSTARD PUDDING

⅓ cup unsweetened cocoa
4 tablespoons sifted flour
1 tablespoon sugar
3 egg yolks
2 cups skim milk
1½ tablespoons liquid Sucaryl
2 teaspoons vanilla extract
3 egg whites

Turn oven on and set at 350°.

Sift the cocoa, flour and sugar into a bowl. Beat the egg yolks, milk, Sucaryl and vanilla together; add to the cocoa mixture, beating until well blended.

Beat the egg whites until stiff but not dry, and fold them into the chocolate mixture. Turn into a 1½-quart round baking dish and set in a shallow pan with 1 inch hot water. Bake 45 minutes, or until set. Serve hot or cold.

Serves 6—110 calories in each serving.

## LEMON-CAKE PUDDING

2 egg whites
¼ teaspoon salt
4 tablespoons sugar
3 teaspoons liquid Sucaryl
2 egg yolks
⅓ cup lemon juice
1 tablespoon grated lemon rind
1 tablespoon melted butter or margarine
3 tablespoons flour
1 cup skim milk

Turn oven on and set at 350°.

Beat the egg whites and salt until peaks form. Add 2 tablespoons sugar and 2 teaspoons Sucaryl, beating until stiff but not dry.

Beat the egg yolks with the lemon juice, rind, butter and the remaining 1 teaspoon Sucaryl. Mix the flour and remaining sugar and add to the yolks. Mix well and stir in the milk. Fold into the egg whites. Turn into a 1-quart casserole. Place in a shallow pan containing ½ inch hot water. Bake 1 hour, or until top is browned and set.

Serve warm or cold. Don't be surprised at the liquid in the dish, it is the correct consistency.

Serves 6—105 calories in each serving.

## APPLE SNOW

2 egg whites
2 tablespoons sugar
1 teaspoon liquid Sucaryl
2 cups unsweetened apple sauce
1 teaspoon vanilla extract
⅛ teaspoon nutmeg

Beat the egg whites until stiff but not dry. Beat in the sugar and Sucaryl. Mix the applesauce, vanilla and nutmeg together. Fold into the egg whites. Serve very cold.

Serves 6—80 calories in each serving.

## APPLESAUCE

- 8 large sour apples
- ⅓ cup water
- 2 tablespoons brown sugar
- 1 tablespoon liquid Sucaryl
- ⅛ teaspoon lemon juice

Quarter the apples and remove the core and pits. Combine the apples and water in a saucepan; cover and cook over low heat 15 minutes. Force through a food mill or purée in an electric blender. Stir in the sugar, Sucaryl and lemon juice. Serve warm or chilled.

Serves 6—105 calories in each serving.

*Note:* You may pare the apples first, if you prefer. Add ½ teaspoon cinnamon or ⅛ teaspoon mace, if you like.

## APPLE BETTY

- 1 teaspoon butter or margarine
- 2 cups cornflakes, crushed
- 1 teaspoon cinnamon
- 1 teaspoon grated lemon rind
- 4 apples, pared and sliced
- 2 tablespoons brown sugar
- ⅓ cup orange juice
- 1 teaspoon liquid Sucaryl

Turn oven on and set at 375°.

Butter a 1-quart casserole. Mix the cornflakes, cinnamon and lemon rind together. Arrange alternate layers of cornflakes and apples, starting and ending with the cornflakes. Mix the sugar, orange juice and Sucaryl together. Pour over the top. Bake 30 minutes, or until apples are tender and top browned.

Serves 6—115 calories in each serving.

## APPLE CHARLOTTE

- 3 slices white bread
- 2 tablespoons melted butter or margarine
- 5 large apples
- 2 tablespoons water
- 2 teaspoons sugar
- 1 teaspoon liquid Sucaryl
- 2 teaspoons lemon juice

Cut the slices of bread in half (to make them half as thick). Brush with the melted butter and arrange on the bottom and sides of a charlotte mold or casserole (buttered side against the mold).

Pare and slice the apples. Combine with the water, sugar and Sucaryl. Cook over low heat 5 minutes, stirring frequently. Stir in the lemon juice and turn into the mold. Bake in a 350° oven 40 minutes or until browned. Carefully unmold and serve hot.

Serves 6—160 calories in each serving.

## BAKED APPLES

- 6 baking apples
- 1 tablespoon brown sugar
- 1 teaspoon liquid Sucaryl
- 2 tablespoons seedless raisins
- ½ cup white wine

Core the apples and pare the skin about 2 inches down from the stem end. Mix the brown sugar, Sucaryl and raisins together. Stuff the apples with the mixture and arrange in a baking dish. Pour the wine over the apples. Bake in a 350° oven 45 minutes or until apples are soft. Baste frequently. Serve hot or cold.

Serves 6—110 calories in each apple.

*Note:* 2 tablespoons mincemeat may be substituted for the raisins.

## BAKED PEARS

- 6 large pears
- 3 tablespoons seedless raisins
- 1 tablespoon brown sugar
- 1 teaspoon liquid Sucaryl
- 3 tablespoons cognac
- ¾ cup orange juice

Pare and core the pears. Mix the raisins, sugar, Sucaryl and 1 tablespoon cognac together. Stuff the pears with the mixture. Arrange in an upright position in a casserole or baking dish; pour the orange juice around them.

Bake in a 350° oven 40 minutes, or until tender but still firm; baste frequently. Heat the cognac in a ladle, set it aflame and pour over the pears. Serve the pears directly from the casserole.

Serves 6—140 calories in each serving.

## CHERRY COMPOTE

- 1 pound cherries
- ½ cup water
- 2 tablespoons sugar
- 10 Sucaryl tablets
- 1 tablespoon cognac
- ⅛ teaspoon almond extract

You may use sour red or black cherries, but you'll have to adjust the sweetening with Sucaryl depending on the type of cherries.

Wash and stem the cherries. Combine the water, sugar and Sucaryl in a saucepan; bring to a boil and drop the cherries into it. Cover and cook over low heat 5 minutes or until the cherries are tender. Remove from the heat and add the cognac and extract. Chill.

Serves 6—100 calories in each serving.

## SPICED APPLES

- 6 cooking apples
- 2 tablespoons brown sugar
- 1½ tablespoons liquid Sucaryl
- ½ cup water
- ½ teaspoon cinnamon
- ¼ teaspoon nutmeg
- 2 cloves
- ½ lemon, thinly sliced

Wash the core the apples; cut into eighths. In a saucepan, combine the sugar, Sucaryl, water, cinnamon, nutmeg, cloves, lemon and apples. Bring to a boil and cook over low heat 10 minutes, or until apples are soft but still retain their shape. Chill. Serve as a dessert or with bland meat dishes.

Serves 6—100 calories in each serving.

## BAKED BANANAS

- 3 firm bananas
- 1 teaspoon cornstarch
- ¼ cup orange juice
- 1 tablespoon melted butter or margarine
- ½ teaspoon liquid Sucaryl
- 1 tablespoon brown sugar
- ¼ cup shredded coconut

Turn oven on and set at 375°.

Peel the bananas and cut in half crosswise, then lengthwise. Arrange in a shallow baking dish. Mix the cornstarch, orange juice and Sucaryl until smooth. Pour over the bananas. Sprinkle with the brown sugar and coconut.

Bake 15 minutes or until easily pierced with a fork. Serve warm.

Serves 6—95 calories in each serving.

## BANANA DELIGHT

- 1 tablespoon gelatin
- 1½ cups water
- ½ cup raspberry juice (fresh or canned)
- 2 teaspoons liquid Sucaryl
- 1 banana, mashed
- 2 tablespoons chopped walnuts
- 2 marshmallows, cut in small pieces

Soften the gelatin in the water; place over hot water and stir until dissolved. Stir in the Sucaryl. Chill until it begins to set and then beat until fluffy. Fold in the banana, walnuts and marshmallows. Turn into a mold or 6 individual glasses. Chill.

Serves 6—50 calories in each serving.

## ORANGE COMPOTE

- 6 oranges
- ¾ cup water
- ⅛ teaspoon salt
- 2 tablespoons sugar
- 40 Sucaryl tablets
- 1 tablespoon orange liqueur

Peel the oranges, reserving the peel of 2. Cut the peel into julienne strips and combine in a saucepan with the water, salt, sugar and Sucaryl. Cook over low heat 25 minutes.

Segment the oranges and place in a heatproof bowl. Pour the hot syrup over them. Chill and stir in the orange liqueur.

Serves 6—90 calories in each serving.

## ORANGE WHIP

- 1 tablespoon gelatin
- ½ cup cold water
- 1½ cups hot water
- ½ cup orange juice
- 1 teaspoon lemon extract
- 2 tablespoons sugar
- 2 teaspoons liquid Sucaryl
- 1 tablespoon lemon juice
- 1 tablespoon grated orange rind
- 1 egg white, stiffly beaten
- 2 tablespoons heavy cream, whipped

Soften the gelatin in the cold water, then dissolve in the hot water. Stir in the orange juice, lemon extract, sugar, Sucaryl, lemon juice and orange rind. Chill until it begins to set. Blend the egg white and whipped cream; fold into the gelatin mixture. Chill in a mold or 6 individual bowls.

Serves 6—50 calories in each serving.

## PEAR COMPOTE

- 12 canned pear halves
- ½ cup orange juice
- 2 tablespoons lemon juice
- 2 tablespoons sugar
- 2 teaspoons liquid Sucaryl
- ¼ cup water
- 1 teaspoon grated lemon rind
- 2 teaspoons preserved ginger, minced or 1 teaspoon powdered ginger

Wash the pears to remove any syrup. Combine the orange juice, lemon juice, sugar, Sucaryl, water, lemon rind and ginger in a saucepan. Cook over low heat 10 minutes. Add the pears and cook 5 minutes. Chill.

Serves 6—135 calories in each serving.

## RHUBARB COMPOTE

- 2 pounds rhubarb
- 2 tablespoons sugar
- 30 Sucaryl tablets
- 1 teaspoon vanilla extract

Wash the rhubarb and cut into 1-inch pieces. Combine in a skillet with the sugar and Sucaryl. Cook over low heat 10 minutes, stirring frequently. Remove from the heat and add the vanilla. Chill.

Serves 6—40 calories in each serving.

## PINEAPPLE FLUFF

- 1 tablespoon gelatin
- ½ cup orange juice
- 1 can (#2) crushed pineapple
- 2 egg whites, stiffly beaten
- ¼ cup heavy cream, whipped

Soften the gelatin in the orange juice; place over hot water and stir until dissolved. Drain the pineapple and combine the syrup with the gelatin mixture. Mix well and chill until it begins to set. Fold in the drained pineapple (reserve a few pieces for the top), the egg whites and cream. Turn into a mold or 6 sherbet glasses. Decorate with reserved pieces. Chill.

Serves 6—115 calories in each serving.

## PINEAPPLE MÉLANGE

1 pineapple
1 cup sliced strawberries or whole raspberries
1 banana, sliced
1 teaspoon liquid Sucaryl
1 tablespoon Kirsch (cherry brandy)

Cut the pineapple in half and scoop out the centers with a melon-ball cutter. Combine with the berries, banana, Sucaryl and Kirsch. Mix well and let marinate for 30 minutes in the refrigerator before serving. You may use the pineapple shells as a container for the melange, or serve it in a glass bowl.

Serves 6—55 calories in each serving.

## STEWED PLUMS

¾ cup water
2 tablespoons sugar
20 Sucaryl tablets
12 firm plums, red, green or blue

Combine the water, sugar and Sucaryl; bring to a boil and carefully drop the plums into the syrup. Cover and cook over low heat 10-15 minutes or until tender but still firm. Taste for sweetness and add more Sucaryl if needed. Chill.

Serves 6—75 calories in 1 serving.

## BERRY BAVARIAN CREAM ✻

1 tablespoon gelatin
2 tablespoons water
1 cup crushed strawberries or raspberries
3 tablespoons confectioner's sugar
1 tablespoon Sucaryl
2 egg whites, stiffly beaten
¼ cup heavy cream, whipped

Soften the gelatin in the water; place over hot water and stir until dissolved. Combine with the berries and chill until it begins to set. Fold in the sugar, Sucaryl, egg whites and cream. Pour into a wet mold and chill. Carefully unmold and garnish with whole berries, if you like.

Serves 6—65 calories in each serving.

## COFFEE SPONGE

1 tablespoon gelatin
½ cup milk
1½ cups hot coffee
3 egg yolks
2 tablespoons sugar
2 tablespoons liquid Sucaryl
¼ teaspoon salt
3 egg whites, stiffly beaten
½ teaspoon vanilla extract

Soften the gelatin in the milk. Add the hot coffee, stirring until dissolved.

Beat the egg yolks, sugar, Sucaryl and salt in the top of a double boiler. Gradually add the coffee mixture, stirring steadily to prevent curdling. Place over hot water and cook 5 minutes, stirring steadily. Chill until mixture begins to thicken, then fold in the egg whites and vanilla. Turn into a mold or 6 individual glasses. Chill.

Serves 6—70 calories in each serving.

## STRAWBERRIES PARISIENNE

2 egg whites
¼ cup heavy cream
1 teaspoon liquid Sucaryl
½ teaspoon vanilla extract
3 cups strawberries, washed and drained

Beat the egg whites until stiff but not dry. Whip the cream and fold into the egg whites with the Sucaryl and vanilla. Fold in the berries and serve in sherbet glasses. If you like a really sweet dessert, sprinkle the berries with 1 teaspoon liquid Sucaryl before combining with the cream mixture. Serve cold.

Serves 6—60 calories in each serving.

## NEGRITOS (CHOCOLATE DESSERT)

2 squares (ounces) unsweetened chocolate
1 tablespoon sugar
1 tablespoon liquid Sucaryl
3 egg yolks, beaten
Dash salt
1 tablespoon cognac
3 egg whites, stiffly beaten

Break the chocolate into small pieces and let it melt over hot water. Add the sugar, Sucaryl, egg yolks, salt and cognac, stirring constantly. Remove from the heat and immediately fold in the egg whites.

Turn into 6 individual serving glasses. Chill for at least 5 hours. Serve with 1 tablespoon of fluffy whipped cream (see recipe) on top.

Serves 6—95 calories in each serving.

## STRAWBERRY SPONGE

2 cups strawberries, washed and drained
1 tablespoon gelatin
1 cup orange juice
1 tablespoon sugar
1 tablespoon liquid Sucaryl
2 egg whites, stiffly beaten
⅛ teaspoon almond extract
Dash salt

Select 6 large berries and reserve. Force the remaining berries through a food mill or mash very fine.

Soften the gelatin in the orange juice, then place over hot water and stir until dissolved. Add the sugar and Sucaryl. Cool until it begins to set. Add the berry pulp and beat with a rotary beater until foamy. Fold in the egg whites and almond extract. Arrange the reserved berries in a 1-quart mold or place one each in 6 individual molds. Pour the mixture over the berries and chill until firm. Unmold carefully or serve in the molds (if china).

Serves 6—65 calories in each serving.

## CHARLOTTE RUSSE

9 lady fingers, split
1½ cups fluffy whipped cream (see recipe)
6 maraschino cherries

Arrange 3 halves of the lady fingers upright in each of 6 sherbet glasses. Divide the whipped cream among them and place a cherry in the center of each.

Serves 6—125 calories in each serving.

## SABAYON

6 egg yolks
2 tablespoons sugar
1 teaspoon liquid Sucaryl
⅔ cup Marsala or sherry

Beat the egg yolks, sugar and Sucaryl in the top of a double boiler until well blended (use a rotary beater or wire whisk). Add the wine; place over hot water and beat until thick and creamy. Serve warm in tall sherbet glasses, or cold.

Serves 6—130 calories in each serving.

## BERRY ICE ❄

3 cups berries (strawberries, blueberries or blackberries)
½ cup sugar
2 cups water
2 tablespoons lemon juice

Force the berries through a sieve and measure the resulting juice. You should have 1½ cups.

Boil the sugar and water together 5 minutes. Add the juice and lemon juice. Cool and pour into the refrigerator tray. Freeze until mushy, then beat very hard; freeze again until mushy and beat again. The more times you beat the better the ice.

Makes about 4 cups—75 calories in ½ cup.

## COCOA ICE CREAM ❄

1 cup light cream
1 cup milk
2 egg yolks
2 tablespoons sugar
1 tablespoon liquid Sucaryl
3 tablespoons unsweetened cocoa
1 teaspoon vanilla
2 egg whites
⅛ teaspoon salt

Scald the cream and milk. Beat the egg yolks, gradually adding the sugar, Sucaryl and cocoa. Beat until smooth. Gradually add the scalded cream mixture, beating constantly to prevent curdling. Cook over low heat, mixing constantly until mixture coats the spoon. Remove from the heat and stir in the vanilla. Pour into a refrigerator tray and freeze until mushy. Beat with a rotary beater or electric mixer until frothy.

Beat the egg whites and salt until stiff but not dry. Fold into the chocolate mixture and freeze until almost set. Beat again and freeze.

Serves 6—135 calories in each serving.

## BISCUIT TORTONI ❋

1 cup water
1 cup nonfat dry milk
¼ cup lemon juice
1 tablespoon sugar
1 tablespoon liquid Sucaryl
1 tablespoon sherry
½ teaspoon almond extract
½ teaspoon vanilla extract
16 almonds, ground

Combine the water and dry milk in a bowl. Beat with an electric mixer or rotary beater until thickened. Add the lemon juice and beat until thick. Add the sugar and Sucaryl. Beat until the consistency of whipped cream. Fold in the sherry, almond and vanilla extracts.

Spoon into 8 4-ounce paper cups or an ice tray. Sprinkle with the almonds. Freeze.

Serves 8—65 calories in each serving.

## FRENCH CREAM ❋

3 tablespoons cornstarch
3 tablespoons nonfat dry milk
2 tablespoons sugar
1½ cups skim milk
1 egg
¼ teaspoon liquid Sucaryl
1 teaspoon orange extract
1 tablespoon cognac
6 lady fingers, split

Mix the cornstarch, dry milk and sugar in the top of a double boiler. Gradually add the milk, stirring until smooth. Place over hot water and cook, stirring steadily until the boiling point. Cook 15 minutes longer, stirring occasionally.

Beat the egg and Sucaryl together. Add a little of the hot-milk mixture, stirring steadily to prevent curdling. Return to balance of hot mixture and cook 2 minutes, stirring almost constantly. Add the orange extract and cognac. Cool 20 minutes.

Arrange 2 lady-finger halves in an upright position in each of 6 sherbet glasses. Fill with the cream and chill.

Serves 6—100 calories in each serving.

## LEMON ICE CREAM ❋

1 tablespoon butter or margarine
1 tablespoon flour
⅛ teaspoon salt
3¼ cups milk
2 teaspoons liquid Sucaryl
½ cup lemon juice
2 teaspoons lemon rind

Melt the butter in a saucepan; stir in the flour and salt. Gradually add half the milk, stirring constantly to the boiling point. Cook over low heat 5 minutes. Remove from the heat and add the balance of the milk. Pour into a refrigerator tray and freeze in the freezer or refrigerator, set at the coldest point, until mixture begins to freeze on the sides. Turn into a bowl; add the Sucaryl, lemon juice and rind. Beat until frothy. Return to tray and freeze.

Makes 1½ pints—105 calories in ½ cup serving.

2 teaspoons gelatin
1 cup cold water
¾ cup nonfat dry milk
1½ cups milk
3 tablespoons sugar
1 tablespoon liquid Sucaryl
2 teaspoons vanilla
1 tablespoon lemon juice

## ICE-CREAM DESSERT ❄

Soften the gelatin in ½ cup water. Mix ¼ cup dry milk with the milk and then scald. Dissolve the gelatin in it and stir in 2 tablespoons sugar, the Sucaryl and vanilla. Chill until slightly thickened.

Beat the remaining ½ cup dry milk with remaining ½ cup water until it begins to thicken. Add the lemon juice and beat until thick. Beat in the sugar and continue beating until the consistency of whipped cream. Fold in the chilled gelatin mixture. Turn into 2 refrigerator trays and freeze in the freezer or refrigerator (set at coldest point) until the edges are set. Beat with a rotary beater or electric mixer and then freeze until set.

Serves 8—80 calories in each serving.

### Chocolate Ice-cream Dessert

Melt 2 squares unsweetened chocolate when heating the milk, and use 1½ tablespoons liquid Sucaryl.

Serves 8—105 calories in each serving.

### Strawberry Ice-cream Dessert

Add 1 cup mashed strawberries to the cooled gelatin mixture. Use 1½ tablespoons liquid Sucaryl.

Serves 8—85 calories in each serving.

### Banana Ice-cream Dessert

Add 2 mashed bananas to the cooled gelatin mixture.

Serves 8—105 calories in each serving.

## MOCHA BISCUIT ❋

- 2 tablespoons flour
- 2 tablespoons sugar
- 2 cups milk
- 2 cups double-strength coffee
- 1 tablespoon liquid Sucaryl
- 4 eggs
- 1 teaspoon vanilla extract
- 1 tablespoon ground nuts

Mix the flour and sugar in a saucepan. Combine the milk, coffee and Sucaryl; gradually add to the saucepan, stirring until smooth. Cook over low heat, stirring steadily to the boiling point. Cook 5 minutes longer.

Beat the eggs lightly. Gradually add some of the hot mixture, stirring steadily to prevent curdling. Return to the balance of the hot mixture. Place over hot water and cook 5 minutes, still stirring constantly. Remove from heat and add the vanilla. Pour into 8 paper cups and freeze in the freezer or the freezing compartment of the refrigerator (set at coldest point). Sprinkle with the nuts.

Serves 8—110 calories in each serving.

## MOCHA CREAM ❋

- 1 teaspoon gelatin
- ½ cup milk
- ½ cup double-strength coffee
- 2 egg yolks
- 3 tablespoons sugar
- 1 tablespoon liquid Sucaryl
- ⅛ teaspoon salt
- 1 square (ounce) unsweetened chocolate, grated
- ⅓ cup water
- ⅓ cup nonfat dry milk
- 1 tablespoon lemon juice
- 2 egg whites, stiffly beaten

Soften the gelatin in ¼ cup milk. Scald the remaining milk and coffee. Beat the egg yolks, 2 tablespoons sugar, the Sucaryl and salt in the top of a double boiler. Gradually add the hot coffee mixture, stirring steadily to prevent curdling. Place over hot water and cook, stirring constantly until mixture coats the spoon. Stir in the chocolate and gelatin. Mix well and cool.

Beat the dry milk and water together until it begins to thicken. Add the lemon juice and beat until thick, then beat in the remaining sugar. Continue to beat until the consistency of whipped cream.

Fold into the coffee mixture with the beaten egg whites. Turn into refrigerator trays and freeze in the freezer or refrigerator (set at coldest point) until the edges are icy. Beat with a rotary beater or electric mixer. Freeze again until mushy. Beat again and then freeze.

Serves 6—90 calories in each serving.

## CUSTARD SAUCE

- 2 eggs
- 1 tablespoon sugar
- ½ teaspoon liquid Sucaryl
- ⅛ teaspoon salt
- 1 cup skim milk, scalded
- ½ teaspoon vanilla

Beat the eggs, sugar, Sucaryl and salt in the top of a double boiler. Gradually add the milk, beating steadily. Place over hot water and cook, stirring steadily until the mixture coats the spoon. Remove from heat, stir in the vanilla and cool. Serve on fruits, plain cake or puddings.

Makes about 1½ cups—15 calories in 1 tablespoon.

## LEMON SAUCE

- 1 tablespoon cornstarch
- ⅛ teaspoon salt
- 2 tablespoons sugar
- 1 cup skim milk
- 1½ teaspoons liquid Sucaryl
- 3 tablespoons lemon juice
- 2 teaspoons grated lemon rind
- 2 teaspoons butter

Combine the cornstarch, salt and sugar in a saucepan. Gradually blend in the milk and Sucaryl. Cook over low heat, stirring constantly until thick. Remove from heat and stir in the lemon juice, rind and butter. Serve warm or cold on puddings, gelatine desserts, ice cream or plain cake.

Makes 1¼ cups—15 calories in 1 tablespoon.

## MAPLE SAUCE

- 2 tablespoons cornstarch
- 1 tablespoon sugar
- ¼ teaspoon salt
- 1 cup water
- 1½ teaspoons liquid Sucaryl
- 2 teaspoons maple flavoring

Mix the cornstarch, sugar and salt in a saucepan. Add a little water, stirring until smooth, then gradually add the remaining water and Sucaryl. Cook over low heat, stirring constantly, until the boiling point. Cook 5 minutes. Stir in the flavoring. Serve warm or cold.

Makes 1 cup—5 calories in 1 tablespoon.

## MILK CHOCOLATE SAUCE

- 1 tablespoon cornstarch
- 2 tablespoons unsweetened cocoa
- 1 tablespoon sugar
- 1 cup skim milk
- 1½ teaspoons liquid Sucaryl
- 2 teaspoons butter or margarine
- ½ teaspoon vanilla extract

Mix the cornstarch, cocoa and sugar in a saucepan. Stir in a little milk, mixing until smooth. Gradually add the remaining milk, Sucaryl and butter. Cook over low heat, stirring constantly until thick, about 5 minutes. Place over ice or in ice water and stir until cool. Add the vanilla. Serve cold with puddings, ice cream or cake.

Makes 1 cup—15 calories in 1 tablespoon.

## CHEESE FROSTING

1 cup cottage cheese
2 tablespoons cream cheese
2 tablespoons confectioners' sugar
¼ cup orange juice
1 tablespoon grated orange rind

Force the cottage cheese and cream cheese through a sieve. Beat in the sugar, orange juice and orange rind. Makes enough to frost two 8-inch layers.

—380 calories in entire recipe.

## PEAKED FROSTING

⅓ cup white corn syrup
2 egg whites
Dash salt
1 teaspoon vanilla, almond, lemon or orange extract

Bring the syrup to a boil. Beat the egg whites and salt until stiff but not dry. Gradually add the syrup and flavoring, beating constantly until stiff peaks are formed.

Use to frost cakes or cupcakes. Makes enough for a 9-inch layer cake or about 24 cupcakes.

—340 calories in entire recipe.

## CREAM FILLING

¼ package vanilla or chocolate pudding
½ cup skim milk

Prepare pudding as package directs. Cool and use as a filling for cakes.

—125 calories in entire recipe.

## FLUFFY WHIPPED CREAM

3 egg whites
1 tablespoon sugar
½ cup heavy cream
½ teaspoon vanilla extract

Beat the egg whites until stiff; beat in the sugar. Whip the cream and fold into the egg whites with the vanilla.

Makes about 3 cups—enough to cover a 9-inch layer cake.

—490 calories in entire recipe.

### Chocolate Fluffy Cream

Add 3 tablespoons unsweetened cocoa and 1 teaspoon liquid Sucaryl to the beaten egg whites.

—550 calories in entire recipe.

## CAKES

1. Always read the recipe and instructions before starting the procedure.

2. Measure the ingredients carefully and accurately. For best results, don't make changes in cake recipes. A little more flour, butter or liquid can completely change the consistency.

   A. The type of flour and baking powder specified in the recipes should be used.

      (1) Throughout this book, flour means all-purpose flour unless a specific flour is called for. Always sift it just before measuring.

      (2) Cake flour is used in some recipes. It is a finer-textured flour and should be used when specified.

      (3) There are three types of baking powder available, double-acting, tartar and phosphate. You may use any of the three unless a definite type is specified. Be sure to use it if it is.

3. Use the freshest and best ingredients.

4. The size of the pan specified in the recipe is important—use it. Prepare the pans as the recipe specifies before beginning.

5. If your oven does not have a temperature gauge or regulator, buy a thermometer which you can place in the oven as a guide.

6. Preheat the oven at least 10 minutes, but to be very sure develop the habit of turning on and setting the oven at the proper temperature before you begin the preparation of the recipe. Oven temperature is one of the most important factors for successful cakes.

7. The center of the oven is the best place to bake a cake. Arrange the rack so that when the cake is on it the top will reach the center. When baking more than one cake, be sure the pans are separated and don't touch. If you bake them on two levels, have at least two inches between the levels and never place one pan directly above or below the other.

8. Don't open the oven door to peek until five minutes before the end of the suggested baking time. If cake appears browned, test it by lightly inserting a cake tester or toothpick into the center of the cake. If it comes

out clean and dry, the cake is finished. You can also test a cake for "doneness" by gently pressing the top with your finger. If it is springy it is done.

9. Remove the pan and place on a cake rack for a few minutes. (The cake will shrink from the sides of the pan.) Then run a spatula around the edge, carefully remove, and complete the cooling on the cake rack. (Sponge, angel and chiffon cakes have different instructions for cooling, so follow them carefully.)

## GOLD CAKE ❋

- 1¾ cups sifted flour
- 1 tablespoon baking powder
- ¼ teaspoon salt
- ½ cup butter or margarine
- ⅓ cup sugar
- 2 tablespoons liquid Sucaryl
- 1 tablespoon grated orange rind
- 8 egg yolks
- ½ cup skim milk

Turn oven on and set at 375°. Grease two 9-inch layer-cake pans and dust lightly with flour.

Sift the flour, baking powder and salt together. Cream the butter, gradually adding the sugar. Continue creaming until very smooth. Add the Sucaryl, orange rind and egg yolks. Beat until thick and light. Add the flour mixture alternately with the milk. Turn into the pans. Bake 30 minutes, or until a cake tester comes out clean. Cool on a cake rack.

Put together with orange- or chocolate-flavored fluffy whipped cream (see recipe).

Serves 16—145 calories in each serving of cake (without cream).

*Note:* The batter makes excellent cup cakes. Bake 20 minutes or until a cake tester comes out clean.

Makes 24—100 calories in each.

## SPONGE CAKE ❋

- 1¼ cups sifted cake flour
- 6 egg yolks
- ¾ cup powdered sugar
- 1 tablespoon liquid Sucaryl
- 4 tablespoons boiling water
- ¼ teaspoon salt
- 1 teaspoon cream of tartar
- 6 egg whites
- 1 teaspoon vanilla extract

Turn oven on and set at 350°. Sift the flour twice.

Beat the egg yolks with an electric mixer or rotary beater until very thick. Add half the sugar, a tablespoon at a time, beating well after each addition, until thick. Add the Sucaryl and the water gradually, beating well. Set aside for 5 minutes.

Sift the salt, cream of tartar and remaining sugar over the egg whites. Beat until stiff peaks form.

Beat the egg-yolk mixture again. Place ¼ the egg whites and the vanilla on the yolk mixture. Sift ¼ the flour over them. Fold in. Repeat, using the same proportion of egg white and flour until the ingredients are used up. Turn into a 9-inch tube pan. Bake 50 minutes, or until delicately browned and cake springs back into place when pressed with the fingertip. Invert and let cool, allowing an air space under the cake. Carefully run a spatula around the cake and turn out.

Serves 16—95 calories in each.

### Chocolate Sponge Cake

Substitute 4 tablespoons unsweetened cocoa for 4 tablespoons flour. Sift together twice, then proceed as directed.

Serves 16—95 calories in each serving.

### Mocha Sponge Cake

Substitute 2 teaspoons coffee extract for the vanilla extract. Proceed as directed.

Serves 16—95 calories in each serving.

## CHOCOLATE SQUARES ❋

- 2 squares (ounces) unsweetened chocolate
- 2 tablespoons butter
- 1 tablespoon brewed coffee
- 1 cup sifted cake flour
- 1½ teaspoons baking powder
- ¼ teaspoon salt
- 2 eggs
- ½ cup sugar
- 1 tablespoon liquid Sucaryl
- ½ cup skim milk

Turn oven on and set at 350°. Grease an 8-inch-square pan and dust it lightly with flour.

Melt the chocolate and butter in the coffee. Sift the flour, baking powder and salt together. Beat the eggs, gradually adding the sugar and chocolate mixture. Beat until fluffy. Add the flour alternately with the milk, beating just until smooth. Turn into the pan. Bake 30 minutes, or until a cake tester comes out clean. Cool on a cake rack.

Serves 12—120 calories in each serving.

## LADY FINGERS ❋

- 3 egg whites
- ⅓ cup sifted confectioners' sugar
- 3 egg yolks
- 1 teaspoon vanilla extract
- 2 teaspoons lemon juice
- ⅛ teaspoon salt
- ½ cup sifted cake flour
- 2 tablespoons sugar

Turn oven on and set at 350°. Line a cooky sheet with white paper or aluminum foil.

Beat the egg whites until stiff. Gradually add the confectioners' sugar, beating until stiff peaks are formed.

Beat the egg yolks until thick and lemon-colored. Add the vanilla, lemon juice and salt. Fold into the whites. Sift the flour over the mixture and fold in carefully but thoroughly. Force the mixture through a pastry tube with a plain tube onto the cooky sheet in 3-inch lengths, or spread 3-inch x ½-inch strips. Sprinkle with the sugar. Bake 12 minutes, or until delicately browned. Let cool on a cake rack.

Makes about 18—40 calories in each.

## ANGEL CAKE ❋

- 1 cup sifted cake flour
- ¾ cup sugar
- 10 egg whites (1¼ cups)
- ¼ teaspoon salt
- 1 teaspoon cream of tartar
- ½ teaspoon vanilla extract
- 1½ tablespoons liquid Sucaryl

Turn oven on and set at 350°.

Sift the flour and 4 tablespoons sugar together.

Beat the egg whites, salt and cream of tartar until thickened and foamy. Add 2 tablespoons of the remaining sugar at a time, beating until stiff peaks form. Beat in the vanilla and Sucaryl.

Sift 2 tablespoons of the flour mixture at a time over the egg whites and fold in gently after each addition. Turn into a 9-inch spring form pan.

Bake 40 minutes, or until delicately browned and springy when pressed. Invert pan and let cool. Allow air to circulate underneath. Run a spatula around the edges and turn out.

Serves 16—75 calories in each serving.

### Chocolate Angel Cake

Substitute 4 tablespoons sifted unsweetened cocoa for 4 tablespoons of the flour. Proceed as directed.

Serves 16—75 calories in each serving.

## CINNAMON CAKE ✻

- 4 tablespoons butter or margarine
- ¼ cup sugar
- 1½ teaspoons liquid Sucaryl
- 2 egg yolks
- 2 tablespoons milk
- 2 teaspoons grated orange rind
- ⅔ cup sifted cake flour
- 1 teaspoon baking powder
- ⅛ teaspoon salt
- 2 egg whites, stiffly beaten
- 2 tablespoons brown sugar
- 1 tablespoon cinnamon

Turn oven on and set at 375°. Lightly grease an 8-inch square pan.

Cream the butter; gradually add the sugar, beating until light and fluffy. Add the Sucaryl, egg yolks, milk and orange rind. Mix well. Sift the flour, baking powder and salt over the mixture, mixing until just blended. Fold in the egg whites. Turn into the pan and sprinkle with the brown sugar and cinnamon mixed together.

Bake 20 minutes or until a cake tester comes out clean. Cool on a cake rack.

Serves 12—100 calories in each serving.

## CHOCOLATE ROLL ✻

- 3 eggs
- ½ cup sugar
- 2 tablespoons water
- ¼ cup unsweetened cocoa
- ½ cup sifted flour
- ¼ teaspoon salt
- 1 teaspoon vanilla extract

Turn oven on and set at 350°. Grease an 11-inch x 16-inch (jelly roll) pan, line with waxed paper and grease again.

Beat the eggs until light. Gradually beat in the sugar until thick. Beat in the water. Sift the cocoa, flour and salt over it and blend in. Stir in the vanilla. Turn into the pan, spreading it evenly.

Bake 15 minutes. Carefully turn out onto a towel sprinkled with cocoa and peel off the paper. Roll up and let cool 1 hour. Then unroll and spread with the selected filling.

Serves 16—60 calories in each serving; cake only.

### Peppermint Chocolate Roll

Spread roll with peaked frosting flavored with 10 drops of oil of peppermint. Roll up.

Serves 16—80 calories in each serving.

### Chocolate Whipped-cream Roll

Spread the chocolate roll with 2 cups fluffy whipped cream.

Serves 16—90 calories in each serving.

## GINGERBREAD ✲

1 cup sifted flour
½ teaspoon baking soda
¼ teaspoon salt
1 teaspoon cinnamon
1½ teaspoons ginger
¼ teaspoon nutmeg
1 egg
2 tablespoons dark-brown sugar
1⅛ teaspoons liquid Sucaryl
¼ cup molasses
½ cup buttermilk or sour skim milk
3 tablespoons melted butter or margarine

Turn oven on and set at 350°. Grease an 8-inch square pan and dust lightly with flour.

Sift the flour, soda, salt, cinnamon, ginger and nutmeg together.

Beat the egg, sugar, Sucaryl and molasses together until light. Add the buttermilk and butter, then the flour. Beat until smooth. Turn into the pan.

Bake 35 minutes, or until a cake tester comes out clean. Cool on a cake rack.

Serves 12—35 calories in each serving.

## UPSIDE-DOWN APPLE CAKE

2 apples, peeled and sliced
1 teaspoon lemon juice
1 tablespoon brown sugar
½ teaspoon cinnamon
1 cup sifted cake flour
1½ teaspoons baking powder
Dash salt
2 egg yolks
¼ cup sugar
1½ tablespoons liquid Sucaryl
6 tablespoons hot water
1 teaspoon vanilla extract
2 egg whites, stiffly beaten

Turn oven on and set at 350°. Lightly grease an 8-inch square pan.

Combine the apples, lemon juice, brown sugar and cinnamon. Spread on the bottom of the pan.

Sift the flour, baking powder and salt together. Beat the egg yolks, gradually adding the sugar and Sucaryl. Beat until thick and light. Beat in the water, and then the flour and vanilla. Fold in the egg whites. Turn into the pan.

Bake 35 minutes, or until a cake tester comes out clean. Cool on a cake rack 10 minutes, run a spatula around the edges and turn out carefully.

Serves 10—100 calories in each.

### Pineapple Upside-Down Cake

Substitute 1½ cups crushed drained pineapple for the apples.

Serves 10—105 calories in each serving.

### Bing Cherry

Substitute 1½ cups drained pitted bing cherries for the apples.

Serves 10—95 calories in each serving.

## ORANGE CHIFFON CAKE ❋

- 1 cup plus 2 tablespoons sifted cake flour
- ½ cup sugar
- 1½ teaspoons baking powder
- ½ teaspoon salt
- 2 egg yolks
- 3 tablespoons salad oil
- 1½ teaspoons grated orange rind
- ⅓ cup orange juice
- 1 teaspoon liquid Sucaryl
- 4 egg whites
- ¼ teaspoon cream of tartar

Turn oven on and set at 325°

Sift the flour, sugar, baking powder and salt into a bowl. Make a well in the center and add the yolks, oil, orange rind, orange juice and Sucaryl. Beat until smooth.

Beat the egg whites and cream of tartar until very stiff. Slowly pour the orange mixture over them and fold in gently until just blended. Turn into a 9-inch tube pan.

Bake 50 minutes, or until a cake tester comes out clean. Invert pan and let cool, but be sure air circulates under it.

Place a spatula between the cake and pan and carefully press it away from the pan. Loosen center and turn out.

Serves 12—115 calories in each serving.

## NUT TORTE ❋

- 4 egg yolks
- ½ cup sugar
- 1½ teaspoons liquid Sucaryl
- ¾ cup ground walnuts
- 1 teaspoon double-acting baking powder
- 1 cup dried fine bread crumbs
- 4 egg whites

Turn oven on and set at 375°. Grease and dust lightly with flour an 8-inch spring-form pan or two 8-inch layer-cake pans.

Beat the egg yolks, gradually add half the sugar, beating until thick and light. Lightly beat in the Sucaryl, walnuts, baking powder and crumbs.

Beat the egg whites until peaks form. Gradually add the remaining sugar, beating until stiff. Fold into the nut mixture. Turn into the pan or pans.

Bake the spring-form 30 minutes or the layer pans 20 minutes, or until a cake tester comes out clean. Cool on a cake rack 10 minutes, then remove from pans. Cover or put together with fluffy whipped cream (see recipe) or dust with confectioners' sugar.

Serves 12—120 calories in each serving of cake (without cream).

## LOAF CAKE ❋

1⅔ cups sifted cake flour
2½ teaspoons double-acting baking powder
¼ teaspoon salt
⅓ cup (⅜ pound) butter or margarine
½ cup sugar
2 eggs
2 tablespoons liquid Sucaryl
1 teaspoon vanilla extract
½ cup skim milk

Turn oven on and set at 350°. Grease a 9-inch loaf pan and dust lightly with flour. Sift the flour, baking powder and salt together.

Cream the butter, gradually adding the sugar. Beat until light and fluffy. Add one egg at a time, beating well after each addition. Beat in the Sucaryl and vanilla. Add the flour mixture alternately with the milk. Beat only until smooth. Turn into the pan. Bake 55 minutes, or until a cake tester comes out clean. Cool on a cake rack.

Serves 18—105 calories in each serving.

## ONE-EGG CAKE ❋

2 cups sifted cake flour
2½ teaspoons double-acting baking powder
½ teaspoon salt
⅓ cup soft shortening
⅓ cup sugar
1 egg
2 teaspoons liquid Sucaryl
¾ cup skim milk
1 teaspoon vanilla extract

Turn oven on and set at 350°. Grease the bottom of an 8 x 8 x 2 inch square pan or two 8-inch layer-cake pans. Dust lightly with flour.

Sift the flour, baking powder and salt together. Cream the shortening; add the sugar. Add the egg and beat until very light and fluffy. Add ¼ the flour mixture alternately with ⅓ the milk and vanilla. Beat only until smooth. Turn into the pan or pans.

Bake the square cake 40 minutes or the 2 layers 30 minutes, or until a cake tester comes out clean. Cool on a cake rack, then carefully turn out. The layers may be put together as you like.

Serves 12—155 calories in each serving.

### Chocolate Cake

Add 2 tablespoons melted semisweet chocolate to the egg-sugar mixture. Bake 5 minutes less.

Serves 12—165 calories in each serving.

### Coconut Cake

Add ½ cup chopped shredded coconut to the batter.

Serves 12—165 calories in each serving.

## NUT CAKE ❋

- 4 egg yolks
- ⅓ cup powdered sugar
- 2 teaspoons liquid Sucaryl
- ½ teaspoon vanilla extract
- 1 teaspoon baking powder
- ⅔ cup graham-cracker crumbs
- ½ cup ground walnuts
- 4 egg whites

Turn oven on and set at 350°.

Beat the egg yolks, gradually adding the sugar. Beat until light and fluffy. Add the Sucaryl, vanilla, baking powder and crumbs. Mix well, then blend in the walnuts.

Beat the egg whites until stiff but not dry and fold into the nut mixture. Turn into an 8-inch spring-form pan or two 9-inch layer-cake pans.

Bake in the spring form 40 minutes or the layers 25 minutes, or until a cake tester comes out clean. Cool on a cake rack.

Serves 10—100 calories in each serving.

*Note:* Cake layers may be covered with fluffy whipped cream (see recipe).

## WHITE CAKE ❋

- 2 cups sifted cake flour
- 2 teaspoons baking powder
- ¼ teaspoon salt
- ½ cup butter or margarine
- ⅓ cup sugar
- 4½ teaspoons liquid Sucaryl
- ½ teaspoon vanilla extract
- ⅔ cup skim milk
- 4 egg whites

Turn oven on and set at 350°. Grease an 8 inch square pan or two 8 inch layer-cake pans. Dust lightly with flour.

Sift the flour, baking powder and salt together. Cream the butter, gradually adding half the sugar. Beat until light and fluffy. Add the Sucaryl and vanilla. Add the flour mixture alternately with the milk. Beat only until smooth.

Beat the egg whites until peaks form; gradually beat in the remaining sugar. Fold into the previous mixture. Bake the square pan 35 minutes or the layers 25 minutes, or until a cake tester comes out clean. Cool on a cake rack.

Ice the square cake, or put the layers together as you like.

Serves 12—170 calories in each serving of plain cake.

## CHEESE CAKE ❋

½ cup water
½ cup nonfat dry milk
1 tablespoon butter
8 zweiback, crushed
½ cup sugar
4 eggs
2 teaspoons liquid Sucaryl
¼ teaspoon salt
2 tablespoons lemon juice
1 teaspoon grated lemon rind
½ teaspoon vanilla
1 pound cottage cheese
¼ cup sifted flour

Turn oven on and set at 250°.

Beat the water and skim milk until the consistency of heavy cream.

Spread the butter on the bottom of an 8-inch spring-form pan. Mix the zweiback crumbs with 1 tablespoon sugar and press onto the butter (reserve 1 tablespoon).

Beat the eggs, gradually add the remaining sugar, Sucaryl, lemon juice, rind and vanilla. Force the cheese and flour through a sieve or food mill and add to the egg mixture with the beaten milk. Mix well. Pour into the prepared pan. Sprinkle the crumbs on top. Bake 1 hour; turn off the heat and leave in oven 1 hour longer. Chill.

Serves 10—140 calories in each serving.

## REFRIGERATOR CHEESE CAKE ❋

2 teaspoons butter
¾ cup graham-cracker crumbs
3 cups cottage cheese
2 tablespoons gelatin
¾ cup water
2 egg yolks
¾ cup skim milk
2 tablespoons sugar
2 teaspoons liquid Sucaryl
¼ teaspoon salt
1 tablespoon lemon juice
1 teaspoon grated lemon rind
1 teaspoon vanilla extract
½ cup nonfat dry milk
2 egg whites

Rub the butter into the bottom and sides of an 8-inch spring-form pan. Press the cracker crumbs against it and chill while preparing the filling.

Force the cheese through a sieve. Soften the gelatin in ¼ cup water. Beat the egg yolks in the top of a double boiler. Add the milk, sugar, Sucaryl and salt. Place over hot water and cook, stirring constantly until thickened. Add the gelatin, lemon juice, rind and vanilla, stirring until gelatin dissolves. Remove from the heat; cool 20 minutes, then stir in the cheese.

Beat the dry milk and remaining ½ cup water until the consistency of whipped cream. Beat the egg whites until stiff but not dry. Fold into the cheese mixture with the whipped milk. Turn into the spring-form. Chill until set, about 4 hours.

Serves 10—100 calories in each serving.

## POUND CAKE ✻

- ½ pound butter
- ½ cup sugar
- 1 tablespoon liquid Sucaryl
- 1 tablespoon cognac
- 5 egg yolks
- 2 cups sifted cake flour
- ½ teaspoon baking powder
- ¼ teaspoon mace
- 5 egg whites, stiffly beaten

Turn oven on and set at 300°. Grease a 9-inch loaf pan and dust lightly with flour.

Cream the butter until very smooth. Gradually beat in the sugar, Sucaryl and cognac until light and fluffy. Beat the egg yolks until thick and lemon-colored and add to the butter mixture. Beat until very light and fluffy.

Sift the flour, baking powder and mace together; add to the butter mixture alternately with the egg whites. Turn into the pan. Bake 1¼ hours, or until a cake tester comes out clean. Cool on a cake rack and carefully turn out.

Serves 18—135 calories in each serving.

## DESSERT PANCAKES

- 3 egg whites
- 3 egg yolks
- ¼ teaspoon salt
- ¾ cup cottage cheese, drained
- ¼ cup sifted flour
- 1 tablespoon butter or margarine

Beat the egg whites until stiff but not dry. Beat the egg yolks and salt until thick. Add the cottage cheese and flour, mixing lightly. Fold in the whites.

Melt half the butter in a skillet or on a griddle. Drop the batter by the spoonful onto it and brown lightly on both sides. Serve with maple sauce (see recipe).

Serves 6 (makes 18)—115 calories in each serving.

## CHOCOLATE FUDGE CAKE ✻

- 4 squares (ounces) unsweetened chocolate
- 3 tablespoons double-strength coffee
- 4 eggs
- ⅓ cup powdered sugar
- ¾ teaspoon liquid Sucaryl
- ½ cup sifted flour

Turn oven on and set at 350°. Grease an 8-inch spring-form pan and dust lightly with flour.

Melt the chocolate in the coffee. Beat the eggs in a bowl; place in a pan of hot water and gradually add the sugar and Sucaryl, beating until stiff peaks are formed. Fold in the flour a tablespoon at a time. Stir in the chocolate just enough to blend it. Turn into the pan.

Bake 45 minutes. Cool on a cake rack and carefully remove the spring-form. This cake has almost the consistency of candy.

Serves 10—120 calories in each serving.

## MOCHA CAKE ✻

- 1 square (ounce) unsweetened chocolate
- ½ cup double-strength coffee
- 3 tablespoons softened butter or margarine
- ⅓ cup sugar
- 2 teaspoons liquid Sucaryl
- 1 egg
- 1 egg yolk
- ¼ teaspoon vinegar
- 1 teaspoon vanilla extract
- 1 cup sifted cake flour
- ½ teaspoon baking soda
- ¼ teaspoon salt

Turn oven on and set at 375°. Grease an 8-inch-square pan and dust lightly with flour.

Melt the chocolate in 2 tablespoons of the coffee. Cream the butter, gradually adding the sugar. Add the Sucaryl, egg and egg yolk. Beat until thick and light. Add the chocolate mixture, the vinegar and vanilla.

Sift the flour, baking soda and salt together, and add half to the chocolate mixture. Beat until smooth. Beat in the remaining coffee and then the remaining flour mixture. Turn into the pan. Bake 30 minutes, or until a cake tester comes out clean. Cool on a cake rack.

Serves 12—105 calories in each serving.

## DEVIL'S-FOOD CAKE ✻

- 2 squares (ounces) unsweetened chocolate
- 1 tablespoon coffee
- 2 cups sifted cake flour
- 1 teaspoon baking soda
- ½ teaspoon salt
- ½ cup butter or margarine
- ½ cup sugar
- 2 tablespoons liquid Sucaryl
- 1 teaspoon vanilla extract
- 3 egg yolks
- 1 cup buttermilk or sour skim milk
- 3 egg whites, stiffly beaten

Turn oven on and set at 350°. Grease two 9-inch layer-cake pans and dust lightly with flour. Melt the chocolate in the coffee.

Sift the flour, soda and salt together. Cream the butter, gradually adding the sugar. Beat until light and fluffy. Beat in the Sucaryl, vanilla and egg yolks. Stir in the chocolate. Add the flour mixture alternately with the buttermilk. Beat only until smooth. Turn into the pans. Bake 30 minutes, or until a cake tester comes out clean. Cool on a cake rack, then carefully remove. Put the layers together with fluffy whipped cream or peaked frosting (see recipes).

Serves 16—160 calories in each serving (without whipped cream or frosting).

## ANISE COOKIES ⁂

- 2½ teaspoons aniseed
- ¼ cup boiling water
- 2 cups sifted flour
- ¼ cup sugar
- ⅛ teaspoon salt
- ½ cup shortening
- 2 tablespoons ice water

Combine the aniseed and boiling water and let soak until cool.

Sift the flour, sugar and salt into a bowl. Cut in the shortening with a pastry blender or 2 knives until the consistency of coarse sand. Stir in the aniseed mixture, tossing lightly with a fork. Add a little ice water at a time, adding just enough to make the dough stick together. Chill 2 hours. Turn oven on and set at 350°.

Roll out the dough ⅛-inch thick between two sheets of waxed paper. Peel off the top layer and cut with a 2-inch lightly floured cooky cutter. Transfer to an ungreased cooky sheet with a spatula. Bake 15 minutes, or until delicately browned.

Makes about 4½ dozen—30 calories in each cooky.

## BUTTERSCOTCH SLICES ⁂

- 1½ cups sifted flour
- 1½ teaspoons baking powder
- ¼ teaspoon salt
- ½ cup butter or margarine
- ⅔ cup firmly packed brown sugar
- ½ teaspoon vanilla extract
- 1 egg

Sift the flour, baking powder and salt together. Cream the butter; gradually beat in the sugar. Beat until fluffy. Add the vanilla and egg. Mix well, then stir in the flour mixture. Shape into rolls about 1½ inches in diameter. Wrap in waxed paper and chill 2 hours. Turn oven on and set at 400°.

Cut the rolls into ⅛-inch slices. Arrange on an ungreased cooky sheet. Bake 7 minutes, or until browned.

Makes about 4½ dozen—40 calories in each cooky.

## BUTTER COOKIES ❋

¼ pound butter
¼ cup sugar
1 egg
1 tablespoon milk
1½ teaspoons liquid Sucaryl
1 teaspoon vanilla extract
1¾ cups sifted flour
1 teaspoon baking powder
¼ teaspoon salt

Have the butter at room temperature. Cream with the sugar until smooth. Beat the egg until foamy and add, mixing again until well blended. Mix the milk, Sucaryl and vanilla, and add. Sift the flour, baking powder and salt together. Add half to the butter mixture, beating until well combined. Add remaining flour mixture, beat again. Divide in two parts and shape into smooth balls. Chill 15 minutes. Turn oven on and set at 375°.

Roll the dough ⅛-inch thick between two pieces of waxed paper. Peel off the top paper and cut the dough with a 2-inch cooky cutter which has been lightly dipped in flour. Carefully transfer to an ungreased cooky sheet with a spatula. Repeat with the balance of the dough, chilling if it gets too soft. Bake 10 minutes, or until delicately browned.

Makes about 5 dozen—30 calories in each cooky.

### Nut Sprinkles

⅓ cup finely chopped nuts—sprinkle a little on each cooky before baking or place ½ nut on each cooky.

—35 calories in each cooky.

### Sugar-Cinnamon Cookies

3 tablespoons sugar mixed with 1 tablespoon cinnamon—sprinkle a little on each cooky before baking.

—35 calories in each cooky.

### Cherry Cookies

Place ½ candied cherry on each cooky before baking.

—35 calories in each cooky.

## CHOCOLATE KISSES

½ cup sifted cake flour
⅓ cup sugar
4 egg whites
¼ teaspoon salt
¼ teaspoon cream of tartar
1¾ teaspoons liquid Sucaryl
2 squares (ounces) unsweetened chocolate, melted

Turn oven on and set at 275°. Grease a baking sheet lightly. Sift together the flour and 2 tablespoons sugar.

Beat the egg whites, salt and cream of tartar until stiff. Gradually beat in the remaining sugar and Sucaryl. Sift ¼ cup of the flour mixture at a time over the egg whites and fold in. Then fold in the chocolate. Drop by the teaspoon onto the baking sheet, leaving 1 inch between each. Bake 45 minutes, or until dry to the touch.

Makes about 24—30 calories in each kiss.

## DROP COOKIES ❋

1¼ cups sifted flour
¼ teaspoon salt
¼ teaspoon baking powder
¼ teaspoon baking soda
2 tablespoons butter
½ cup sugar
1 tablespoon liquid Sucaryl
1 egg
1 teaspoon vanilla extract
¼ cup sour cream

Turn oven on and set at 375°. Sift the flour, salt, baking powder and baking soda.

Cream the butter, gradually adding the sugar. Blend in the Sucaryl, egg, vanilla and sour cream. Add the flour mixture, beating until smooth. Drop by the teaspoon onto a cooky sheet leaving 1½ inches between each. Bake 15 minutes or until browned.

Makes about 3½ dozen—35 calories in each cooky.

## NUT CRESCENTS ❋

½ cup shelled almonds
¾ cup butter
Dash salt
2 tablespoons sugar
2 cups sifted flour

Grind the nuts very fine. Cream the butter and work in the salt, sugar and flour until smooth. Add the nuts, mixing until well blended. Chill 3 hours.

Turn oven on and set at 350°.

Shape the dough into long rolls as thick as a pencil. Cut 1½-inch lengths and place on a lightly floured cooky sheet. Bend them into crescents. Bake 12 minutes. Remove from the cooky sheet at once with a spatula.

Makes about 4 dozen—50 calories in each cooky.

## HERMITS ✻

½ cup raisins
1 cup plus 2 tablespoons sifted flour
1½ teaspoons baking powder
¼ teaspoon salt
¼ cup sugar
½ teaspoon cinnamon
½ teaspoon allspice
½ teaspoon ginger
⅛ teaspoon nutmeg
1 tablespoon boiling water
1 egg
1 tablespoon milk
1½ teaspoons liquid Sucaryl
¼ cup melted butter or margarine, cooled

Turn oven on and set at 375°. Lightly grease a cooky sheet.

Chop the raisins into small pieces. Sift the flour, baking powder, salt and sugar into a bowl. Dissolve the cinnamon, allspice, ginger and nutmeg in the boiling water. Beat the egg, milk, Sucaryl and butter together. Add to the flour mixture with the spices. Mix vigorously until throughly blended, then stir in the raisins.

Drop by the teaspoon (in small mounds) onto the cooky sheet leaving about 1½ inches between each. The cookies will spread in baking. Bake 15 minutes, or until browned, and a toothpick inserted in the center comes out clean.

Makes about 2 dozen—45 calories in each cooky.

## OATMEAL COOKIES ✻

1 cup uncooked oatmeal
⅓ cup milk
1½ teaspoons liquid Sucaryl
¾ cup sifted flour
1 teaspoon baking powder
¼ teaspoon salt
⅓ cup raisins, chopped
¼ cup coarsely chopped nuts
¼ pound butter
¼ cup brown sugar

Turn oven on and set at 375°.

Mix the oatmeal with the milk and Sucaryl.

Sift the flour, baking powder and salt together. Stir in the raisins and nuts until they are well coated and separate.

Cream the butter and brown sugar together. Add the oatmeal mixture and the flour mixture. Mix well.

Drop by the teaspoon in mounds onto an ungreased cooky sheet, leaving 1½ inches between each. Bake 15 minutes, or until browned.

Makes about 3 dozen—50 calories in each cooky.

## SHORTBREAD ⁂

½ pound butter
½ cup light brown sugar, packed
2¼ sups sifted flour

Have the butter at room temperature and cream it until smooth. Add 1 tablespoon of the sugar at a time, beating until fluffy. Add ¼ of the flour at a time, mixing thoroughly after each addition. Divide in 2 balls and smooth them with the hands. Chill for 20 minutes. Turn oven on and set at 375°.

Roll the dough ¼-inch thick between two pieces of waxed paper. Cut with a lightly floured 2-inch cooky cutter. Use a spatula to transfer to an ungreased baking sheet, leaving ½ inch between each. Repeat until all the dough is used up, and chill the pieces in between if necessary.

Bake 12 minutes, or until delicately browned.

Makes about 36—80 calories in each cooky.

## SCHNECKEN ⁂

1½ cups sifted flour
1 tablespoon sugar
⅛ teaspoon salt
6 tablespoons butter
1 cake or package yeast
¼ cup skim milk, scalded and cooled
2 egg yolks

Sift the flour, sugar and salt into a bowl. Work in the butter with the hand.

Soften the yeast in the milk for 5 minutes. Add the egg yolks and beat with a rotary beater until light and frothy. Add to the butter mixture, stirring until a dough is formed. Wrap and chill overnight.

Remove from the refrigerator 1 hour before it is to be baked. Prepare the filling:

½ cup ground walnuts
2 tablespoons brown sugar
2 teaspoons cinnamon
1 teaspoon liquid Sucaryl
2 egg whites, stiffly beaten

Mix the nuts, sugar, cinnamon and Sucaryl together. Divide the dough in two and roll out ⅛-inch thick. Spread half the egg whites and half the nut mixture on each. Roll up like a jelly roll. Cut into ½-inch slices and place on a buttered baking sheet. Let rise in a warm place 30 minutes.

Turn oven on and set at 400°. Bake 15 minutes, or until browned.

Makes about 36—50 calories in each.

## BASIC YEAST CAKE ❋

1 cake or package yeast
¼ cup lukewarm water
6 tablespoons skim milk
2 tablespoons sugar
½ teaspoon salt
3 tablespoons butter or margarine
2 cups plus 2 tablespoons sifted flour
1 egg
½ teaspoon vanilla extract

Soften the yeast in the water. Scald the milk; stir in the sugar, salt and butter. Cool to lukewarm. Add 1 cup flour and beat well. Add the egg, vanilla and yeast. Beat again. Add enough flour to make a stiff batter (it may not be necessary to add all the flour). Beat until smooth and elastic. Cover and let rise in a warm place for 1 hour. Turn oven on and set at 375°.

Punch the batter down and turn into a lightly greased 8-inch square pan. Cover and let rise 30 minutes. Bake 30 minutes, or until browned.

Serves 16—80 calories in each serving.

## DANISH PASTRY ❋

1 cake or package yeast
¼ cup lukewarm water
2 tablespoons sugar
1 teaspoon liquid Sucaryl
1 teaspoon salt
1¼ cups butter or margarine
1 cup hot scalded milk
2 eggs
½ teaspoon vanilla extract
1 teaspoon lemon juice
¼ teaspoon mace
3½ cups sifted flour
3 tablespoons powdered sugar
¼ cup chopped walnuts

Soften the yeast in the water; stir until dissolved. Combine the sugar, Sucaryl, salt, ¼ cup butter, and milk. Stir until smooth. Cool, then beat in the eggs. Add the yeast, vanilla, lemon juice, mace, and 3 cups flour. Beat until smooth, and add a little more of the flour, if necessary, to make a dough. Cover and let rise in a warm place until double in bulk. Keep remaining butter at room temperature.

Roll the dough into a square ¼-inch thick. Dot with half the butter. Fold dough in half and press the edges together. Roll out and dot with remaining butter. Roll out into a square and fold in quarter. Roll out again, fold again and roll again. Fold the dough, and place in a bowl. Cover and chill 30 minutes.

Roll out the dough ⅓-inch thick. Cut into 2½-inch squares. Sprinkle with a mixture of the powdered sugar and walnuts, and roll up diagonally. Turn ends together and place on a baking sheet. Cover and let rise 30 minutes. Bake in a 475° oven 8 minutes or until browned.

Makes about 32—130 calories in each.

*Note:* You may bake just the number you want and keep the remaining dough for a week.

**Cheese-filled Danish Pastries**

Combine 1 cup cottage cheese with 1 egg yolk, 1 tablespoon sugar, ¾ teaspoon liquid Sucaryl and ½ teaspoon vanilla extract. Roll out the dough and cut into 2½-inch squares; place a tablespoon of the cheese mixture on each. Fold 2 opposite corners to the center and press to seal. Let rise and bake as directed.

Makes about 32—125 calories in each.

## DOUGHNUTS

- 2 cups sifted flour
- 2 teaspoons baking powder
- ¼ teaspoon salt
- ⅛ teaspoon nutmeg
- 1 egg
- 2 tablespoons sugar
- 1½ tablespoons liquid Sucaryl
- ½ cup skim milk
- 2 tablespoons melted butter or margarine
- Fat for deep frying
- 3 tablespoons confectioners' sugar

Have ready a saucepan with the fat, and another one with boiling water.

Sift together the flour, baking powder, salt and nutmeg.

Beat the egg; add the sugar and Sucaryl, beating constantly. Stir in the milk and butter. Add the flour mixture, stirring until a dough is formed. Chill 15 minutes.

Roll out the dough ¼-inch thick and cut with a doughnut cutter. Gather up the small pieces and roll out again. Let the doughnuts stand for 15 minutes before frying. Turn oven on and set at 375°.

Heat the fat to 370°. There should be enough fat to more than cover the doughnuts. Bring the water to a boil. Use two forks, one for turning the doughnuts in the fat, and the other for the water, to avoid spattering the water into the fat.

Fry the doughnuts until browned on both sides, about 3-4 minutes. Don't crowd the pan. Quickly dip the doughnuts one by one into the boiling water and remove immediately to a baking pan. Bake 10 minutes, or until crisp. Sprinkle with the confectioners' sugar.

Makes 18—125 calories in each doughnut.

## KUGELHOF ✻

- 1 cake or package yeast
- ¼ cup lukewarm water
- 2½ cups sifted flour
- 2 eggs
- 1 cup skim milk, scalded and cooled
- ¼ cup butter
- ½ teaspoon salt
- 1½ tablespoons powdered sugar
- ¼ cup seedless white raisins
- 8 blanched almonds, halved

Combine the yeast and water in a bowl. Let soften 5 minutes, then sift in ½ cup flour. Mix, then sift the remaining flour over it. Don't mix; cover and set in a warm place until the yeast mixture pushes through the dry flour. Mix lightly with the hand while adding one egg at a time, then the milk. Beat with the hand until smooth and elastic.

Cream the butter, salt and sugar together and work it into the yeast mixture. Beat in the raisins. Butter a 9-inch Kugelhof or tube pan. Arrange the almonds on the bottom and turn the dough into it. Cover and set in a warm place until double in bulk, about 45 minutes.

Turn oven on and set at 400°. Bake 40 minutes, or until browned. Remove the cake from the pan and cool on a cake rack.

Serves 18—110 calories in each serving.

## COOKING TERMS

Bake —To cook food in a heated oven; also applies to pancakes "baked" on a griddle or skillet on top of the range.

Barbecue —To roast slowly over coals, wood or under electric heat, sometimes on a spit. Also a highly seasoned sauce.

Baste —To spoon liquid or fat over food while marinating, roasting, cooking or baking.

Beat —To make a mixture smooth and light with the use of a spoon, fork, rotary beater or electric mixer.

Blanch —To place in cold water, then bring to a boil; nuts are then placed in cold water, and the skin slipped off between the fingers.

Blend —To combine two or more ingredients and mix together until smooth.

Boil —To bring liquid or food to 212° F (sea level) at which time bubbles rise to the surface and break. Boiling can then be continued over low heat.

Braise —To brown food slowly in a little hot fat over low heat. Turn to brown all sides (it usually takes about 20 minutes). Season and add a little liquid. Cover and cook over low heat until tender.

Bread —To coat with crumbs. Sometimes food is coated with crumbs, then dipped into eggs and crumbs again.

Broil —To cook under the heat of the broiler. Also over hot coals, wood, or between two surfaces.

Brown —To cook food in a little fat (usually over medium heat) until browned. Turn when one side is browned and continue until all sides are browned.

Brush with—To cover a surface lightly with a liquid or oil, using a pastry brush or waxed paper.

Caramelize—To melt granulated sugar in a pan over low heat, stirring constantly until it forms a golden-brown syrup.

Chill —To cool foods in the refrigerator.

Chop —To cut foods into small pieces with a knife or chopper. You can chop coarse, medium or fine.

Coat —To roll food in flour or other specified ingredients until coated with it. Food may be shaken in a bag with the dry ingredients until coated, or the dry ingredients may be shaken onto it.

Cream —To work shortening or other ingredients with a spoon against the side of a bowl until creamy. The electric mixer will simplify the process. Turn indicator to "cream."

Cut in Shortening—To mix shortening and flour with a pastry blender or 2 knives until shortening is evenly distributed.

Deep fry —To cook food in hot fat that completely covers it. Fat should be heated over low heat to temperature specified in the recipe (use thermometer). Watch thermometer all through the frying process, as the fat cools when cold food is added.

Dice —To cut food into very small (about ⅛″) cubes.

Dissolve —To mix dry or solid ingredients with liquid until it liquefies.

Dot —To scatter small pieces of food (usually butter) over the surface of another food or utensil.

Dredge —To dust or sprinkle food lightly with flour or other dry ingredient until coated.

Fold in —To heap on top of another mixture, and using a spoon, wire whisk or rubber spatula, cut down gently to the bottom, run utensil across the bottom and bring up some of the mixture in a gently rolling circular motion. Usually applies to beaten egg whites or whipped cream, but can be a dry ingredient. Continue until ingredients are evenly combined.

Fry out —Solid fat or fat meat fried until fat melts away.

Garnish —To decorate food.

Grate —To rub food into small pieces on a grater.

Grease —To rub a pan, other utensil or food lightly with oil, butter, margarine or shortening.

Grind —To put food through a food chopper.

Knead —To shape the dough into a round flat ball on a floured surface and fold over the edge farthest from you toward you. Use the heels of the hands to press down away from you. Turn dough one quarter way around and repeat steps until dough is smooth.

Lard —To place strips of bacon, salt pork or fat on top of or in gashes of meat, poultry or fish. To insert strips of fat under the skin or into the meat with a pointed instrument or needle.

Marinate —To soak food in a liquid, usually spiced and with wine or vinegar.

Melt —To heat until the ingredient is changed from solid to liquid.

Mince —To cut or chop into very fine pieces.

Pan broil —To cook on top of the range in a lightly greased or ungreased skillet, pour off fat as it accumulates.

Parboil —To cook foods partially in a liquid.

Pare —To remove the outer skin or covering of food such as potato or apple.

Peel —To remove outer covering by pulling or cutting it off.

Pit —To remove the seeds or pits of a food, usually a fruit.

Poach —To cook in a liquid just below the boiling point.

Preheat —To turn oven on and set it at temperature specified in recipe 10-15 minutes before it is to be used.

Purée —To press food through a sieve or food mill. You can also put the food in a blender for a few seconds. A purée is also the result of this process.

Render —To melt solid fat away from other tissue.

Roast —To cook in an oven by dry heat.

Sauté —To cook food in a little fat or oil (without the addition of water) usually over low or medium heat. This step is very often used in cooking preliminary to longer cooking with liquid added.

Scald —To heat just under the boiling point, that is until tiny bubbles begin to form on the sides.

Score —To make shallow gashes on food with a knife or fork.

Sear —To brown surface of food over high heat.

Season —To sprinkle, rub into or add salt, pepper and other specified flavorings.

Shallow fry—To fry in hot fat, about 1½ inches deep. Follow temperature specified in recipe.

Sift —To put dry ingredient through a flour sifter or fine sieve. Some sifters sift 3 times at once.

Simmer —To cook just below the boiling point over low heat.

Singe —To hold poultry over a flame to burn off the feathers.

Shred —To cut or tear into narrow pieces.

Skewer —To fasten opening or hold in place by means of metal or wooden skewers.

Sliver —To cut into long thin pieces.

Snip —To cut into small pieces with kitchen shears.

Steam —To cook in steam in a double boiler, pressure cooker or on a rack in a tightly closed saucepan.

Steep —To let stand in hot liquid.

Stir —To blend, using a spoon, fork or whisk with a circular motion.

Toss —To mix lightly with fork and spoon, 2 forks or 2 spoons.

Truss —To secure the body of a fowl so that it holds its shape in cooking.

Whip —To beat rapidly with an egg beater, whisk or electric mixer to incorporate air and increase volume.

## TEMPERATURE GUIDE

| | |
|---|---|
| Very slow oven | 225° |
| Slow oven | 250° to 300° |
| Moderate oven | 325° to 375° |
| Hot oven | 400° to 450° |
| Very hot oven | 475° and over |

## COOKING MEASUREMENTS

| | |
|---|---|
| Dash | = less than ⅛ teaspoon |
| 3 teaspoons | = 1 tablespoon |
| 2 liquid tablespoons | = 1 ounce |
| 4 tablespoons | = ¼ cup |
| 16 tablespoons | = 1 cup |
| 1 cup | = ½ pint (8 ounces) |
| 2 liquid cups | = 1 pound |
| 16 ounces | = 1 pound |
| 4 cups | = 1 quart |

## CONVERSION TABLE
**(approximate)**

*Weight:*

15 grams = ½ ounce
30 grams = 1 ounce
50 grams = 1¾ ounces
75 grams = 2½ ounces
100 grams = 3½ ounces
500 grams = 17 ounces
1 kilogram = 35 ounces

*Liquid:*

1 decilitre = 3½ ounces
1 demilitre = ⅞ pint
1 liter = 1¾ pints
1 American pint = 16 fluid ounces
1 American cup = 8 ounces
1 teaspoon = 4.9 cubic centimeters
1 tablespoon = 14.8 cubic centimeters
1 cup = 236.6 cubic centimeters

*Can sizes:*

8 ounces = 1 cup
#1 Picnic = 1¼ cups
#1 = 1½ cups
#300 = 2 cups
#303 = 2 cups
#2 = 2½ cups
#2½ = 3½ cups
#1 square = 1 pound

## TABLE OF EQUIVALENT WEIGHTS AND MEASURES

| | | | |
|---|---|---|---|
| Baking powder | 1 ounce | equals | 3½ tablespoons |
| Beans, dried | ½ pound | " | 1 cup |
| Bread crumbs | 3 ounces (approx.) | " | 1 cup |
| Butter and solid fats | 1 pound | " | 2 cups |
| Butter and solid fats | ¼ pound | " | 8 tablespoons |
| Butter and solid fats | ¼ pound | " | ½ cup |
| Cheese, cottage | ½ pound | " | 1 cup |
| Cheese, cream | ½ pound | " | 1 cup |
| Cheese, grated | ¼ pound | " | 1 cup |
| Chocolate | 1 ounce | " | 1 square |
| Cinnamon | 1 ounce | " | 4½ tablespoons |
| Coconut, grated dried | ¼ pound | " | 1 cup, packed |
| Consommé | 1 can | " | 10½ ounces |
| Corn meal | 1 pound | " | 3 cups |
| Cornstarch | 4½ ounces | " | 1 cup |
| Cream | ½ pint | " | 1 cup |
| Dates, pitted | ½ pound | " | 1¼ cups |
| Eggs | 2 ounces | " | 1 egg |
| Egg whites | 8 to 10 | " | 1 cup |
| Flour | 1 pound | " | 4 cups, sifted |
| Flour | ¼ ounce | " | 1 tablespoon |
| Honey | 12 ounces | " | 1 cup |
| Lemon juice | 1 lemon | " | 2 to 3 tablespoons |
| Lemon rind, grated | 1 lemon | " | 2 to 3 teaspoons |
| Nuts, ground | ¼ pound | " | 1 cup |
| Oil | 7½ ounces | " | 1 cup |
| Peanut butter | 1 pound | " | 1¾ cups |
| Potatoes | 1 pound | " | 3 average |
| Raisins | 1 pound | " | 3 cups |
| Rice, uncooked | 1 pound | " | 2 cups |
| Rice, uncooked | 1 cup | " | 3 cups, cooked |
| Sugar, brown | 1 pound | " | 2¼ cups, packed |
| Sugar, confectioner's | 1 pound | " | 3½ to 4 cups, sifted |
| Sugar, granulated | 1 pound | " | 2 cups |
| Tomatoes, fresh | 1 pound | " | 3 average |
| Tomato sauce (1 can) | 7¾–8 ounces | " | 1 cup |

## MANAGING THE FREEZER

A food freezer is one of the greatest aids to modern living. No matter how small the kitchen may be, there is a freezer or refrigerator-freezer designed for it. Whether or not you can afford the space for a 13-cubic-foot bookshelf freezer or a 5-cubic-foot roll-out freezer, you *should* have one.

You will not only save money but time with proper use of the freezer. Unless you live in an isolated area, *don't* load the freezer with uncooked foods. Of course, an extra steak, chicken, fish, a few vegetables, breads and ice cream are handy to have, but by all means cook for the freezer, and then you'll have meals in minutes for emergencies or just have the luxury of days without cooking. Be sure to label everything carefully with the date, name of dish and number of servings, i.e. "Nov. 16, Beef in Red Wine for 3." Follow the rules for individual foods, but a blanket rule is *don't overcook.*

Many people have a wrong impression as to the length of time that frozen foods can be kept. If kept too long, there is a loss in flavor, texture, and quality; the various frozen foods can be kept only for the length of time specified. Spoilage also results from improper wrapping; when air hits foods in a freezer, "freezer burn" results. Raw foods may, of course, be cooked and then frozen. However, once the dish has been thawed, do not refreeze.

*Breads* — Baked breads of all types freeze very well. Store in polyethelene bags. Defrost in bag for 1 hour or heat in a 350° oven for 10 minutes. Yeast breads keep up to 3 months, baking-powder biscuits or breads up to 2 months.

*Cakes* — Wrap cooled unfrosted cakes or cupcakes carefully in freezer wrapping. Defrost in the wrapping for 1 hour. Keep up to 3 months; fruitcakes keep up to 1 year.

*Cookies* May be frozen baked or unbaked. Cool baked cookies and pack in boxes or freezer containers, with waxed paper between layers. Wrap carefully and freeze. Defrost in package for 30 minutes. Keep up to 6 months. Unbaked cooky dough should be rolled and cut; pack in layers with aluminum foil between. Bake unthawed. Keep up to 4 months.

*Fish* *Fish* and *Shellfish* cook in a short time, so it isn't a time saver to freeze them.

*Meats* Cooked meats and stews are wonderful for freezing. Of course, leftovers can be frozen, but to really enjoy the dish, undercook it 20%. As an example, if the recipe says cook 2 hours, you cook the dish 25 minutes less, or only 1 hour and 35 minutes. Remove the portion you want to freeze and place it in a bowl or saucepan. Cool quickly in cold water or over ice, then chill it. Pack in freezer containers, label and freeze. When ready to use, reheat, taste for seasoning and serve. Do not add potatoes, rice or noodles to meat dishes that are to be frozen. Add when reheating. Keep up to 2 months.

*Meatloaves* and *meat balls* may be thawed and eaten cold or reheated and served hot. Keep up to 2 weeks.

*Baked and cooked hams* may be thawed and served cold or reheated in the oven. Keep up to 4 months.

*Cooked poultry* may be frozen whole or cut up. Remove all stuffing and freeze separately. Chill thoroughly before wrapping or packing in freezer containers. To reheat a whole bird, place in a roasting pan and reheat in a 300° oven. Allow 3 hours for larger birds, about 1½ hours for small ones. Keep up to 1 month.

*Pies* Fruit pies may be frozen baked or unbaked, but are superior when frozen unbaked. Prepare as usual, but don't prick the top. Wrap carefully and freeze. When ready to bake, unwrap, prick top or cut vents and bake in a 400° oven 1 hour. Keep up to 3 months.

*Soups* Soups are excellent for freezing. Chill them before pouring into glass, plastic or metal containers. Allow 1-inch head room for expansion. Seal carefully and freeze. Reheat in a covered saucepan and taste for seasoning. Don't add potatoes, rice or macaroni to soups that are to be frozen until ready to reheat. Keep up to 2 months.

*Vegetables* These cook too quickly to warrant freezing in the cooked stage. *White* or *sweet potatoes* may be frozen many styles. Heat in a 350° oven for about 30 minutes. Keep up to 3 months.

*Baked beans* should be packed in covered containers and frozen until needed. Reheat in a covered baking dish in a 325° oven 1 hour. Keep up to 9 months.

Foods should be wrapped in special freezer materials and care should be taken to force out any air before sealing. This will prevent "freezer burn" which causes food to lose its flavor. You may use freezer foil (heavier than ordinary foil) polyethelene wrap or bags for wrapping. Containers are available in foil, plastic or glass. Just be sure everything is air-tight.

## CALORIE CHARTS

### Alcoholic Beverages

| | | |
|---|---|---|
| Ale | 8 ounces | 140 |
| Beer, Bock | 8 ounces | 175 |
| Beer, Lager | 8 ounces | 110 |
| Bourbon whiskey | 1 ounce | 100 |
| Brandy | 1 ounce | 80 |
| Canadian whiskey | 1 ounce | 100 |
| Champagne, dry | 4 ounces | 110 |
| Champagne, sweet | 4 ounces | 140 |
| Cognac | 1 ounce | 80 |
| Gin | 1½ ounces | 125 |
| Irish whiskey | 1 ounce | 100 |
| Liqueurs | 1 ounce | 80 |
| Manhattan | 2½ ounces | 250 |
| Martini, dry | 2½ ounces | 180 |
| Martini, sweet | 2½ ounces | 200 |
| Port wine | 3½ ounces | 100 |
| Rum | 1½ ounces | 150 |
| Rum and cola | Tall glass | 225 |
| Rye whiskey | 1 ounce | 100 |
| Scotch whiskey | 1 ounce | 100 |
| Sherry, dry | 3½ ounces | 110 |
| Sherry, sweet | 3½ ounces | 140 |
| Sloe gin | 1½ ounces | 150 |
| Stout | 8 ounces | 160 |
| Vermouth, dry | 1 ounce | 40 |
| Vermouth, sweet | 1 ounce | 60 |
| Vodka | 1½ ounces | 125 |
| Whiskey sour | 3½ ounces | 225 |
| Wine, dry | 3½ ounces | 70 |
| Wine, sweet | 3½ ounces | 125 |

## Fish

| | | |
|---|---|---|
| Abalone | 4 ounces | 125 |
| Anchovies | 1 | 10 |
| Anchovy paste | 1 tablespoon | 35 |
| Bass | 2″ x 2″ x 1″ | 100 |
| Bluefish | 2″ x 2″ x 1″ | 100 |
| Butterfish | 4 ounces | 125 |
| Brook Trout, broiled | 8 ounces | 125 |
| Caviar | 1 tablespoon | 30 |
| Clam juice | 6 ounces | 50 |
| Clams | 4 ounces meat | 90 |
| Clams, round | 6 | 100 |
| Clams, soft shell | 12 | 100 |
| Cod | 2″ x 2″ x 1″ | 90 |
| Crab | 4 ounces meat | 100 |
| Crab meat, canned | 4 ounces | 110 |
| Eel | 4 ounces | 125 |
| Finnan Haddie | 4 ounces | 125 |
| Fishballs, chopped | 2 small | 70 |
| Flounder | 2″ x 2″ x 1″ | 75 |
| Frogs' Legs | 4 ounces | 75 |
| Haddock | 2″ x 2″ x 1″ | 100 |
| Halibut | 2″ x 2″ x 1″ | 125 |
| Herring, Atlantic | 4 ounces | 210 |
| Herring, pickled | 4 ounces | 100 |
| Herring, smoked | 4 ounces | 225 |
| Herring, sour-cream | 4 ounces | 250 |
| Lake Trout, sautéed | 4 ounces | 325 |
| Lobster | 4 ounces meat | 100 |
| Lobster, 1 pound | 4 ounces meat | 100 |
| Lobster, canned | ½ cup meat | 75 |
| Mackerel | 2″ x 2″ x 2″ | 100 |
| Mackerel, salt | 4 ounces | 160 |
| Muskalunge | 2″ x 2″ x 1″ | 100 |

| | | |
|---|---|---|
| Oysters | 6 average | 90 |
| Oysters, fried | 6 average | 400 |
| Oyster stew | 1 cup | 250 |
| Perch | 4 ounces | 90 |
| Pike | 4 ounces | 80 |
| Porgy | 4 ounces | 100 |
| Salmon, broiled | 3″ x 3″ x 1″ | 200 |
| Salmon, creamed | ½ cup | 300 |
| Salmon, canned | 1 cup | 375 |
| Salmon, smoked | 4 ounces | 325 |
| Sardines, canned | 4 ounces | 225 |
| Scallops | 4 ounces | 90 |
| Shad | 3″ x 3″ x 1″ | 150 |
| Shad roe | 3 ounces | 125 |
| Shrimp | 9 average | 100 |
| Shrimp, canned | 4 ounces | 100 |
| Smelts | 3 average | 100 |
| Sole, fillet of | 4 ounces | 90 |
| Sturgeon, smoked | 4 ounces | 175 |
| Swordfish | 3″ x 3″ x ½″ | 225 |
| Trout, brook | 8 ounces | 125 |
| Trout, lake | 8 ounces | 160 |
| Tuna, canned with oil | 4 ounces | 300 |
| Tuna, drained | 4 ounces | 200 |
| Tuna, fresh | 4 ounces | 180 |
| Turtle | 4 ounces | 175 |
| Whitefish | 4 ounces | 150 |

## Meats and Poultry

| | | |
|---|---|---|
| Bacon | 2 slices | 100 |
| Bacon, Canadian | 1 slice | 60 |
| Beef, boiled | 4 ounces | 200 |
| Beef, chipped | 1 slice | 30 |
| Beef, chuck | 3 ounces | 265 |
| Beef, corned (lean) | 4 ounces | 200 |
| Beef, ground | 3 ounces | 310 |
| Beef liver, fried | 4 ounces | 240 |
| Beef, pot-roast | 4 ounces | 275 |
| Beef, rib-roast | 1 large slice | 300 |
| Beef, round | 3 ounces | 200 |
| Beef, rump | 3 ounces | 320 |
| Beef, sirloin | 3 ounces | 260 |
| Beef, stewing | Average serving | 325 |
| Beef, tongue | 4 thin slices | 160 |
| Beef, canned corn-beef hash | 3 ounces | 120 |
| Bologna | 1 average slice | 80 |
| Brains | 3 ounces | 105 |
| Calf's liver | 4 ounces | 160 |
| Chicken, broilers | ½ average | 330 |
| Chicken, canned | 4 ounces | 200 |
| Chicken, fried | 4 ounces boneless | 275 |
| Chicken, hens | 4 ounces boneless | 350 |
| Chicken, roasters | 4 ounces boneless | 225 |
| Chicken fat | 1 tablespoon | 100 |
| Chicken livers | 4 ounces | 150 |
| Duck, roasted | 4 ounces boneless | 350 |
| Duck, roasted | 3″ x 3″ x 1″ | 250 |
| Frankfurters | 1 small | 125 |
| Frankfurters | 1 large | 200 |
| Goose, roast | 4 ounces boneless | 325 |
| Ham, boiled | 4 ounces | 375 |
| Ham, fresh | 4 ounces boneless | 450 |
| Ham, hocks | 4 ounces | 410 |
| Ham, prosciutto | 1 ounce | 120 |

| | | |
|---|---|---|
| Ham, smoked | 4 ounces | 420 |
| Hamburger | 3 ounces | 310 |
| Heart, beef | 3 ounces | 110 |
| Kidneys, beef | 4 ounces | 150 |
| Lamb chop | 4 ounces | 350 |
| Lamb chop, rib | 1 small | 225 |
| Lamb, roast leg | 3 ounces boneless | 230 |
| Lamb, shoulder | 3 ounces boneless | 290 |
| Lamb stew | 1 cup | 250 |
| Liverwurst | 1 average slice | 90 |
| Mutton | 2 thin slices | 200 |
| Pastrami | 4 ounces | 350 |
| Pigs' feet | 4 ounces meat | 160 |
| Pork chop, loin | 4 ounces | 440 |
| Pork chop, rib | 4 ounces | 375 |
| Pork loin | 4 ounces | 350 |
| Pork sausage | 1 average | 225 |
| Pork, spareribs | 4 ounces | 360 |
| Rabbit | 4 ounces | 190 |
| Sausage, bologna | 1 thick slice | 100 |
| Sausage, liverwurst | 1 thin slice | 75 |
| Sausage, salami | 1 thin slice | 75 |
| Sausage, summer | 1 thin slice | 60 |
| Sausage, Vienna | 4 ounces | 240 |
| Squab | 1 average | 275 |
| Sweetbreads, broiled | 4 ounces | 100 |
| Sweetbreads, fried | 4 ounces | 325 |
| Tongue, beef | 4 thin slices | 160 |
| Tripe | 4 ounces | 150 |
| Turkey | 4 ounces | 300 |
| Veal cutlet, breaded | 4 ounces boneless | 240 |
| Veal cutlet, broiled | 4 ounces boneless | 210 |
| Veal, shouder | 4 ounces | 270 |
| Veal stew meat | 4 ounces | 330 |
| Venison | 4 ounces | 225 |
| Vienna sausage | 4 ounces | 240 |

## Vegetables

| | | |
|---|---|---|
| Artichokes | 1 | 100 |
| Artichokes, hearts | 4 | 30 |
| Asparagus | 10 spears | 25 |
| Asparagus | 1 cup spears | 35 |
| Bamboo shoots | 4 ounces | 35 |
| Beans, baked | 1 cup | 240 |
| Beans, kidney | 1 cup | 300 |
| Beans, lima | 1 cup | 150 |
| Beans, green | 1 cup | 25 |
| Beans, pork, molasses | 1 cup | 325 |
| Beans, pork, tomatoes | 1 cup | 295 |
| Beans, white marrow | 4 ounces dried | 320 |
| Beets | 1 cup | 70 |
| Beets, pickled | 4 ounces | 25 |
| Broccoli | 1 cup | 40 |
| Brussels sprouts | 1 cup | 40 |
| Cabbage, Chinese | 4 ounces | 25 |
| Cabbage, cooked | 1 cup | 40 |
| Cabbage, raw | 1 cup | 25 |
| Carrots | 1 medium | 20 |
| Carrots, cooked | 1 cup | 45 |
| Cauliflower | 1 cup | 30 |
| Celeriac (celery root) | 1 root | 10 |
| Celery, raw | 1 large stalk | 6 |
| Celery, cooked | 1 cup | 25 |
| Chives | 1 ounce | 10 |
| Corn | 1 ear | 90 |
| Corn, cooked | 1 cup kernels | 140 |
| Cucumber | 1 average | 20 |
| Eggplant | 3 large slices | 50 |
| Endive | 4 ounces | 20 |
| Garbanzos (chick peas) | 4 ounces dried | 375 |
| Garlic | 1 clove | 5 |
| Ginger, fresh | 1 root | 15 |

| | | |
|---|---|---|
| Kohlrabi | 1 cup | 40 |
| | | |
| Leeks | 1 cup | 40 |
| Lentils | 4 ounces | 360 |
| Lettuce | 1 large leaf | 3 |
| Lettuce | 1 head | 65 |
| | | |
| Mung-bean sprouts | 1 cup raw | 20 |
| Mushrooms | 1 cup | 30 |
| Mustard greens | 1 cup | 30 |
| | | |
| Okra | 1 cup | 40 |
| Olives, green | 1 | 7 |
| Olives, black | 1 | 10 |
| Onions, cooked | 1 cup | 80 |
| Onions, green | 10 large | 100 |
| Onions, raw | 1 average | 35 |
| | | |
| Parsley, chopped | 1 tablespoon | 1 |
| Parsnips | 1 cup | 90 |
| Peas, cooked | 1 cup | 110 |
| Peas, dried | 4 ounces | 375 |
| Peas, fresh | 4 ounces (in shell) | 115 |
| Peppers | 1 average | 20 |
| Pigeon peas, cooked | 4 ounces | 125 |
| Pimentos | 1 average | 10 |
| Potatoes | 1 average | 100 |
| Potatoes au gratin | 4 ounces | 275 |
| Potato chips | 10 medium | 100 |
| Potatoes, baked | 1 Idaho | 150 |
| Potatoes, boiled | 1 average | 100 |
| Potatoes, French-fried | 8 pieces | 160 |
| Potatoes, fried raw | ½ cup | 250 |
| Potatoes, hashed brown | ½ cup | 240 |
| Potatoes, mashed | ½ cup (with milk) | 80 |
| Potatoes, mashed | ½ cup (milk, butter) | 120 |
| Potatoes, sweet | 1 average | 190 |
| Pumpkin | 1 cup | 75 |
| Pumpkin seeds | 1 ounce | 150 |

| | | |
|---|---|---|
| Radishes | 10 | 25 |
| Rice, boiled | 1 cup | 200 |
| Rice, brown | ½ cup raw | 375 |
| Rice, wild | ½ cup raw | 300 |
| Rutabagas | 1 cup | 50 |
| Sauerkraut | 1 cup | 40 |
| Scallions, young | 6 small | 25 |
| Soybean sprouts | 1 cup | 45 |
| Spinach, boiled | ½ cup | 50 |
| Squash, Hubbard (winter) | 1 cup | 100 |
| Squash, summer | 1 cup | 30 |
| Succotash | 1 cup | 175 |
| Sweet potatoes | 1 average | 190 |
| Tomatoes | 1 medium | 25 |
| Tomatoes, stewed | 1 cup | 50 |
| Turnips | 1 cup | 40 |
| Watercress | 4 ounces | 20 |
| Yams, baked | 1 average | 200 |
| Yams, candied | 1 average | 375 |
| Zucchini | 1 cup | 45 |

### Fruits, Fresh

| | | |
|---|---|---|
| Apples | 1 small | 60 |
| Apples | 1 medium | 75 |
| Apples | 1 large | 115 |
| Apple butter | 1 tablespoon | 30 |
| Applesauce | 1 cup unsweetened | 100 |
| Applesauce | 1 cup sweetened | 180 |
| Apricots, fresh | 1 medium | 20 |
| Apricots, dried | ½ cup | 200 |
| Apricots, cooked | ½ cup (with sugar) | 240 |
| Avocado | ½ average | 280 |

| | | |
|---|---|---|
| Banana | 1 small | 80 |
| Banana | 1 large | 120 |
| Blackberries, raw | 1 cup | 80 |
| Blueberries, raw | 1 cup | 85 |
| Cantaloupe | ½, 5″ melon | 40 |
| Cherries, raw | 1 cup unpitted | 65 |
| Cherries, raw | 1 cup pitted | 95 |
| Coconut, fresh | 1 cup shredded | 350 |
| Coconut, dried | 4 ounce package | 630 |
| Coconut milk | 1 cup | 60 |
| Crab apple | 1 average | 20 |
| Cranberries, raw | 1 cup | 55 |
| Cranberry sauce | 1 cup | 550 |
| Currants, red, raw | 1 cup | 60 |
| Dates | ½ cup pitted | 250 |
| Figs, fresh | 1 average | 30 |
| Figs, dried | 1 average | 50 |
| Fruit cocktail, fresh | ½ cup | 65 |
| Gooseberries, raw | 1 cup | 60 |
| Grapefruit | ½ large, 5″ | 105 |
| Grapefruit | ½ medium, 4″ | 75 |
| Grapefruit | ½ small, 3½″ | 45 |
| Grapefruit | 1 cup sections | 80 |
| Grapes, Concord | ½ pound | 125 |
| Grapes, Delaware | ½ pound | 125 |
| Grapes, Malaga | ½ pound | 150 |
| Grapes, Muscat | ½ pound | 150 |
| Grapes, Niagara | ½ pound | 125 |
| Grapes, Scuppernong | ½ pound | 125 |
| Grapes, Sultanina | ½ pound | 150 |
| Grapes, Thompson, seedless | ½ pound | 150 |
| Guavas | 1 average | 50 |
| Honeydew melon | 1 medium wedge | 45 |
| Huckleberries | 1 cup | 80 |
| Lemon juice | 1 tablespoon | 4 |
| Lemons | 1 medium | 20 |

| | | |
|---|---|---|
| Limes | 1 medium | 20 |
| Loganberries | 1 cup | 90 |
| Mangos | 1 average | 85 |
| Muskmelons | ½, 5″ melon | 40 |
| Nectarines | 1 medium | 40 |
| Orange juice | 1 cup | 108 |
| Oranges | 1 large | 105 |
| Oranges | 1 medium | 75 |
| Oranges | 1 small | 50 |
| Oranges, sections | 1 cup | 85 |
| Papaya | 1 average serving | 65 |
| Peaches | 1 medium | 45 |
| Peaches | 1 large | 65 |
| Pears | 1 average | 95 |
| Pears | 1 small | 70 |
| Persimmon, seedless | 1 average | 95 |
| Persimmon, seeds | 1 average | 75 |
| Pineapple, raw | 1 slice, ½″ thick | 35 |
| Pineapple, raw | 1 cup cubes | 75 |
| Plums | 1 average | 30 |
| Pomegranate | 1 average | 75 |
| Prunes | 1 large | 25 |
| Quince | 1 average | 40 |
| Raisins | 1 cup | 430 |
| Raspberries, black | 1 cup | 100 |
| Raspberries, red | 1 cup | 70 |
| Rhubarb, raw | 1 cup diced | 20 |
| Rhubarb, cooked | 1 cup (with sugar) | 385 |
| Strawberries | 1 cup | 55 |
| Tangerines | 1 medium | 35 |
| Tangerines, juice | 1 cup | 95 |
| Watermelon | 1 wedge, 4″ x 8″ | 120 |
| Watermelon, ¾″ cut | ½ slice | 50 |

## Dairy Products

| | | |
|---|---|---|
| Acidophilus milk | 1 cup | 95 |
| American cheese | 1 average slice | 105 |
| American cheese | 1 ounce | 105 |
| Bleu cheese | 1 ounce | 95 |
| Brie cheese | 1 ounce | 100 |
| Butter | 1 cup | 1600 |
| Butter | 1 tablespoon | 100 |
| Butter | 1 pat | 50 |
| Buttermilk, skim milk | 1 cup | 85 |
| Camembert | 1 ounce | 85 |
| Cheddar, cheese foods | 1 ounce | 95 |
| Cheddar, processed | 1 ounce | 105 |
| Cheeses, processed | 1 ounce | 105 |
| Condensed milk | 1 tablespoon sweetened | 60 |
| Cottage cheese | ½ cup | 105 |
| Cottage cheese | 1 ounce | 25 |
| Cream cheese | 1 ounce | 105 |
| Cream cheese | 1 tablespoon | 55 |
| Crcam, light | ½ pint | 490 |
| Cream, light | 1 tablespoon | 30 |
| Cream, heavy | ½ pint | 780 |
| Cream, heavy | 1 tablespoon | 50 |
| Cream, heavy sour | 1 tablespoon | 50 |
| Edam cheese | 1 ounce | 120 |
| Evaporated milk | 1 tablespoon, unsweetened | 25 |
| Gorgonzola cheese | 1 ounce | 100 |
| Goat's milk | 1 cup | 165 |
| Grated cheese | 1 tablespoon | 35 |
| Gruyère cheese | 1 ounce | 100 |
| Limburger | 1 ounce | 100 |
| Malted milk | Tall glass | 325 |
| Malted milk (ice cream) | Tall glass | 625 |
| Milk, whole | 1 cup | 165 |
| Milk, skim | 1 cup | 85 |

| | | |
|---|---|---|
| Milk, evaporated | 1 cup | 345 |
| Milk, condensed | 1 cup | 980 |
| Milk, dried whole | 1 tablespoon | 39 |
| Milk, dried skim | 1 tablespoon | 28 |
| Milk, malted | 1 ounce powder | 115 |
| Milk, goat's | 1 cup | 165 |
| Ovaltine, half milk | 1 cup | 110 |
| Parmesan cheese | 1 ounce | 110 |
| Parmesan, grated | 1 tablespoon | 30 |
| Pot cheese | 1 tablespoon | 30 |
| Provolone cheese | 1 ounce | 105 |
| Roquefort cheese | 1 ounce | 90 |
| Sour cream | 1 tablespoon | 50 |
| Stilton cheese | 1 ounce | 110 |
| Swiss cheese | 1 thin slice | 100 |
| Velveeta cheese | 1 ounce | 100 |
| Welsh rarebit | 1 cup | 390 |
| Yeast, dry | 1 tablespoon | 20 |
| Yogurt, skim milk | 1 cup | 115 |
| Yogurt, whole milk | 1 cup | 180 |

**Beverages**

| | | |
|---|---|---|
| Apple juice | 1 cup | 125 |
| Buttermilk | 1 quart | 350 |
| Buttermilk | 1 cup | 85 |
| Carbonated drinks | 8 ounces | 100 |
| Carbonated water (unflavored) | | 0 |
| Chocolate milk | 8 ounces | 225 |
| Chocolate syrup | 1 tablespoon | 40 |
| Club soda | | 0 |
| Cider | 1 cup | 125 |

| | | |
|---|---|---|
| Cocoa, whole-milk | 1 cup | 235 |
| Cocoa, dry powder | 1 tablespoon | 20 |
| Coffee, black | | 0 |
| Coffee, with milk | 1 cup | 25 |
| Coffee, cream, sugar | 1 cup | 100 |
| Cola drinks | 1 cup | 100 |
| Ginger ale | 8 ounces | 100 |
| Grape juice | 8 ounces | 130 |
| Grapefruit juice (canned) | 8 ounces | 130 |
| Grapefruit juice (fresh) | 8 ounces | 90 |
| Grapefruit juice (frozen) | 1 can (6 oz.) | 395 |
| Grapefruit-orange (canned) | 8 ounces | 130 |
| Ice-cream soda | 1 average | 325 |
| Lemonade | 8 ounces | 115 |
| Malted milk | 12 ounces | 325 |
| Malted milk (with ice cream) | 12 ounces | 625 |
| Milk, chocolate | 8 ounces | 225 |
| Milk, whole | 1 cup | 165 |
| Milk, skim | 1 cup | 85 |
| Orange juice, fresh | 1 cup | 108 |
| Orangeade | 12 ounces | 135 |
| Ovaltine, half milk | 1 cup | 110 |
| Pineapple juice (canned) | 1 cup | 125 |
| Postum, black | | 0 |
| Postum, half milk | 1 cup | 85 |
| Postum, cream, sugar | 1 cup | 100 |
| Root beer | 8 ounces | 105 |
| Seltzer | | 0 |
| Soda, flavored, carbonated | 8 ounces | 100 |
| Soda, ice-cream | 1 average | 325 |
| Tea, plain | | 0 |
| Tea, sugar, milk | 1 cup | 50 |
| Tomato juice | 1 cup | 50 |

## Breads

| | | |
|---|---|---|
| Bagel | 1 | 120 |
| Bread crumbs | ½ cup | 170 |
| Boston brown bread | ¾″ slice | 105 |
| Cinnamon buns | 1 medium | 165 |
| Cinnamon toast | 1 slice | 125 |
| Cornbread | 1 medium | 130 |
| Cracked-wheat bread | ½″ slice | 60 |
| Croutons | ½″ cubes | 5 |
| Date-and-nut bread | ½″ slice | 155 |
| Frankfurter roll | 1 | 155 |
| French bread | ½″ slice | 50 |
| Gingerbread | 2″ square | 205 |
| Gluten bread | ½″ slice | 45 |
| Graham bread | ½″ slice | 90 |
| Hamburger roll | 1 | 150 |
| Italian bread | ½″ slice | 40 |
| Melba toast | 1 slice | 20 |
| Muffins | 1 average | 120 |
| Muffin, blueberry | 1 average | 135 |
| Muffin, bran | 1 large | 125 |
| Muffin, English | 1 | 125 |
| Muffin, raisin | 1 | 105 |
| Parkerhouse rolls | 1 large | 125 |
| Protein bread | ¼″ slice | 30 |
| Pumpernickel | ½″ slice | 105 |
| Raisin bread | ½″ slice | 65 |
| Rolls, plain | 1 medium | 120 |
| Rye bread | ½″ slice | 55 |
| Rye bread, toast | ½″ slice | 55 |
| Rye Krisp | 1 piece | 15 |
| Soy bread | ½″ slice | 80 |
| Swedish rye wafers | 1 wafer | 20 |

| | | |
|---|---|---|
| White bread | ½″ slice | 65 |
| White bread, toast | ½″ slice | 65 |
| Whole-wheat bread | ½″ slice | 55 |
| Zweiback | 1 piece | 25 |

**Cereals & Flours**

| | | |
|---|---|---|
| Barley, raw | 1 tablespoon | 40 |
| Bran, 100% | ½ cup | 75 |
| Bran, flakes | ½ cup | 55 |
| Bran, raisin | ½ cup | 80 |
| Buckwheat flour | ½ cup | 175 |
| Cereals, most cooked | 1 cup | 150 |
| Cheerios | 1 cup | 100 |
| Cornflakes | 1 cup | 90 |
| Corn flour | 1 cup | 405 |
| Cornmeal, cooked | 1 cup | 125 |
| Cornmeal, dry | 1 cup | 400 |
| Cream of wheat | 1 cup | 120 |
| Farina | 1 cup | 105 |
| Flour, pastry | 1 cup | 365 |
| Flour, rye | 1 cup | 285 |
| Flour, wheat | 1 cup | 400 |
| Grapenuts | ½ cup | 160 |
| Griddle cakes, wheat | 1 (5″) | 75 |
| Grits, cooked | 1 cup | 120 |
| Kix | 1 cup | 130 |
| Krispies | 1 cup | 135 |
| Noodles, dry | 1 cup | 280 |
| Noodles, egg, cooked | 1 cup | 105 |
| Oat cereal | 1 cup | 100 |
| Oatmeal, cooked | 1 cup | 150 |
| Oatmeal, dry | 1 cup | 310 |
| Pancake mix, dry | 1 cup | 470 |
| Pancakes, wheat | 1 (5″) | 75 |

| | | |
|---|---|---|
| Pancakes, buckwheat | 1 (5″) | 65 |
| Pep | 1 cup | 125 |
| Pie crust, plain | Double crust (9″ pie) | 1315 |
| Pie crust, plain | Lower crust (9″ pie) | 655 |
| Puffed Rice | 1 cup | 55 |
| Puffed Wheat | 1 cup | 40 |
| Ralston | 1 cup | 190 |
| Rice Flakes | 1 cup | 120 |
| Rice, brown raw | 1 cup | 750 |
| Rice, converted raw | 1 cup | 680 |
| Rice, white raw | 1 cup | 690 |
| Rice, converted cooked | 1 cup | 205 |
| Rice, white cooked | 1 cup | 200 |
| Rice, precooked dry | 1 cup | 420 |
| Shredded Wheat | 1 large | 100 |
| Shredded Wheat | 1 medium | 80 |
| Soybean flour, low fat | 1 cup | 230 |
| Soybean flour, medium fat | 1 cup | 235 |
| Soybean flour, full fat | 1 cup | 250 |
| Soybean grits | 1 cup | 365 |
| Spaghetti, dry | 1 cup | 355 |
| Spaghetti, cooked | 16 ounces | 680 |
| Spaghetti, cooked | 1 cup | 220 |
| Starches (corn, arrowroot, etc.) | 1 cup | 465 |
| Starches | 1 tablespoon | 30 |
| Tapioca, dry | 1 cup | 545 |
| Tortillas (5″) | 1 | 50 |
| Waffle flour | 8 ounces | 650 |
| Waffles | 1 average | 215 |
| Wheat flakes | 1 cup | 125 |
| Wheat flour | 1 cup | 400 |
| Wheat germ | 1 cup | 245 |
| Wheat, rolled | 1 cup | 175 |
| Whole meal | 1 cup | 175 |
| Wheat-barley cereal | 1 cup | 410 |
| Yeast, dry | 1 tablespoon | 20 |

## Commercially Canned Foods
(Average)

| | | |
|---|---|---|
| *Fruits* | | |
| Apricots | 4 medium halves, 2 T. syrup | 105 |
| Blackberries | ½ cup | 95 |
| Blueberries | ½ cup | 50 |
| Cherries, red | ½ cup | 60 |
| Grapefruit sections | ½ cup | 85 |
| Peaches, cling | 2 medium halves, 2 T. syrup | 95 |
| Peaches, freestone | 2 medium halves, 2 T. syrup | 100 |
| Pears | 2 medium halves, 2 T. syrup | 90 |
| Pineapple, sliced | 2 small or 1 large slice, 2 T. syrup | 125 |
| Purple plums | 3 plums, 2 T. syrup | 115 |
| *Juices* | | |
| Grapefruit juice | 4 ounces | 50 |
| Orange juice | 4 ounces | 55 |
| Pineapple juice | 4 ounces | 65 |
| Tomato juice | 4 ounces | 25 |
| *Vegetables* | | |
| Asparagus | 6 medium | 20 |
| Beans, baked | ½ cup | 140 |
| Beans, green cut | ½ cup | 20 |
| Beans, green lima | ½ cup | 75 |
| Beets, cubed | ½ cup | 40 |
| Carrots, cubed | ½ cup | 30 |
| Corn, cream-style | ½ cup | 105 |
| Corn, kernel, white | ½ cup | 80 |
| Corn, kernel, yellow | ½ cup | 85 |
| Mushrooms | ½ cup | 20 |
| Peas, Alaska | ½ cup | 70 |
| Peas, sweet | ½ cup | 60 |
| Pimentos | 1 medium | 10 |

| | | |
|---|---|---|
| Sauerkraut | ½ cup | 25 |
| Spinach | ½ cup | 20 |
| Sweet potatoes | ½ cup | 145 |
| Tomatoes | ½ cup | 25 |
| Turnip greens | ½ cup | 20 |

*Fish*

| | | |
|---|---|---|
| Mackerel | ½ cup | 210 |
| Salmon | ½ cup | 170 |
| Sardines in oil | 5 medium, drained | 165 |
| Sardines, tomato sauce | 1½ large | 225 |
| Shrimp, dry pack | 10–12 medium | 80 |
| Shrimp, wet pack | 10–12 medium | 45 |
| Tuna | ½ cup, drained | 255 |

*Soups*

(Entire contents of can, 1¼ cups, before milk or water is added; compute additional calories for milk, if added.)

| | | | |
|---|---|---|---|
| Asparagus, cream of | 175 | Consommé | 100 |
| Bean with bacon | 435 | Green pea | 330 |
| Beef | 275 | Mock turtle | 225 |
| Beef noodle | 155 | Mushroom, cream of | 340 |
| Black bean | 250 | Oxtail | 230 |
| Bouillon (beef broth) | 77 | Pepper pot | 270 |
| Celery, cream of | 220 | Scotch Broth | 290 |
| Chicken, cream of | 220 | Tomato | 205 |
| Chicken with rice | 110 | Vegetable | 205 |
| Chicken gumbo | 155 | Vegetable-beef | 220 |
| Chicken noodle | 160 | Vegetarian vegetable | 200 |
| Clam chowder | 190 | | |

*Meats and Poultry; Luncheon Dishes*

| | | |
|---|---|---|
| Beef goulash | 8 ounces | 190 |
| Beef stew | 8 ounces | 180 |
| Chicken-noodle dinner | 8 ounces | 170 |
| Chicken stew, dumplings | 8 ounces | 190 |
| Chili con carne, beans | 8 ounces | 300 |

| | | |
|---|---|---|
| Chop suey with meat | 8 ounces | 150 |
| Corned-beef hash | 8 ounces | 320 |
| Lamb stew | 8 ounces | 180 |
| Macaroni, cheese sauce | 8 ounces | 210 |
| Macaroni creole | 8 ounces | 150 |
| Pork and beans | 8 ounces | 310 |
| Spaghetti, tomato sauce | 8 ounces | 210 |
| Spanish rice | 8 ounces | 130 |

### Commercially Frozen Foods
(Average of ⅓ of 9–10 ounce package)

*Fruits*

| | | | |
|---|---|---|---|
| Apples, sliced | 90 | Cherries, red, unsweetened | 55 |
| Apricots | 100 | Peaches, sliced | 90 |
| Blueberries, sweetened | 105 | Pineapples, chunks | 85 |
| Blueberries, unsweetened | 55 | Raspberries, red | 100 |
| Boysenberries, sweetened | 95 | Rhubarb | 75 |
| Boysenberries, unsweetened | 50 | Strawberries, sliced | 110 |
| Cherries, red, sweetened | 110 | Strawberries, whole | 90 |

*Vegetables*

| | | | |
|---|---|---|---|
| Asparagus, cuts and tips | 20 | Mixed vegetables | 65 |
| Asparagus, spear | 25 | Mustard greens | 20 |
| Beans, cut wax | 30 | Okra | 40 |
| Beans, green cut | 30 | Peas and carrots | 55 |
| Beans, French style | 30 | Peas, black-eyed | 130 |
| Beans, baby lima | 125 | Peas, green sweet | 75 |
| Beans, Fordhook | 100 | Potatoes, hash-browned | 75 |
| Broccoli, chopped | 30 | Potatoes, French fried | 170 |
| Broccoli, spears | 30 | Potatoes, mashed | 75 |
| Brussels sprouts | 35 | Spinach | 25 |
| Cauliflower | 20 | Squash, winter | 40 |
| Collard greens | 30 | Squash, crookneck | 20 |
| Corn, cut | 80 | Succotash | 95 |
| Corn on the cob | 100 | Turnip greens | 25 |
| Kale, chopped | 30 | | |

### *Soups, Frozen*

| | | | |
|---|---|---|---|
| Oyster stew, 6 ounces | 190 | Shrimp, cream of, 6 ounces | 260 |
| Pea with ham, 6 ounces | 190 | | |

### *Fruit Juices*

(About 3½ ounces prepared from concentrated, frozen can, according to instructions on label)

| | | | |
|---|---|---|---|
| Grape juice, sweetened | 55 | Orange juice | 45 |
| Grapefruit juice | 45 | Orange-grapefruit juice | 45 |
| Lemonade, sweetened | 45 | Pineapple juice | 55 |

## Commercially Packaged Crackers

| | each piece | | each piece |
|---|---|---|---|
| Bleu Cheese crackers | 7 | Saltina biscuit | 15 |
| Butter Thins | 18 | Sky Flake wafer | 15 |
| Cheese Nip crackers | 10 | Snow Flake crackers | 14 |
| Cheese Tidbits | 2 | Soda crackers | 31 |
| Corn Thins | 3 | Sugar honey grahams | 29 |
| Crown pilot | 100 | Trentons | 25 |
| Holland Rusk | 55 | Triangle Thins | 9 |
| Malted milk wafers | 17 | Triscuits | 20 |
| Nabisco graham crackers | 28 | Uneeda Biscuits | 23 |
| Oysterettes | 3 | Uneeda Lunch Biscuits | 14 |
| Ritz crackers | 16 | Waverly Wafers | 18 |
| Ritz cheese crackers | 17 | Wheat Thins | 9 |
| Royal Lunch milk crackers | 48 | Zwieback, sweetened | 31 |
| Saltines | 14 | | |

### Commercially Packaged Sweet Cakes
(average)

| | each piece | | each piece |
|---|---|---|---|
| Animal crackers | 9 | Mello squares | 57 |
| Chocolate Chip cookies | 56 | Mickey Mouse cookies | 7 |
| Chocolate grahams | 58 | Nabisco sugar wafers | 5 |
| Chocolate snaps | 17 | National arrowroot biscuits | 22 |
| Devil's-food squares | 59 | Oatmeal cookies | 18 |
| Fig Newtons | 53 | Oreo Creme Sandwich | 57 |
| Frutana biscuits | 34 | Raisin fruit biscuit | 34 |
| Gaiety Creme Sandwiches | 110 | Social tea biscuit | 20 |
| Lemon snaps | 16 | Trio Creme Sandwich | 55 |
| Lorna Doone shortbread | 38 | Vanilla wafers | 15 |
| Macaroon cookies | 21 | Zuzu ginger snaps | 15 |
| Mallomars | 61 | | |

### Cakes and Pies

(as purchased commercially—not in accordance with recipes in this book)

| | | |
|---|---|---|
| Almond coffee cake | 3″ x 2″ x 1″ | 200 |
| Angel food | 3″ x 2″ x 2″ | 300 |
| Apple crumb | 3″ x 2″ x 1″ | 200 |
| Apple turnover | 1 average | 290 |
| Butter cake | 3″ x 2″ x 1″ | 200 |
| Cheesecake, cream | 2½″ wedge | 320 |
| Chocolate cake, iced | 3″ x 2″ x 1″ | 220 |
| Chocolate cake, plain | 3″ x 2″ x 1″ | 150 |
| Coconut cake, iced | 3″ x 2″ x 1″ | 300 |
| Coffee cake | 3″ x 3″ x 1″ | 150 |
| Cup cake | 1 average | 120 |
| Cup cake, iced | 1 average | 170 |
| Fruit cake | 3″ x 3″ x 1″ | 225 |

| | | |
|---|---|---|
| Ginger cake | 2" x 2" x 1" | 175 |
| Gold cake | 3" x 3" x 1" | 175 |
| Jelly roll | 1" slice | 250 |
| Pie, most varieties | 1 average cut (4") | 300 |
| Pie, custard | 1 average cut | 265 |
| Pie, mince | 1 average cut | 385 |
| Pie, pumpkin | 1 average cut | 265 |
| Pound cake | 2" x 2" x 1" | 200 |
| Spice cake | 2" x 2" x 1" | 220 |
| Strawberry shortcake | 3" wedge | 350 |
| White cake, plain | 2" x 2" x 1" | 240 |
| White cake, iced | 2" x 2" x 1" | 310 |

# Index